SEXUAL BEHAVIOR: Psycho-Legal Aspects

SEXUAL BEHAVIOR
Psycho-Legal Aspects

by FRANK S. CAPRIO, M.D.
and DONALD R. BRENNER, LL.B.

107109

THE CITADEL PRESS
NEW YORK

FIRST EDITION

Copyright © 1961 by The Citadel Press
All rights reserved
Manufactured in the United States of America
Library of Congress Catalog Card Number 61-9938
Published by The Citadel Press,
222 Park Avenue South, New York 3, N. Y.

preface

The intelligent management of sexual problems is everybody's concern. There is widespread anxiety today about the increasing incidence of sex offenses. Psychiatrists know that sex crimes are motivated by unconscious forces and may represent the symptom expression of sick minds.

Many judges and lawyers feel that all sex offenders are criminals and should be treated as such. Too often the attitude of the police toward the whole problem of sex offenders is callous, arbitrary, and routine, although the problem is one that concerns vital interests of society. How can it best be met? Prosecution of sex offenders does not always solve the problem. The authors are convinced that the answer is not to be found in bigger jails, more policemen, and longer sentences, but in a more enlightened understanding and treatment of offenders—treatment that is directed toward discovering and correcting the psychological causes. Statistics prove that psychiatric treatment, when properly instituted, gives better results than punitive measures.

Contrary to public opinion, not all sex offenders are dangerous. Many are exhibitionists, Peeping Toms, or nonaggressive homosexuals, whose behavior is more accurately classified

5

as public nuisances than as public dangers. It is the minority of sex offenders, those who rape, assault children, or commit lust murders, who constitute the real danger necessitating institutional treatment. All offenders who refuse treatment and are unwilling to conform to acceptable social behavior should be ordered by the court to obtain treatment from a psychiatrist or at a psychiatric clinic. If they fail to cooperate, they should be segregated from society, institutionalized, and subjected to the study and treatment they need.

Judges are often reluctant to give the sex offender the benefit of the doubt, particularly as to whether or not he is dangerous to society. Exhibitionists, for example, are not necessarily dangerous "sexual psychopaths." Generally they suffer from a deep-seated neurosis which impels them not to violence but to seek thrills from shocking or embarrassing the opposite sex. Confining exhibitionists behind bars solves nothing, but when placed on probation under psychiatric supervision, they usually respond to treatment.

The judges of our courts should understand that sexual deviations are not congenital or incurable, and cannot be eliminated by mere statutory regulations. Dr. Bernard Wortis stated: "A just administration of the law requires that separate considerations be given to individual cases and circumstances. Though punishment and isolation are necessary in some cases, the courts should also have easy recourse to custodial probationary agencies for psychiatric surveillance or treatment of the sex offender."

The authors have become increasingly conscious, in their respective practices of psychiatry and law, of the divergence of opinions between members of the two professions in their attitudes towards crime and the treatment of criminals. This divergence is most marked in that criminal area commonly referred to as "sexual offenses" which include rape, lust murder, homosexuality, incest, crimes against children, various types of sexual assault, exhibitionism, and other sexual misconduct. It may be that the current emphasis on sex crimes is the product of headline sensationalism, or the rage of a community which deems it expedient to rid its streets of the "heinous" sex offender. Or it could be that the term "sex" carries some singular connotation of "dirt and filth" which demands drastic decisions from the uninformed.

Our law is generally concerned with the problem of sexual misconduct in two respects: the occurrence of the offense; and the punishment of the offender. The idea prevails that to punish will deter, but the history of criminology makes it clear that punishment has not been altogether successful as a deterrent to further crime. In the Dark Ages of criminology, when executions were public and often included tortures, the ghastly scenes did not lessen the incidence of crime.

Likewise, psychiatry is also particularly concerned with two aspects of sexual offenses: the psychological and sociological reasons for the occurrence of the crime; and the psychiatric evaluation and study of the offender, with a view toward preventing further abnormal sexual behavior.

It is true that there are isolated instances of enlightened thinking by both doctors and lawyers in regard to the management of sex cases, but these are all too infrequent, uncorrelated, and therefore ineffective.

We are greatly disturbed by this deplorable situation because we feel, and actual case histories prove, that the sex offender does not, in most cases, receive responsible or knowledgeable handling. There is no concerted effort on the part of law-enforcement officials, lawyers, or judges to delve into their problems so that the source of the trouble can be exposed and treated. We are concerned further because, among doctors, definitions of mental illnesses are vague and varied, and are often the expression of personal prejudice rather than of factual information. The result is the mismanagement of sex cases to the detriment of the offender, the family, and the community.

It must be assumed, therefore, that deficiencies in the administration of this type of criminal case are attributable to a lack of understanding and knowledge. Webster defines "ignorant" as follows: *destitute of knowledge; uninstructed or uninformed; unaware; one without knowledge in general or in a particular matter.* Our experience shows that a vast amount of ignorance—in the strict sense of this definition—exists in the field of sexual problems. One of the coauthors will not forget the caustic and illiberal comment of a judge on the bench of a court of one of our great states. After hearing a plea for hospitalization and psychiatric counseling for a convicted homosexual, the judge bellowed, "But he's a pervert, isn't he?" and refused to entertain further argument. "Jail," he said, "is the only cure for the defendant." Many thousands of cases have been similarly mismanaged.

This book is not intended as criticism of any group. We do not think it fair to censure any segment of the legal or medical profession; we are certain that all are honest and sincere. We do believe, however, in the need for a re-education and scientific enlightenment of those who find themselves faced with the management of sex cases. This book is intended to help those who are confronted with these problems, and those whose homes (married couples among them) are threatened because of sex complications. By making proper information readily accessible, their difficulties may be alleviated. Finally, we hope this book will succeed in clarifying the psycho-legal issues involved in sex offenses.

The plan of the book is to present by discussion, explanation, case history, and constructive recommendations, various types of sex offenses, including marital sex problems. We wish to communicate to the reader, both professional and nonprofessional, our knowledge and experience in this field.

To summarize, this book intends to answer such provocative questions as: 1) Is society's attitude toward sex still influenced by ancient sex taboos? 2) What are the psycho-legal aspects of sex problems in marriage? 3) Is homosexuality a crime, a sickness, or a way of life? 4) Should rapists be given the death penalty? 5) What is the best method for civil and military authorities to deal with sex offenders? 6) Is "red-light" prostitution on its way out? 7) What about the problem of sex censorship? 8) Should our sex laws be changed? 9) What can be done to prevent sex crimes? 10) Can sex offenders be cured? 11) Should we have compulsory sex education in our schools? 12) Should the United Nations adopt a world-wide sex-health program?

Finally, we hope that the information contained in this book will lead to better legislation covering the misunderstood aspects of sexual behavior, improved management of sex cases, and significant advancement of psycho-legal research in sex crimes and aberrations, with benefit to both society and the individual.

FRANK S. CAPRIO, M.D.
DONALD R. BRENNER, LL.B.

Washington, D.C.
January 1961

contents

chapter one

PSYCHIATRY AND THE LAW

INTRODUCTORY REMARKS

Only in close cooperation between psychiatrists and lawyers can there be real progress in dealing with cases involving mental or emotional disorders. The District of Columbia and the State of New Hampshire have, to a degree, abandoned obsolete, unscientific, and unsound criteria, but there is need for change throughout the entire country.

The law is slow to change. The psychiatrists, perhaps, should devise better approaches to the tasks of determining just when a person is "insane" or not responsible for his acts because of mental illness. It is only through cooperative advances by both professional groups that real productivity will be achieved.

For this psychiatric legal cooperation, the authors have found it convenient to use the term they have coined, the "psycho-legal" approach, to distinguish it from the more common term, "medico-legal." The term applies to considerations of mental and emotional disorders and problems encountered in matters brought to the attention of the authorities or the courts. And it places a needed emphasis on the cooperative work of psychiatrist and lawyer, especially in cases involving sexual problems.

But society will also have to cooperate if this alignment between psychiatrist and lawyer is to be as fruitful as it can

13

be. Society must be ready to change obsolete methods of handling sex offenders since it is in reality partially responsible for those offenses.

Dr. Karl Bowman, Professor Emeritus in psychiatry at the University of California, writes: "In the sexual sphere, particularly, our society is split between a publicly professed culture of sex denial and rejection and a clandestine culture of sex acceptance and affirmation.

"Under this dual system, individuals are expected to release their sexual tensions in secret and often in violation of publicly professed rules. . . .

"This inconsistency . . . creates much confusion in the minds of youths. It may be a factor in producing the emotional distortion and behavior pathologies found in many serious sex offenders."

We believe that every sex offender should be given a thorough pretrial physical and psychiatric examination. Investigation by a social-service worker to determine his family background should be a *must*. Psychiatric treatment, when needed and properly instituted, has proved more effective than punitive measures.

Dr. Manfred Guttmacher points out: "In most states the way that homosexual offenses are dealt with in courts depends greatly on the religious beliefs and social orientation of the law-enforcement agents and judge. This results in a deplorable inequality in convictions and in sentencing."

Our judges should realize, as Guttmacher suggests, that "isolated acts of deviant behavior do not necessarily make the individual a sexual offender and that many nonsexual offenses have in reality a definite sexual basis."

Sex offenders who are psychotic or psychopathic and thus dangerous should be committed to mental institutions. In cases where the diagnosis is disputed, the offender, perhaps, should be required to appear before a board or panel of psychiatrists who have no interest in the ultimate outcome of the case for final diagnosis. Under such a system, the judge and jury, would not be called on to appraise the testimony of opposing psychiatrists.

Although there has been great progress in the use of psychiatric testimony in court matters, there is still much to be done. It may be that changes in some of our laws will benefit, although it is our opinion that the real advancement is to be made by a better understanding between the psychiatrists and lawyers, and closer cooperation by them in the evaluation and disposition of those matters which require psychiatric help and legal counsel.

THE ROLE OF THE PSYCHIATRIST IN COURT

The psychiatrist may be called into a case involving a sexual offense for two reasons generally. He may be asked to examine an accused with the view in mind of determining the man's mental ability to comprehend the nature of his act and assist in the defense of his case; or psychiatric aid may be sought in order to establish the presence of an emotional involvement which, with proper treatment, may be alleviated.

When an accused has been arrested and charged, his lawyer may wish to have him examined psychiatrically. If the judge permits bond, thus permitting the man to remain free pending trial, he may be examined in the psychiatrist's office. If, however, the defendant is remanded to jail awaiting trial, any such examination would be made there.

A psychiatric examination usually consists of a series of interviews, not less than three in number, after the psychiatrist submits a written report to the attorney. The report may be presented to the court for consideration legally. The authors have worked on many cases where such a report formed the basis for probation of an accused with the provision that psychiatric treatment be obtained.

There are those cases where the defense counsel deems it necessary to have a determination made as to the legal ability of his client to stand trial. Ordinarily, the lawyer raises the issue although the judge, himself, may invoke it. A request for mental examination may be made on oral motion in court. In the District of Columbia, the judge may order a defendant confined in a mental hospital for determination of his mental capacity to stand trial.

Title 24, D. C. Code, Sec. 301 (1951), as amended, provides:

1. Authority for the court to order an accused committed for examination and observation to a mental hospital.

2. A finding by the court on whether the accused is mentally competent to stand trial.

The above section states in part: "Whenever a person is arrested by information, or is charged in the juvenile court of the District of Columbia, for or with an offense and, prior to the imposition of sentence or prior to the expiration of any period of probation, it shall appear to the court from the court's own observations, or from prima facie evidence submitted to the court, that the accused is of unsound mind or is mentally incompetent so as to be unable to understand the proceedings against him or properly to assist in his own defense, the court may order the accused committed . . . for such reasonable period as the court may determine for examination and observation and care and treatment if such is necessary." The statute provides further that, if after such examination and observation, a report is made to the court that the accused is of unsound mind or mentally incompetent, the court may on the basis of such report order the accused committed to a hospital. If either the defense or prosecution objects to the above finding, then the court may—within its own discretion and without a jury—make a judicial determination of the competency of the accused to stand trial, and can order the accused confined to a hospital until such time as the hospital superintendent certifies to the court that he is competent to be tried.

Provided, however, the psychiatric report finds him sane and able to stand trial the defendant is then afforded a trial on the issues involved. This does not preclude the defense from availing itself of testimony from its own psychiatrist at trial to dispute the issue of sanity, for the government must then prove sanity beyond a reasonable doubt, just as it must prove every other element of the crime in order to convict.

If trial is held and the accused found not guilty by reason of insanity by a jury, he will then be committed to a mental institution until such time as he is free from mental disease or defect as would make him dangerous to hismself or the community in the foreseeable future.

On the other hand, the jury may find that the defendant was sane at the time of the offense and convict him accordingly.

There are, of course, cases in which psychiatric testimony as to the mental condition of a defendant differs. The jury must then decide the issue on the merits of the case and after careful consideration of all such testimony.

An interesting case was decided in the District of Columbia, in 1958. (Williams vs. United States, U. S. App. D. C. No. 14,460, November 12, 1958.) This was an appeal from an order denying a motion for a new trial on the grounds of newly discovered evidence.

The facts were as follows:

On February 8, 1957, the defendant assaulted his wife with a deadly weapon. On July 20, 1957, he stabbed his daughter to death. He was tried and convicted for assaulting his wife on November 7, 1957, during which trial two government psychiatrists testified that the accused was not suffering from a mental disease when the assault took place.

On April 28, 1958, trial was held on the murder charge. The same two psychiatrists testified that they had reviewed their records—without further examination—and had decided that the defendant was suffering from mental disease on the date of the fatal stabbing. They further stated that they "would guess the mental disease goes back several years."

A verdict was entered of acquittal by reason of insanity. The appeal was brought for a new trial on the assault charge alleging insanity at the time of the assault.

A new trial was ordered.

In his book, *Murder, Madness and the Law,* Dr. Louis Cohen observes that disagreements between law and psychiatry arise out of the approach to two questions: 1) What is the mental condition of the accused? 2) How may society be protected?

Dr. Cohen explains: "The attitude of the psychiatrist with regard to law is that when the court asks the question, 'Is the defendant insane?' it is the same as if it were asking, 'Is he psychotic?' The court thinks of insanity in terms of the responsibility of the defendant while the psychiatrist is thinking in terms of mental disease.

"The legal standards for responsibility have been set up by the courts and have been more or less inclusively written into the legal rules. Insanity has been legally defined by the following standards: whether the accused lacks appreciation of what he has done, lacks knowledge of the consequences of his act, whether his act is based on deluded motivation, whether he has the ability to distinguish between right and wrong.

"Psychiatrically, the problem is seen somewhat differently. All of these standards may apply, or some of them may, or none of them may, but the person may be psychotic nevertheless. Conflict and disagreement often arise because of this arbitrary legal definition of insanity. For example, a psychotic person may commit a crime and may, strictly speaking, appreciate what he has done, but that does not mean to the psychiatrist that the person is not insane."

In another section of his book, Dr. Cohen writes: "Less psychiatric-legal disagreement is found in pre-trial hearings than when the question of responsibility is raised, as in a trial. It is here that much of the hope lies for improving the legal handling of the insane. Increasing use is being made in many states of pre-trial examinations by nonpartisan or court-appointed experts.

"By this method, when the court and the expert are using the same approach to what I have already said is a common problem, they can come to a reasonable solution of that problem. If the courts used a common-sense rule in a trial, as they do in a pre-trial hearing, they would come much closer to arriving at a common-sense judgment.

"The courts will never be perfect, nor the laws, nor the experts. Everyone is fallible, and our profession and our institutions are as fallible as the people of whom they consist. But there is always room for progress within the limits of that fallibility, and there is much room for progress, I believe, in the handling of the insanity issue in criminal cases."

As an example of the confusion that can arise, Dr. Cohen describes the case of a certain Albert Fish, a sex offender, who suffered from delusions, hallucinations, and sadistic wishes. He had the compulsive urge to bribe, seduce, and attack children. According to Cohen, he had had sexual experience with children in every state. "He was also a masochist and inflicted the most horrible tortures on himself.

"In the Grace Budd murder, the intended victim of Fish had been Grace's brother, whom he wished to castrate. However, the boy did not appeal to him, so he chose Grace instead. After he had strangled her, he cut up her body. It took him nine days to eat the parts of her body. All during this period, he was in a state of great sexual excitement.

"Dr. Wertham, who declared Fish insane, testified: 'He does not know the nature and quality of his acts. He does not know right from wrong. He is insane now, and he was insane then.'

"But the four psychiatrists called by the prosecution testified that Fish was sane, legally and medically. They said, in effect, that a person could kill and eat children, and still not be suffering from a psychosis.

"The jury, paying less heed to the psychiatric testimony than to their own sense of indignation aroused by the hideous crime, pronounced Albert Fish guilty as charged. He was sentenced to die in the electric chair."

Psychiatrists are sometimes accused of defending a sex offender, whether guilty or not, or of testifying on either side of a case depending on the fee. But is it likely that a reputable psychiatrist would deliberately prostitute his ethics and conscience and testify contrary to his honest opinion merely for a fee? He surely would not describe an offender as not "dangerous" when he believes otherwise. However, the allegation is often heard that a psychiatrist always tries to get a defendant "off the hook." These suspicions are nurtured by conflicting testimony of two psychiatrists who may testify that a defendant was insane at the time he committed a crime while two other psychiatrists testify that he was sane. But psychiatry is not yet such an exact science that findings will always coincide. Psychiatrists often differ in a diagnosis, but judges, too, often disagree on a verdict. Even the Justices of the Supreme Court of the United States disagree on many issues.

However, psychiatry has established a sufficient authority to be increasingly valued in court procedures. The legal profession is giving greater heed to the psychiatric evaluation of criminals and sex offenders. Even so, much remains to be done to clarify problems which confront both the lawyer and the psychiatrist.

Dr. Winfred Overholser writes: "There is much room for improvement in the use of psychiatric expert testimony. We may safely expect that with the development of mutual understanding between the representatives of law and psychiatry the adoption of the needed improvements which we have discussed may be accelerated."

CASE ILLUSTRATIONS

Case 1. The following case is an unusual one in that the ultimate outcome, obtained by close cooperation between psychiatrist, lawyer, and court, shows that an enlightened attitude in the handling of sex offenders can both protect society and further the rehabilitation of the offender.

The defendant, a middle-aged male, married and the father of four children, is a college graduate and holds a responsible business position in which he has won a reputation for reliability. His home life appears happy and normal, and his relationship with his family is close and pleasant. He is a tall and rather heavy-set man, and his features are masculine. One might well believe him to have been an athlete in his college days.

This man was arrested on the complaints of four boys whose ages ranged from nine to twelve years. Each boy alleged that the defendant picked him up near the school, drove him to a secluded spot at the edge of town, and there performed an act of fellatio on him. It was alleged that the four acts took place within a three-day period and that the boys, all friends, decided to report the incident to the principal when the youngest, in the presence of the other three, divulged his experience. Comparing notes, the boys concluded that the same man had accosted each of them. Having seen him driving by the school that afternoon, they thought it best to seek out the authorities.

The defendant was arrested, identified in a line-up by each of the boys involved, and released on bond. He protested his innocence and disclaimed knowledge of the acts complained of, or of having ever seen any of the complainants. Indignantly he proclaimed that he was the victim of mistaken identity. The fact that there was positive identification of his person and his automobile made no difference. He continued to protest his innocence.

The first office consultation with the author proved fruitless, the defendant refusing to cooperate. He maintained that he was "framed," that the charges were false, and that, for some reason, the boys "had it in for me." His wife, who accompanied him on this occasion, shared his indignation and suggested bringing a lawsuit against the boys.

Subsequent interviews, however, proved more fruitful. In the absence of his wife, the defendant admitted a past record of sexual offenses, including conviction for homosexuality, sexual assault, an indecent exposure. In addition to the convictions the defendant recited instances where he had been picked up by the police for sexual offenses, later to be released because of insufficient evidence. At no time, however, did he admit having committed the offenses for which he was being held.

Although several interviews were held between the initial arrest and the trial date, no admission of guilt was elicited from the defendant nor did he seem in doubt about the outcome in court. He was certain that he would be completely exonerated.

The trial opened, the cases were consolidated, and the state called each of the four boys to testify. With few variations they testified as expected. The man had enticed them into his car with the promise of an after-school job, stating that he wanted to talk with them about it. Once in the car the defendant drove away from the school and to a strange neighborhood. On the way he gave them candy and said that his business partner was waiting for them.

The testimony went like this:

Q. What did he do then?

A. He started feeling my leg and fooling around with it.

Q. While he was driving?

A. Yes, sir; and he pulled my zipper down and began playing with my penis, and when we stopped, he took my penis into his mouth.

Q. Now, when he stopped, did he do this?

A. Yes, sir.

Q. Now, when he stopped the car, just what did he do? You said that he had been playing with your penis before the car stopped?

A. Yes, sir.

Q. And did he pull off to the side of the road?

A. Yes, sir.

Q. And then what did he do?

A. He put my penis in his mouth.

Q. Did he unzip your pants?

A. Yes, sir.

Q. Did you try to stop him?

A. No, sir. I was scared.

Q. Do you know how long he kept your penis in his mouth?

A. About five minutes.

Q. Have you ever done anything like this before, with this man or anyone else?

A. No. sir.

Q. Where were you when he put your penis in his mouth?

A. Lying on the ground near the side of the car.

Q. Did he force you to lie down?

A. No, sir. He asked me to get out of the car, take my pants off, and lie down on the ground.

Q. Did you try to get away?

A. No, sir. I was too scared.

Q. Did he use any force against you?

A. No, sir.

Q. What happened then?

A. After he got through, he told me to put my pants on and that he would drive me back to town.

Q. Did he do that?

A. Yes, sir.

The testimony of all four boys was essentially the same and cross-examination did not alter their stories. The defendant did not take the stand nor was there any evidence introduced on his behalf. The defendant was found guilty on all four charges and sentenced to two years in the State penitentiary on each charge. The case was appealed to the State Supreme Court and conviction upheld in its entirety.

Up to this time the defendant had been free on bond and working every day. His employers maintained that he was loyal, dependable, honest, and completely reliable. At this point in the case word was awaited from the court for the defendant to surrender himself to begin serving his sentence. He had received no psychiatric treatment nor had he been examined by a psychiatrist. Pending word from the court it was arranged for the defendant to be evaluated psychiatrically by Dr. Caprio. The report indicated that this man was suffering from a neurosis which could be treated effectively, and it was recommended that, from a medical standpoint, jail would do neither the man nor society any good.

Armed with the psychiatric report, Mr. Brenner immediately gained an interview with the sentencing judge who, after much deliberation and study, in addition to several consultations with the authors and defendant, made a momentous decision.

The conviction would be suspended on the following terms: the defendant was required, for a period of six months, to report daily to an officer of the court; he was required to receive psychiatric treatment at his own expense and at such times as the doctor deemed necessary; and he must report to work as usual. The judge made it clear that any variation of the above conditions without his approval would result in an immediate revocation of the sentence suspension. If, at the end of the trial period, progress was favorable—as indicated by psychiatric reports furnished to the judge—the sentence would be generally suspended. The judge reserved the right, at any time and for any reason during the trial period, to revoke the suspension and commit the defendant to the State penitentiary for the full term.

The following psychiatric report was submitted to the court.

> TO WHOM IT MAY CONCERN
>
> This is to certify that I have given —— a comprehensive psychiatric examination consisting of three consultation interviews.
>
> Based on the findings of this examination, it is my opinion that he is suffering from a psychoneurosis associated with a sexual maladjustment. His antisocial offenses involving sex conflicts are definitely the product of a mental illness.
>
> It is my understanding that he has never received psychiatric treatment before and has served a prison sentence for his offenses. In view of this fact, I would see no point in having him serve another prison incarceration without the benefit of psychiatric treatment.
>
> Judging from my own experiences with numerous cases of sex offenders, which I have treated at the request of the Court, I feel that —— can be cured of his sexual neurosis and consequently am of the opinion that society's interest would best be served by having him rehabilitated so that he can live out his life as a law-abiding citizen in some gainful type of employment.
>
> Respectfully yours,

This interesting and rather amazing judicial conclusion was put into operation with unquestionable success. The defendant, long in need of psychiatric help, was cured of his neurosis, and society was rid of a potentially dangerous person. At last report this man was completely readjusted, had continued on his job, and was a happy husband and father as well as a useful citizen in the community. A long prison term would inevitably have had tragic consequences to himself, his family, and probably others.

The case illustrates what benefits can be derived from proper and intelligent handling of sex cases. The enlightened judge, working in close harmony with the defense lawyer and the doctor, rejected the easy, harsh traditional treatment of this sexual offender. His ruling had the future of the man foremost in mind and helped to demonstrate that understanding and treatment can do more good than a term behind bars.

Case 2. Another case involved a man holding a responsible position, who had sexually seduced numerous young girls, getting them to indulge in sexual deviations. He also managed to get a husband and wife to perform certain sexual activities in his presence. This, he said, was a form of therapy called "psychodrama" by which, in acting out their repressed sexual desires, they would be cured of their emotional ailments.

He was arrested and sent to jail. In court he pleaded "not guilty" on the ground that he was putting into practice a theory of treatment which he claimed was associated with sex customs among primitive tribes.

The author had an opportunity to interview the husband who was one of the victims in the case. He brought to me a written account of the entire episode. After reading it, I was convinced that the offender on trial was suffering from a deep-seated sexual neurosis and needed to be institutionalized rather than sent to jail. The husband and his wife, who had been induced to perform in the staged sex orgies, developed, as a consequence, acute states of anxiety from their feelings of guilt and inferiority over allowing themselves to be so used.

It is our opinion that a person who would seduce a husband and wife into the sexual practices as described in this case would have to be mentally ill and in need of psychiatric treatment. We do not deny, however, that the couple should not have become involved. The husband, a neurotic who had been under psychiatric treatment, was susceptible to the influence of the sex offender and described his experiences as follows:

(Note: We will here use pseudonyms and refer to the sex offender as "Jack," the husband as "Robert," and the wife as "Dorothy.")

"I had asked Jack that my wife shouldn't be brought into it. He said he had some other women whom he could employ but it would cost money and wouldn't be as effective. He asked me if I wanted to be cured. I said, 'Yes.' He then said to let him meet my wife, and he would handle her. When he came to my apartment, he sat down on the chair and said what would happen would be more effective than anything else he could think of. My wife asked me who the joker was? He looked like a jerk and was rather repulsive. When I went into the bedroom, he was still talking with my wife. He asked her to help him with me. He wanted her to take off her things. He slapped her on the face and asked if she liked it. My wife refused, at first, to take off more than her coat but finally showed her brassière. I stood by in silence. I didn't like it, My wife consented to cooperate because she said she wanted to help and assured me that she loved me. I was reluctant to have her be a party to all this. However, I got her into it. The next day Jack called. He asked me how I felt. I said what had happened the day before was quite a shock to me. I asked him if I was supposed to feel better. He said, 'Well, a little better.' This was strange therapy but I threw myself into it, resolved to cooperate to the limit. I wanted to be cured. I was hoping it would work. I had no idea what miserable disappointment and unhappiness lay ahead. Jack said he would keep in touch with me. During our subsequent appointments for lunch, he spoke of things pertinent to my condition. He asked me if I didn't feel that I wanted to finish the act of fellatio. He said if I were a good boy, he would let me do it. He gave me a spoonful of white ice cream, and at the time

I wondered why. By that time, I was beginning to feel like a zombie. I was confused. I felt he could do anything with me. I told him I had dreamed about him. He said it was a good sign. It was working. He could call his shots. He never missed. He walked down the street with his arm on mine. 'Don't you feel my strength pouring into you?' I imagined it was. I tried hard to believe that it was. I said, 'Yes, I do.' In the bedroom, he guaranteed that I would be cured in three weeks. I would be a virile man.

"I was going around in a sort of a stupor, and the world was beginning to look unnatural, like in dream scenes. Was this the beginning of a change? I seemed to be reliving the whole past again. I couldn't concentrate. I was losing enthusiasm. My right ear kept ringing. In the morning, I dreaded going to work. I was not awake, and the world looked as though I was not a part of it. I was more anxious than usual. I feared that I wouldn't be able to continue work. He assured me that I would be cured—yes, definitely. I would become a strong, virile, dynamic individual. I wondered what was happening to me.

"I was supposed to be subservient. He was the master and I could not do anything except when he gave me permission. His objective was to get me into a state of mind where he was the authority—undisputed. I was beginning to be as passive as a lamb.

"I hated to drag my wife into it. I wondered what he would do to her. I didn't want him to have my wife sexually. I wondered whether it would be part of the act. I knew Dorothy would refuse. She told me so—none of that business. Jack assured me he would not try that. I still felt guilty about my wife being brought into it but since I had thought it necessary, I would go along.

"He came up to the house for the second time. He grabbed my wife and sat her down on his lap. I was told to sit on the sofa. He put his arms around her and kept slapping her bottom. He then asked Dorothy to go into the bedroom and take off her clothes. He grabbed her hand and put it against his penis. 'You see,' he said. 'It is not hard. I have no erection; this is all for your husband's sake, and you promised to help.' Dorothy took her clothes off and came out in her robe. He said, 'Take everything off, this is necessary; this is the treatment.' He was playing with my wife's breasts. I sat and watched. I was confused. What was he going to do next? He said to her, 'Just put your head down and kiss it for me and watch his reaction.' My wife said it was silly—what was that for? He said, 'All right, just put your head down in my lap and let him think that you are doing it.' He said to me, 'Kiss the same breast that I kissed.' And then he told me to take my penis out and told Dorothy to kiss it. He had my wife get up again and he slapped her bottom and then made her lie down across my lap and made me do the same thing. He picked her up and said to me, 'Here now I give her to you.' He then asked Dorothy, 'Is Robert's big or small?' She said, 'My husband's is very large.' He said, 'Well, mine is very small, you see.' And then he rubbed my wife's hand against it. He said to Dorothy, 'If this has affected you in any way, I will give you some advice and it will be all right.' My wife said, 'As long as you help my husband, I will straighten myself out.'

"For the next few days Dorothy seemed to have lost all feeling for me. I must have felt extremely guilty about bringing her into the act. I hoped it would be finished soon. Jack had told me that this was a form of psychodrama treatment. He made me think it was necessary. He had painted a beautiful picture of a miraculous cure. Gosh, when I was cured, what couldn't I do? It would be wonderful, a new life. He had me believing it.

"One other time he took me by the arm and with all his strength forced me into a kneeling position. He told me to lie down on the bed. He pulled out his penis and told me to reach for it. He repeated this time after time. I made the gesture of reaching for it with my mouth. He jumped back. He slapped me and called me vile names. He said when he cured me his price was to have Dorothy. He called her on the phone and told her that. I was afraid that his dominance was obsessing me. During my periods of fighting to stay on my feet, I felt great sexual excitement. I fantasied having all women, being rough with them, subjecting them to indignities, like Jack. Slapping them on the face, like Jack. There would be no more sense of guilt. I would be like him, forceful, dynamic, a man of overpowering personality. I had, at times, great hostility toward my wife and I wished I were free from her. I wasn't meant for marriage. Why did I get married? I wished for a great deal of money. I wished for power and for many women and fantasied all sorts of sexual behavior with them. I still feared having overt homosexual relations, but perhaps I would get to do as I pleased with no feelings of guilt. Perhaps these were manifestations of the storm before the calm. I wanted desperately for someone to hold on to, someone who would not abandon me. Jack talked about me making the aggressive move in the homosexual act. I guess he tried to egg me on. He wanted to incite me to aggressive action.

"He said, 'A few more meetings and we will be finished.' I was confused and the ringing in my ear kept keeping me anxious for my life. I felt conscious of my brain. Was there an organic change going on? Was I going to develop a tumor? Was I going to develop a psychosis to keep from getting well? I pictured the 'demons' within me calling up all their reserves to discredit Jack. They were putting ideas in my mind about him. He was a charlatan, exploiting my emotions. I was sick and wanted to convince Jack I was sick. I pleaded with him but he wouldn't budge. I was the little boy and he was the master. Jack was becoming an obsession with me. I wanted him to make me feel better. I was tired of fighting and struggling. I told him if he helped me he could ask for any amount of money. He agreed. He seemed so positive he could help me. He said that I should give him a token sum of money. I don't recall ever giving him any money.

"Jack wanted me to get my daughter into the act. He asked me wouldn't I like to have her. He forced me down on my knees and told me to ask for it and say 'please.' He slapped me on the face and told me to say, 'I would like to see my wife perform fellatio in front of me.' He asked if my wife would mind if I got a girl up to my house and had her while he had my wife. He said he would talk to her and arrange it. He filled my thoughts with the wildest sexual fantasies imaginable.

"My wife and I had a fierce argument. She called Jack a Svengali and told me to go to him. Jack told her I never loved her, that I didn't want her. We finally patched things up. I damned Jack; I cursed the bastard. What was he doing to me? I was confused. He said once, 'Now you are better. Enjoy yourself and have a good time. You owe me $150? He wrote it down on a piece of paper. I said, 'Wait until I feel good, and I will gladly pay you.' It had been a nightmare and still no benefit. I felt like killing him. I was panicky, afraid that I was going out of my mind."

Jack was undoubtedly a sex offender who needed hospitalization. Our purpose in quoting Robert's description of his sexual experiences is to enable the reader to arrive at his own conclusion as to whether Jack, the sex offender, was or was not a sick individual. As a matter of fact, his two victims, husband and wife, were also neurotic and had exercised sick judgment in allowing this fantastic sexual exploitation to take place.

As to the psychodynamics of the case, Jack, no doubt, suffered from a strong, latent homosexual component. He also suffered from psychic impotence. He tried to overcompensate for his penis inferiority (which he admitted by saying that he had a smaller penis than Robert) by manifesting a false sense of power, what we might call pseudo-masculinity. We recall how he told Robert that he was 'pouring his strength into him.' His sexual neurosis centered around his sexual sado-masochism. He took sadistic delight in subjecting Robert to the humiliation of seeing his wife indulge in sexual activities with him. This sexual involvement of three people is referred to as troilism or as the French would say, a *ménage à trois*. It may be difficult for the legal profession to understand why a person like Jack should not be held responsible for his acts since he was not insane and, therefore, knew right from wrong. As previously stated, Jack was tried as a criminal and sentenced to prison. There are, however, some forward-thinking judges who, upon reflection and understanding of the sexual psychodynamics involved, would have committed Jack to a mental institution for treatment.

Case 3. The case involved a young man in his early twenties, arrested in a theatre for placing his hand on the thigh of a young boy sitting next to him. He admitted similar acts on previous occasions. Another psychiatrist and I concluded he was not a sexual psychopath but a neurotic, and we recommended probation with treatment. The two psychiatrists for the prosecution, however, disagreed. He was, they insisted, a sexual psychopath.

The judge, who incidentally was a woman, concluded that the case involved a question of diagnosis and that neither she nor the jury knew enough about psychiatry to evaluate it properly. Hence, she proposed that the four psychiatrists retire until we emerged with a diagnosis we all agreed on. This unusual procedure proved a sensible one. The conference resulted in agreement that the defendant was a neurotic. He

was placed on probation and responded favorably to psychotherapy.

Case 4. William B., a handsome young man of twenty-
six, married, and father of one child, consulted the author
after having been arrested for threatening to kill his wife. He
accused his wife of adultery with a neighbor and, ignoring her
denials, continued the threats. Finally they separated. One
day, following a heated telephone conversation and threat,
William was picked up by the police. To the psychiatrist he
confided that his sexual performance was deficient. When his
wife complained, he assumed that she was unfaithful to him.
The pre-trial psychiatric evaluation revealed the possibility of
a psychosis.

When the case came before the judge, the psychiatric findings were made available to him. The defendant was thereupon
committed to a mental hospital for a thirty-day examination to
determine his mental capacity to stand trial.

In brief, then, the issue of mental capacity to stand trial may
be raised either by the court or the defense counsel. There
are reported instances where the defendant himself, when asked
by the judge if he had anything to say, raised the issue.

Case 5. Clark vs. U. S. (U.S. App. D. C. Aug. 1958) is a
case in which the defendant appealed a conviction for murder
in the first degree. At the trial his counsel told the jury that
he thought the case was one of manslaughter not murder, and
said, "We are not asking you to acquit this man, to free him.
We know he must pay a penalty."

The defendant himself, however, testified that he "must have
been insane" when he committed the crime.

The Court of Appeals, in ordering a new trial, said: "Defense counsel's attempt to take the defense of insanity out of
the case was error. We cannot say it was not prejudicial. It

must have tended, and may have tended effectively, to persuade the jury to disregard the court's subsequent instruction that they should find the defendant not guilty by reason of insanity unless they found, beyond a reasonable doubt, that he was sane."

There are unfortunate instances where a judge will order a defendant to trial although competent psychiatric reports indicate that he is psychotic and mentally incompetent to stand trial. And there are also cases where a judge will ignore the recommendations of a psychiatrist that the defendant, though he may not be psychotic, is in need of proper counselling and treatment rather than imprisonment as a sex psychopath.

HISTORICAL CONSIDERATIONS

Although insanity figured as a defense in court for hundreds of years, the criteria for deciding its applicability in a particular case are confusing. Oftentimes they lack both scientific validity and legal soundness.

In the seventeenth century, Lord Coke asserted that a guilty intent was necessary to sustain conviction for criminal behavior and that an insane person could not have such intent. He theorized, therefore, that any person without the mental capacity to form an intention to commit a wrongful act should not be held responsible. Later writers, among them Hale and Hawkins, agreed with Coke's views although with some elaboration. Hale concluded that the judge and jury were the ultimate deciders of the insanity issue. Hawkins injected the concept of right and wrong by maintaining that any person who could not distinguish between "good and evil" should not be held responsible for a criminal act. Overholser cites a further developmental concept in the ruling in the 1800 Hadfield case, which held that a delusion connected with the criminal act must be present to validate the defense of insanity.

These and other tests of insanity were invoked by the judges of the day without benefit of expert advice. The judge informed the jury on the issues involved according to his own views of the subject. Henry Weihofen, in his book *The Urge to Punish,* points out that those early judges used their own earlier rulings as binding legal precedent. Thus, judge-made law became the basis for disposing of the insanity issue. With different judges enouncing different concepts, confusion arose. Furthermore, then as now, law was resistant to change. While, therefore, medical researchers made progress in the field of mental illness, most judges took little note of their findings.

The so-called "McNaughten Rules," set down in England in 1843, became the accepted criteria in both Britain and the United States. The gist of these rules was the "right-and-wrong" test of determining the issue of insanity. But several years earlier, an Ohio court set "irresistible impulse" as a criterion for legal sanity and this test was sometimes used.

CRITERIA OF RESPONSIBILITY

1. *The "Good-and-Evil" Test*

The original concept of "right and wrong" was injected into court usage in the eighteenth century by Hawkins, who wrote: "Those who are under a natural disability of distinguishing between good and evil, as infants under the age of discretion, idiots, and lunatics, are not punishable by any criminal prosecution whatsoever." Also used in England was the test of whether a man "doth not know what he is doing no more than a wild beast."

In the light of recent psychological findings this concept of "good and evil," as applied to sex offenders, is clearly unscientific. Some offenders may know that it is wrong to do a particular act, for example, exhibitionists who expose themselves, knowing it is wrong but do it anyway because of the compulsive nature of their neurosis. Certain psychotic offenders are able to distinguish right from wrong, but still commit sexual acts for which, under this rule, they may be punished.

This old rule of "good and evil" was not developed through

scientific study; the conclusions were reached without inquiry into the mental and emotional nature of the offender. Each judge who followed this rule applied his own individual unscientific view of "insanity." There inevitably arose confusion and discrepancy as to what was meant by "right and wrong" or "good and evil."

2. The McNaughten Rules ("Right-and-Wrong" Test)

The above concepts persisted until 1843 when the McNaughten case was tried. Daniel McNaughten shot to death a man who, he thought, was the British Prime Minister, Sir Robert Peel. The victim was actually Peel's secretary. McNaughten's attorney's defense was "partial insanity," on the ground that McNaughten was suffering from a delusion which affected his mind and compelled his murderous actions. Witnesses, with experience in handling the insane, gave their opinion that he was insane at the time of the commission of the crime and should not be held responsible. The jury found McNaughten not guilty by reason of insanity and committed him to an asylum.

There was much criticism of the decision and members of Parliament demanded clarification of just how far the plea of "partial insanity" could be extended. The House of Lords formulated a series of four questions concerning insanity as a defense and submitted these questions to the fifteen Chief Judges of England. Fourteen of the fifteen agreed on answers which became established as the McNaughten Rules. They may be summed up in the following:

1. If the accused did the alleged act under the influence of insane delusion, but with a view to redress or revenge some supposed grievance or injury, or to produce some public benefit, he was nevertheless punishable according to the nature of the crime committed, if he knew, when he was committing the act, that he was acting contrary to law.

2. In order to establish a defense on the ground of insanity it must be clearly proved that at the time of committing the act, the accused was laboring under such defect of reason from a disease of the mind as not to know the nature and quality of the act he was doing, or if he did know it, that he did not know he was doing what was wrong.

3. If the delusion was only a partial delusion, and if otherwise the individual was not insane, he should then be considered responsible for his act.

Overholser points out: "The knowledge of right and wrong was applied to the particular act charged, not (as formerly in the English law) to right and wrong in general."

Despite growing criticism, the McNaughten Rules remain in general use throughout this country and the English-speaking world.

3. *The "Irresistible Impulse" Test*

Nine years before the McNaughten Rules were set down, an Ohio Court devised the "irresistible impulse" test of insanity. Overholser, commenting on the case of State vs. Thompson (Wright's Ohio Report 617, 1834) quotes part of the court's decision as follows: "If the defendant were in a state of mind in which at the time of the deed he was free to forebear, or to do the act, he is responsible as a sane man." A later Ohio case, tried in the same year as the McNaughten matter, propounded the question: "Was the accused a free agent in forming the purpose to kill" (Clary vs. State, 12 Ohio Reports 495).

Seventeen states recognize the "irresistible impulse" test along with the McNaughten Rules.

4. *The New Hampshire Pike and Jones Cases*

What gives the New Hampshire cases singular importance is that the courts' decisions were the forerunners of the later

Durham ruling; they were the result, at least in part, of the writings of the American physician, Isaac Ray, whose book, *The Medical Jurisprudence of Insanity,* first brought scientific criteria to bear on the subject. Actually these rulings did not catch on in other jurisdictions to any extent until some eighty years later when the Durham rule was enunciated.

The case of State vs. Pike (49 N. H. 399, 1870), involved a defendant who assaulted one Thomas Brown with an axe causing a four-inch head wound which proved fatal. Pike was indicted on a charge of murder in the first degree.

At the trial, evidence was introduced tending to show that Pike had an irresistible appetite for alcohol and that his intake of it was uncontrollable; further that his constant indulgence had resulted in the disease of dipsomania.

The court commented on the fact that whether there is such a disease as dipsomania, and whether the defendant had such a disease, and whether an act done by him was the product of such disease, *are questions of fact for the jury* (emphasis ours). The court instructed jury in the following manner:

"That every person of mature age is presumed to be sane until there is evidence tending to show insanity, but when there is evidence coming from the other side tending to show insanity, then the state must satisfy the jury beyond a reasonable doubt that the prisoner is sane."

The Jones case, decided the following year (State vs. Jones 50 N. H. 369, 1871), went a step further. Jones had been indicted for the first-degree murder of his wife by inflicting a three-inch-long and two-inch-deep razor cut in her throat. The court's charge to the jury included the following: "If the killing was the offspring or product of mental disease in the defendant, the verdict should be not guilty." And in a precedent-setting recognition of the value of psychiatric testimony the court continued: "I may add that it confirms me in the belief that we are right or at least have taken a step in the right direction, to know that the view embodied in this charge meets with the approval of men who, from great experience in the treatment of the insane as well as careful and long study of the phenomena of mental disease, are infinitely better qualified to judge in the matter than any court or lawyer can be."

But the thought and insight expressed in the above decision lay long dormant. Until 1954 few, if indeed any court, ruled in such an enlightened manner.

5. *The Durham Case*

The now famous and controversial Durham case—or cases —began in 1951 and originated in a charge of housebreaking, although he was in trouble with the law even before then.

Monte Durham had a long history of imprisonment and hospitalization because of emotional disorders. He was discharged from the United States Navy in 1945 after a psychiatric evaluation had found him to be suffering from a "profound personality disorder." Shortly thereafter he attempted suicide and was confined in St. Elizabeth's mental hospital for about two months.

In January, 1948, Durham was charged with and convicted on a bad-check indictment. However, he was declared of unsound mind and committed to St. Elizabeth's Hospital on a diagnosis of "psychosis with psychopathic personality." He was released from the hospital in 1950, committed again in February 1951, and released in July of the same year.

In October, 1951, Durham was adjudged of unsound mind, following his indictment on the housebreaking charge, and once again he was committed to the hospital until such time as he was mentally capable of standing trial. Sixteen months later he was tried and convicted. Then, in 1954, the United States Court of Appeals for the District of Columbia, in its history-making decision, rewrote the law and adopted the new test of criminal responsibility: *If the defendant's unlawful act was a product of mental disease or mental defect he is not criminally responsible* (emphasis ours).

The majority decision, written by Judge David L. Bazelon, noting that there had been psychiatric testimony at the trial to the effect that the defendant was of unsound mind when committing the crime, stated in part:

"The 'right-and-wrong' test, approved in this jurisdiction in 1842, was the exclusive test of criminal responsibility in the District of Columbia until 1929 when we approved the 'irresistible impulse' test as a supplementary test in Smith vs. U. S. (36 Fed. 2nd 548). The 'right-and-wrong' test had its roots in England. There, by the quarter of the 18th century, an accused escaped punishment if he could not distinguish 'good and evil,' i.e., if he 'doth not know whether he is doing, no more than . . . a wild beast.' (Glueck, *Mental Diseases and the Criminal Law,* 138, 39; 1925.)

"Later, in the same century, the 'wild beast' test was abandoned and 'right and wrong' was substituted for 'good and evil.' And toward the middle of the 19th century, the House of Lords, in the famous McNaughten case, restated what had become the accepted 'right-and-wrong' test in a form which has since been followed, not only in England but in most American jurisdictions as an exclusive test of criminal responsibility.

"The science of psychiatry now recognizes that a man is an integrated personality and that reason, which is only one element in that personality, is not the sole determinant of his conduct. The 'right-and-wrong' test which considers knowledge or reason alone, is, therefore, an inadequate guide to mental responsibility for criminal behavior.

". . . inadequate because a) it does not take sufficient account of psychiatric realities and scientific knowledge, and b) it is based upon symptoms and so cannot validly be applied in all circumstances. We find that the 'irresistible impulse' test is also characterized by brooding and reflection and so relegates acts caused by such illness to the application of the inadequate 'right-and-wrong' test. We conclude that a broader test should be adopted.

"The rule, we now hold must be applied on the retrial of this case and in future cases, is not unlike that followed in the New Hampshire courts since 1870. It is simply that an accused is not criminally responsible if his unlawful act was the product of mental disease or mental defect.

"We use 'disease' in the sense of a condition which is considered capable of either improving or deteriorating. We use 'defect' in the sense of a condition which is not capable of either improving or deteriorating and which may be either congenital, or the result of injury, or the residual effect of a physical or mental illness." (Durham vs. U. S. 214 Fed. 2nd 862—decided July 1, 1954.)

Thus the Durham rule was born. The Court of Appeals ordered a new trial in a manner consistent with the new standards set down. On retrial Durham was once again found guilty by a jury; however, the Court of Appeals reversed the conviction because of faulty instructions to the jury. (Durham vs. U. S. 237 Fed. 2nd 760—decided Feb. 29, 1956.) Following the second reversal, Durham pleaded guilty to petty larceny and served a year in prison.

In September of 1958, Monte Durham was again in criminal court. He was charged with a $437 robbery. At the trial, Dr. Caprio was the sole psychiatrist testifying in behalf of the defense; the prosecution chose not to counter with any psychiatric testimony of its own. Dr. Caprio testified that Durham had been, in his opinion, "mentally ill since he was fifteen years old," and that the defendant was suffering from "a disintegration of the personality with accompanying delusions" when he committed the alleged crime. Although a jury found

Durham guilty, the Judge reversed the decision, mainly on the basis of Dr. Caprio's psychiatric testimony, and ordered the defendant committed to a mental institution until sane and not dangerous either to himself or to others.

We have traced the evolution of criteria of responsibility from the eighteenth century to the present. There remains the question: What does the future hold?

What Does the Future Hold?

Forward thinking psychiatrists and lawyers are gradually bringing about changes in the thinking on crime and punishment, especially in the field of insanity. As we have previously pointed out, the U. S. District of Columbia Court of Appeals, in the Durham case, modernized the entire concept of insanity, emphasizing medical criteria rather than legal precedent.

Although the new ruling has been hailed by both psychiatrists and lawyers, there has been much confusion and controversy in subsequent court rulings. One U. S. District Judge assailed the Durham rule as "general, indefinite and puzzling in practical application." In a 1956 Court of Appeals decision (Douglas vs. U. S.—U. S. Ct. Appls. D. C. Nos. 12795 and 12879), the Durham decision was held not to bar testimony, if available, in terms of older tests of insanity, and furthermore, not to bar instructions by the court permitting the jury to consider such tests as having evidential support, provided that the Durham decision is followed in its definition of the ultimate jury question to be decided. The court said:

"As to the criteria or tests to be used in resolving this issue Durham gives greater latitude than theretofore had prevailed in this jurisdiction. We had said in Holloway, following the McNaughten Rule (8 Eng. Reprint 718) that 'the ordinary test of criminal responsibility is whether the defendant could tell right from wrong' but we had there added, 'a slightly broader test is whether his reason had ceased to have domain of his mind to such an extent that his will was controlled, not by rational thought, but by mental disease.' (148 Fed. 2nd 666.)

"In the earlier case of Smith vs. U. S. (36 Fed. 2nd 548), we had also added the 'irresistible impulse' test which permitted the jury to consider whether the accused suffered from such a 'diseased mental condition as to deprive him of the will power to resist the insane impulse. . . .' But in Durham we concluded that the advance of psychiatric knowledge demonstrated the fallacy of making these particular 'symptoms, phases or manifestations' the exclusive criteria to guide the jury. In so holding, however, we did not purport to bar all use of the older tests: testimony given in these terms may still be received if the expert witness feels able to give it, and where a proper evidential foundation is laid, a trial court should permit the jury to consider such criteria in resolving the ultimate issue of 'whether the accused acted because of a mental disorder.' In aid of such a determination the court may permit the jury to consider whether or not the accused understood the nature of what he was doing and whether or not his actions were due to a failure, because of mental disease or defect, properly to control his conduct."

In another District of Columbia case, a jury acquitted John Leach on ground of insanity (Overholser vs. Leach, U. S. App. D. C. No. 14480) because psychiatric testimony indicated that he was a "sociopathic personality"—which actually means that he was *antisocial*. Leach was denied release from a mental hospital although he maintained he was sane all the time.

Dr. Winfred Overholser sees a trend toward sending more criminals to hospitals rather than to prison. He has commented further that in his opinion the court should allow more time for mental examination and evaluation of criminals. Judge David L. Bazelon, author of the Durham decision, is of the opinion: "It is both wrong and foolish to punish where there is no blame and where punishment cannot correct. The community security may be better protected by hospitalization (under D.C. Code Sec. 24-301) than by imprisonment." (William vs. U. S. 250 Fed. 2nd 19)

In the State of California there is an unprecedented move by psychiatrists as well as some lawyers to challenge the "right-and-wrong" test of insanity. This challenge has its roots in a case where psychiatric evidence indicates the commission of a criminal act by a defendant who, although knowing the difference between right and wrong, could not control his action. This drive may well be the beginning of a nationwide reappraisal of the prevailing "insanity" rules.

The State of Massachusetts, attempting to circumvent a capricious court ruling which would deny a mental examination to a defendant who needed one, passed, as far back as 1921, the so-called "Briggs Law" which provides that persons indicted for capital offenses, and others bound over or indicted who have previously been convicted of a felony or indicted more than once, are referred automatically to the State Department of Mental Health for examination. Overholser points out that "the examination is made not because anyone raises the issue but because the defendant falls into one of certain legal categories."

The examination is made by medical experts selected by psychiatrists and not by the courts. Such psychiatric examination, then, is taken from court supervision and made automatic and free from outside pressures. If a determination is made that the defendant needs mental care, he is certified to a mental hospital, and if he subsequently recovers, he may be tried in court. If, on the other hand, the defendant is adjudged sane and able to stand trial, it would be difficult for a frivolous plea of insanity to prevail.

Overholser further comments: "Thus justice has been done to the mentally ill defendant. Specious pleas of insanity have been virtually eliminated and the public has been spared the spectacle of seeing apparently equally competent men arrayed against each other on the witness stand."

Dr. Manfred S. Guttmacher, Chief Medical Advisor to the Supreme Court of Baltimore, Maryland, is chairman of a fourteen-member committee which has recommended modernization of the State of Maryland law in which insanity is evaluated by the McNaughten Rules.

Dr. Guttmacher points out that, in current psychiatric concepts, a person may be legally sane under the "right-and-wrong" test and yet "suffer from a mental illness which prevents him from being responsible for his acts."

The Guttmacher Committee recommends:

1. That a person be excused from criminal responsibility if, as a result of mental disease or deficiency at the time of such conduct, he lacks sufficient capacity to either understand and appreciate the criminality of his conduct or to conform his conduct to the requirement of the law.

2. A psychiatrist should be allowed to give testimony regarding the mental capacity of a defendant without danger of denying the defendant his rights.

3. Every defendant, if found insane at the time of commission of a crime but sane at time of trial, should be held at least one year for mental observation.

4. Any defendant in need of emergency psychiatric treatment should immediately be hospitalized.

Dr. Philip Q. Roche, in his award-winning book, *The Criminal Mind,* (Farrar, Straus & Cudahy) comments on the progress made by the courts in determining the issue of medical criteria of insanity as against legal criteria. He notes that a source of conflict between the psychiatrist and the lawyer is the latter's demand that the psychiatrist relate his observations in rather arbitrary language, defining mental illness as any behavior other than that which society calls normal.

Light has finally begun to shine through the clouds of

ignorance, precedent, and out-of-date thinking, mainly through the cooperation of the lawyer and psychiatrist. We hope that the future will bring an even closer study of the emotional personality as a basis for judging wrongful acts in general, and especially in the field of sex offenses where emotion has so much power over behavior. A *psycho-legal approach* must be established so that adequate psychiatric evaluation is accessible to all sex offenders.

Unfortunately, the sex offender remains a marked man in the community. The resulting and usually shameful publicity helps no one, and is especially harmful when small children are involved and the sex offender is stigmatized as a "fiend" or "degenerate."

Sex offenses are of course a community problem, but the problem is generally attacked without knowledge and insight. The emphasis is placed on the moral issue alone, when the problem is an involved psycho-legal matter. Society often fails to distinguish between the offender who commits a crime of violence and who may be a menace and is probably in need of psychiatric treatment, and the offender whose misbehavior involves no violence and which may do no real harm to anyone. There is a vast difference between the two and each should be dealt with accordingly. All sex offenders should not be lumped together for classification, treatment, or punishment.

In treating the problem of the sex offender there are conflicts between the attitude of society, legal precedent, personal bias on the part of lawyer or judge, and the medical standards of the psychiatrist. Too few attempts are seriously made to uncover the real problem—the problem of the individual. There is, then, too little interchange of ideas and too little cooperation in the handling of sex cases. But in such cooperation may well be the ultimate solution.

chapter two

OUR CHANGING CONCEPT
OF SEXUAL BEHAVIOR

Sex is a universal phenomenon, which has involved mankind in problems since the beginning of time. No race, primitive or civilized, has been without problems of sexual behavior.

This great incomprehensible mystery has challenged man's curiosity for ages. Yet he seemed also to fear his knowledge, for he surrounded himself with a shell of sexual ignorance. Only recently has there been a scientific recognition of sex as a major factor in life.

This widespread ignorance of one of the most important aspects of human behavior resulted in an inestimable amount of needless suffering.

ORIGIN OF SEX TABOOS

To understand life, one needs to understand sex. And to understand sex properly, one must have a knowledge of the origin of sex taboos.

The dread of sex as something *inherently* "evil" and harmful persists today. Sex taboos in our culture have their origin, symbolically, in the Garden of Eden. Warned by God not to eat the fruit of a certain tree on penalty of death, Adam, who was not told why he should not do so, ate the forbidden fruit and was expelled from Paradise, along with Eve, his copartner in the crime. According to René Guyon, author of *The Ethics of Sexual Acts,* the forbidden tree symbolized a characteristic taboo.

About this taboo, Frazer wrote in *The Golden Bough:*

1. When a chief priest of the Congo traveled for the purpose of meting out justice, married persons had to refrain from sexual relations; otherwise the priest would meet with disaster.

2. Hunters and fishermen avoided sexual relations before setting out on their expeditions; otherwise they would catch no game or fish.

3. Among the Kochins (Burma) a woman who prepared yeast for making beer abstained from sexual relations during this time; if not, the beer would be bitter.

4. Incestuous relations were avoided because they impaired the fertility of the soil and spoiled the harvest.

5. In Rome at the time of the Kings, incest was forbidden because it caused famine.

6. In the Congo, if a high priest was away from home, he would die if his flock failed to observe chastity.

It would appear from the above that not only refraining from incest, but the sacrifice of all sexual pleasure at certain times, was held to be essential to avoid calamity. Today, of course, we hold such prohibitions to be contrary to scientific knowledge and common sense. Yet we retain a host of prejudices that any sane analysis reduces to absurdity.

Dr. S. Kirson Weinberg, author of *Incest Behavior** observes that the "general incest taboos among the Hebrews were basic to the subsequent taboos in Western culture, especially in England and in the United States."

In Babylonia, incest was punishable by death or exile. In 1650 in England, incest was regarded as a crime and also punishable by death. The Romans considered physical intimacy between members of one's own family "unnatural." The

---

* Weinberg, Kirson, S., *Incest Behavior,* The Citadel Press, N.Y.

ancient Chinese often decapitated persons guilty of incestuous relations.

Sigmund Freud, in attempting to trace the origin of the incest taboo, informs us in his *Totem and Taboo* that, in prehistoric times, the leader of the "primal horde" forced his sons to leave the family while he kept the daughters to himself. The sons later united, returned to kill the father and eat his flesh believing that, in this way, they would acquire his virility and power. However, feeling guilty for their crime, they prohibited the killing of the totemic animal (the father symbol). They also prohibited sexual relations with women in the family horde.

According to Freud, therefore, this ancient taboo marked the beginning of "social organization, moral restriction and religion."

Laws prohibiting incest extended through Europe and the United States. In this country the Mormons practiced incest until 1892 when both incest and polygamy were outlawed by the Utah legislature.

SEX AND RELIGION

In all "primitive" religions, whether ancient or contemporary, the sexual function was mythologized in a great diversity of forms, expressing the ingenious variety of practices which "make mores right." Sacred harlotry, for example, was a widely distributed phenomenon. It survived in disguised form and under rationalizations prompted by the local mores as in the Lupanars (brothels) of medieval cities in Europe. Sex worship as a form of religion was primarily associated with fertility rites. Thus, ancient peoples looked upon the erect phallus (penis) and the yoni (vulva) as symbols of the creative force of nature, representative of reproduction, harvest, and the "mystery" of birth. These procreative images, with attendant myths and rituals, are found in all early cultures. Ceremonial practices, surrounding and dramatizing the sexual functions, often included in religious dances, erotic movements that often culminated in sexual orgies.*

The origin of sex taboos, according to historical documents, runs parallel to the origin of religious rites. Thus, sexuality becomes associated with that which was considered "sinful," "immoral," "shameful," and "unclean."

Today, psychiatrists encounter many patients who suffer from psychosomatic ailments due to sex guilt. Some psychoanalysts interpret their suffering as an unconscious need for self-punishment due to what they consider their sexual transgressions. It is an acknowledged fact that many severe cases of anxiety neuroses among the very religious stem from the fear of punishment for such "sins" after death.

In Orthodox Jewish culture the sin of masturbation was punishable by death. Catholic sex codes—which, as we know, stem from the earliest sex taboos of the Jewish faith—condemned masturbation as a "carnal sin." The Protestants continued this attitude.

Not so long ago, both Jewish and Christian clerics attributed everything from pimples to insanity to "the evil of self-abuse." Fortunately, today there is less evidence of such ignorant and harsh condemnation. The public, too, has adopted a more realistic attitude toward masturbation, and the change is due chiefly to scientific enlightenment. Thus, today, both the universality of self-gratification and its harmlessness are recognized as established facts.

Thanks to psychoanalysis, many people no longer regard their sexual organs with the disgust, shame, or guilt, which stems from the theological concept of "original sin." However, instances recur of neurotic parents instilling in their offspring a fear of punishment should they innocently fondle their genitals.

* *Sexual Deviations*, London, L.S. and Caprio, F.S., Linacre Press, Washington, D.C. 1950.

Our prudery regarding sexual matters thus has its origin in ancient taboos which contravene logic and experience. A good example is the objection of those with a strong puritanical complex to the display of women's lingerie in department stores as being "morally offensive and embarrassing." What, we ask, could be more ridiculous or more farfetched?

A study of sex taboos reveals that the terms "normality" and "abnormality" have relative meanings, predicated on convention rather than nature or instinct.

According to the article entitled "Concepts of Normality and Abnormality In Sexual Behavior" published by the Kinsey Group in 1949: "An examination of the early sex codes shows that they originated in much the same way as the food taboos, the menstrual taboos, the restrictions of nudity, and a host of other such prohibitions. Hittite and Hebraic codes are replete with condemnation by classification, the labeling of certain acts as clean or unclean, as an offense when performed in the sight of the King, of Jehovah, or of some God. . . . Only later did they become prohibitions against all animal intercourse, against all homosexual contacts, against nearly all oral-genital contacts. . . . Masturbation, mouth-genital, anal, homosexual, and animal contacts were considered unnatural, because they were acts that could not lead to reproduction. All of these were greater sins than nonmarital coitus. In light of more modern attitudes on masturbation, it should not be overlooked that 'self-pollution' was rated by some Talmudic scholars as the greatest of all sexual sins. However, at various times in the history of the Christian Church pre-coital sex play, variations in positions assumed in intercourse, and all other variant eroticisms were similarly condemned as perversions. In some church groups the restrictions against erotic play, even including mouth-genital contacts, have been relaxed, *provided* that such activities are not engaged in as an end in themselves, but as adjuncts to the successful consummation of a genital union between married partners. It is interesting to find that many clinicians still use their reproductive criterion as the prime basis for determining the normality or abnormality of the sexual behavior of their patients."

While we recognize that much in our moral and legal codes is a residue of primitive sex taboos, we have done little to revise such residues out of legislation governing sexual behavior.

In summarizing the influence of taboos on our present attitude toward sex, René Guyon writes:

"According to the theory of sex, sex is taboo, the sexual organs are taboo, their names and functions are taboo. All our actual prohibitions are derived from this: they have tended to separate the sexes in order to avoid transgressions; disgrace to him who does not respect the taboo (formerly it would have been death). Since the formulation of this doctrine, the whole of human evolution has had to bear the burden of this heavy mortgage, which still makes itself felt today in our laws and prohibitions, in the fanatical activities of the various societies for opposing sex, in numberless arbitrary interferences with private life."

SEXUAL PROBLEMS IN EARLY TIMES AND THE LAW

Anthropologists point to drawings and markings inside prehistoric caves of males with erect penises as the first expression of the concept of homosexuality inasmuch as the drawings symbolized the "manly" status of the male. Sanger Brown suggests that, during the earliest periods of human society, sex symbols were plentiful, including phallic emblems and figures of Kings and Gods with erect penises. Other sex symbols were fire and trees with subjects of symbolworship.

Clifford Allen, author of *The Sexual Perversions and Abnormalities,* points out that the ancient Hebrews, a small nation, condemned any sexual practice—and in particular any form of homosexual behavior—which might interfere with natural reproduction, which they counted on for their national survival. Bailey believes that the ancient Egyptians disapproved of homosexuality. The Assyrians had laws which penalized homosexuality with flogging or castration. In other ancient cultures, such as the Hittites, while it is not certain what penalties were imposed, evidence points to the condemnation of homosexuality.

With the passsage of time and the advance of civilization, emblematic reverence gave way to other bizarre sex practices. We now call these "perversions," because they are regarded as maladjustments of the sexual life. Brown maintains that later as these inverted practices became more popular, the state, mainly through the influence of Christianity, attempted to stamp them out, though not with complete success.

The male was made dominant as the sex factor and woman was relegated to a humiliating status. Under the influence of such cults, woman was generally held in low estimation, until a new principle came into being, that of the virgin birth. This solemnized the state of womanhood. Once again the female rose in esteem, and womanhood symbolized goodness, purity, and righteousness. The church had conceived an almost infallible concept, that of the married woman in the home as a saintly state. Thus the relationship between man and woman was sanctified, the sacredness of the home made inviolate, and womanhood raised to a high status. A wife who was about to become a mother was considered a messenger from heaven itself. It was hoped that this would solemnize and solidify the relationship between man and woman and lead to sexual purity. Restricting sex relations to the home, where it would be regarded as fine and good, was expected to stamp out the then prevalent "perverted" habits.

But as John Symonds points out, there was once again a strange and unforeseen reversal of form. The high ideas and ideals devised by the church failed, at least in part. The restrictions against variations of sexual behavior seemed to stimulate their recurrence. These included various types of homosexual contact among males and females and also incestuous practices, aberrations involving the abuse of small children, and sodomy. Sexual deviations may also have been a consequence of the sexual licence in Imperial Roman times, when "social diseases" became rampant. Female sexual partners may have deliberately been avoided for fear of venereal infection, and male partners sought instead. As male homosexuality flourished, the lawmakers assumed a lenient attitude. It was not contrary to Greek law, for example, for a Greek citizen to take a male lover.

Elizabeth Drummond points out that the city government of Athens depended for a substantial part of its income on the fees paid by licensed houses of male prostitution. Greek law allowed agreements between young boys and male adults, establishing contractual rights to the sexual use of the persons involved. These same laws went so far as to protect the middleman or procurer who was then a perfectly respectable businessman. These contracts of homosexual prostitution were upheld by the courts as establishing an effective and actionable right, enforceable by law. A young boy not fortunate enough to be under contract was not so well favored in the eyes of the law. The sexual freelance was punished for open-market solicitation. The practice of homosexuality was so widespread in Greece that the army permitted soldiers to consort sexually with each other, believing that it bolstered morale.

Thus a comprehensive study of homosexuality from the historical and sociological standpoint reveals worldwide incidence of this practice, in various forms, differing degrees, and in varying grades of social and legal tolerance.

As we pointed out earlier, Hebraic laws prohibited homosexuality and imposed capital punishment on convicted offenders. Likewise, the Koran of the Mohammedans condemned to death violators of this "crime" against nature. Canon Law, that is the rule or doctrine of discipline confirmed by the Pope, also censured this practice.

It is safe to say, as noted by Drummond, that modern sex laws, although no doubt based on ancient Hebraic principles, derived at least in part, from the Justinian Code (named for Justinian, the Byzantine Emperor [483-565 A.D.], in whose reign laws of the Empire were codified); it imposed penalties for sodomy, rape, adultery, fornication, incest, and sexual corruption of minors. The code so influenced the criminal laws of England and most European countries that sodomy is considered a serious crime in many jurisdictions. Joseph Parke says that the old English sentence for convicted sodomites was burial alive; in Scotland male offenders who violated children were hanged; in France, where homosexuality had gone almost unchecked for centuries, offenders were brought before a church tribunal and, if found guilty, a sentence of hanging or burning (or both) was imposed.

According to J. D. Mercer: "Pious Emperor Theodosius burned homosexuals alive—*sacro-sanctum esse debeter hospitium virilis animal*—classing all manifestations of homosexuality with the calling up of demons, sorcery and witchcraft, worship of pagan deities, and any kind of abominable profanation. Those who were burned, it seems scarcely necessary to mention, were invariably slaves, freemen, peasants, tradesmen, and mechanics."

A most gruesome case of homosexual behavior in the annals of French law, and, indeed, in any legal annals, is that of Gilles de Rais, notorious fifteenth-century sadist. The son of a wealthy and powerful baron, married at the age of sixteen, Gilles was rich, tall, and handsome. But his aversion to women drove him away from his young and lovely wife after a few weeks of marriage. He joined the army and gained fame as a military leader, becoming Marshal of France at the age of twenty-five. As a trusted Court adviser, he made no secret of his preference for male sex companions, especially young ones. Gilles cultivated a fervent friendship with Joan of Arc, but this did not alter his sexual preferences. Following the death of Joan of Arc, whom Gilles was unable to save, his conduct became sadistic. His chief victims were children whom he would befriend, with lavish kindness, then suddenly beat them without mercy. After performing abnormal sexual acts upon their little bodies, he would take a razor-sharp knife and mutilate them. It is estimated that Gilles de Rais thus murdered at least two hundred children. In 1440 he was tried before a tribunal of the Bishop of Nantes and sentenced to be hanged, and, while still alive, to then be burned at the stake. This man was, without doubt, the most "depraved criminal" of early times.

Among the Zulus a man guilty of incest was regarded as an evildoer and put to death. In other primitive cultures, suicide for the offender was compulsory.

Incest was a Biblical offense. The Hebrews incorporated the incest taboo in their Mosaic laws and extended it to half sisters. The penalties were "ostracism, ritualistic curse witnessed by the people, and death."

However, Weinberg notes: "Lot committed incest with his daughters at their instigation because they wanted children; Abraham married his half sister, Sarah; Jacob married the sister of his first wife with her father's consent; Reuben had relations with his father's wife Bilhah, and nothing was done. Moses was the son of an aunt and nephew. Ezekiel protested against the laxity of incest customs during the Babylonian exile. But, during the later stay of the Hebrews in Palestine, the incest taboo became more effective."

The sanctions against adultery, as set down in the Ten Commandments, "Thou shalt not commit adultery" and "Thou shalt not covet their neighbor's wife" were, according to historians, observed even before the time of Moses, and there was strict punishment for a woman found guilty.

Jesus Christ decreed the everlastingness of the marriage contract and the solemnity of the relationship, although amongst the rabbis there was doubt and much debate as to what he actually meant. Richard Lewinsohn, in his recent work, *A History of Sexual Customs,* points out that there were two rabbinical schools of thought by which Christ may have been influenced. The more liberal Hillel School allowed divorce for adultery while the other more conservative group, headed by Rabbi Shammai, made it much more difficult for a man to rid himself of his wife, even on these grounds. According to the strictest teachings of Christ, divorce was forbidden altogether because he decreed the relationship of marriage to have been created by God and not by man, therefore, a relationship which no man himself could put aside. Canon Law, that of the Catholic Church, adopted this dictum, recognizes no exception to it and accordingly, no divorce—no matter what the grounds —is acceptable to the church. Most Protestant denominations, however, hold that Christ meant to allow divorce under certain conditions, and they have relaxed their thinking along that line.

From a reading of the applicable Biblical text, either conclusion might reasonably be reached since there seems to be variance in the Gospel texts. In the Gospel of St. Matthew, one finds: "Whoever shall put away his wife except for fornication and shall marry another shall be guilty of adultery," but the Gospel of Mark, Luke, and St. Paul mention no such exception.

Irrespective of prohibition against adultery, church or otherwise, it does not appear that any of our cultures, past or present, have been able to devise laws effective against adultery. In some periods, such as the Renaissance, adultery was commonplace and condoned by society; the penalties, if any, were light.

THE EVOLUTION OF SCIENTIFIC THEORIES OF SEXUAL BEHAVIOR

Although the physician Henrick Kaan gave a general description of sexual pathology in his book published in 1844, *Psychopathia Sexualis,* it was Karl Ulrichs, a German writer and magistrate who, in 1866, advanced the first theory to account for homosexuality. Ulrichs coined the term "Urning" (derived from Uranos of Plato) for a male homosexual and "Urningin" for a female homosexual. He believed that homosexuality was congenital. He was of the opinion that a homosexual had the body of one sex and the mind and soul of the opposite sex. His book was published under the name of *Numa Numantius.*

In 1869, Carl Fredrich Otto Westphal, professor of psychiatry in Berlin, made a specific scientific study of homosexuality. He established homosexuality as a "disease of inversion." He regarded it as a sexual anomaly, a morbid type of congenital inversion. He also referred to it as "moral insanity" and coined the term "contrary sexual feeling." Westphal was the first to put the study of sexual inversion on a scientific basis.

In 1875 Paolo Mantegazza of Italy investigated sexual anomalies. He concluded that homosexuality represented an "error of nature" and attributed it to two causes: (1) difficulty in practicing normal coitus and (2) desire for pleasure.

A few years after the famous French hypnotist, Jean Martin Charcot, considered homosexuality a morbid entity, caused by hereditary degeneration of some kind.

Richard von Krafft-Ebing, Professor of Psychiatry at Vienna University, presented detailed data regarding homosexuality in his famous work, *Psychopathia Sexualis,* published in 1886. It was considered an authoritative work at the time, but it added little to the understanding of the psychological causes of sexual inversion. Krafft-Ebing divided sexual inversion into (1) acquired homosexuality and (2) congenital homosexuality. The latter he took to be a manifestation or sign of degeneration—a neuropathic and psychopathic state which is hereditary.

Dr. Albert Moll of Berlin, another early investigator, considered inversion an innate anomaly and emphasized heredity as the important factor. Because homosexuality is contrary to the procreation instinct, he assigned it to the realm of pathology (a sickness or disease). However, the sexual instinct cannot be regarded as a procreative instinct, and Moll failed to take into consideration its functions of expressing love and experiencing pleasure.

Ivan Bloch, German author of several important works on sex, including the well-known *The Sexual Life of Our Times,* an encyclopedia of the sexual sciences in relation to our civilization, re-emphasized the conclusions of his predecessors that homosexuality was a "sickness."

Magnus Hirschfeld, sexologist and founder of the Institute of Sexual Science in Berlin (1918) and author of *Sexual Anomalies* unfortunately harbored the misconception that homosexuality is congenital. He stated: "It is therefore conclusive that the homosexual urge is independent of the wish and will and that its phenomenon lies in the individual constitution itself." It was Hirschfeld, moreover, who proposed the term "third sex" (a sexual intermediary stage between man and woman).

It should be noted, however, that Hirschfeld did stress the importance of viewing sexual inversion as a social phenomenon and repeatedly urged revision of legal statutes in keeping with this approach.

In 1897 appeared the first of a series of scientific investigations into expressions of sexual behavior by the English sexologist, Havelock Ellis (1859-1939). Published in seven volumes over a period of years, under the title of *Studies in the Psychology of Sex,* these works constituted, at the time, the most comprehensive contribution to the understanding of human manifestations. One volume was devoted entirely to the subject of sexual inversion.

In the theoretical field, Ellis upheld some of the viewpoints of the earlier investigators, emphasizing at times, a theory of congenital homosexuality. Thus, we find him writing: "Congenital sexual inversion is an anomaly, an inborn variation of which we are beginning to understand the causes; it is, even when extreme, only pathological in the same sense as color-blindness, or albinism, or transposition of the viscera is pathological." Ellis also offered clinical evidence that psychological factors played an important role in causing homosexuality. Though he was not fully aware of the scientific implications of the evidence he presented, Havelock Ellis paved the way for the significant developments that were to begin with Sigmund Freud.

In the opening decade of the twentieth century, Sigmund Freud, father of the new science of psychoanalysis, gave the world a new theory of sexuality. He claimed that all human beings go through a stage of sexual development in infancy and childhood known as the "polymorphous perverse stage" which accounts for the universality of variations in sexual behavior.

Freud formulated the hypothesis that in all human beings there are residual manifestations of "polymorphous perversity;" that we are all basically bisexual by virtue of the fact that each of us is the product of the union of male and female; and that variations in sexual behavior actually represent a regression to the infantile stage of sexual development. Freud attributed certain variations, such as homosexual activities, to arrested development of the sexual impulse. He found that they were caused by "fixated" attachments to one or both parents.

He maintained that a definite interrelationship existed between health and the expression or suppression of sexual desires. This sex hunger, he labeled the "libido." Freud also concluded that the libido drive, present in all human beings, is closely associated with our love component—the most powerful of all our emotions. On this premise all love at the unconscious level is intimately related to sexuality, which accounts for the instinctive reciprocal attraction between the sexes resulting in the perpetuation of the race. Sex is an international language. The sexual instinct, a component of the over-all instinct of self-preservation, is also responsible for man's accomplishments in science, art, literature, and music —all of which sublimate the sexual impulse.

Freud discovered in his psychoanalytic studies that we all have a common sexual nature which begins with infancy and ends with death. He observed that the prohibitions of sexual pleasures in the name of "morality" only serve to make sex more erotic. Excessive modesty about sex stimulates sexual precocity in childhood and keeps some adults preoccupied with sexual matters.

He found that persons who evaded the sexual side of their lives were doomed to neurosis, their sexual repressions being based on the presumption that sex is synonymous with sin. The neurosis declares itself in the language of the unconscious. Thus health complaints of a psychosomatic nature supply evidence of unsatisfied libidinal needs. This clinical Freudian viewpoint was substantiated by dream analysis. What a person may consciously deny is revealed by hidden wishes disguised in dream symbolism. Freud, in this respect alone, made a major contribution to medical knowledge and established psychoanalysis as a permanent scientific technique for the diagnosis and treatment of neurotic disorders.

Dr. Wilhelm Stekel, an original coworker of Freud, made important contributions to the understanding of homosexuality and other sexual aberrations. Between 1920 and 1932 he published in German and English over a dozen books on varieties of aberrant sexual behavior. His findings on bisexual love and the homosexual neurosis are well known. Stekel concluded that there is no inborn homosexuality, no inborn heterosexuality, only bisexuality. He regarded homosexuality as already involving a predisposition to neurosis, viewing sexual inversion as an outgrowth of certain emotional attitudes.

The late Dr. Smith Ely Jelliffe,* famous American psychoanalyst, explained homosexuality as follows:

"Everyone passes through a period of development when he tends to fall in love or be especially interested in persons like himself, that is, of the same sex. This is the homosexual state and is the natural transition between self-love and the state of objective love in which the object is of the opposite sex. A homosexual residual of this state remains as a normal component of every individual, which adequately sublimated, is of great social value as the basic factor in friendships between persons of the same sex, but inadequately sublimated becomes the basis of homosexuality in its various perverse forms."

Dr. Edmund Bergler, contemporary American psychoanalyst, is of the opinion that "every homosexual is an exquisite injustice collector, and consequently a psychic masochist. The psychic masochist is a neurotic who constantly creates, by means of his own unconscious provocations, situations in which he finds himself 'behind the eight-ball.' What he is really after, although consciously he is ignorant of this dreary fact, is defeat, humiliation, rejection."

THE CONCEPT OF THE SEX-LOVE INTERRELATIONSHIP

Sex is an expression of one's basic personality. It can either represent the gratification of a physical desire per se (sex for sex's sake) or what is more desirable, a psycho-physical expression of love.

* *Diseases of the Nervous System*, Smith Ely Jelliffe, M.D.

The term "sex-love impulse" implies that there exists a component of the instinct of self-preservation known as the sex drive. It is an instinct we are born with. No one is born "sexless" or "asexual."

It is this inner biological urge or force that explains the universal desire to mate and accounts for the perpetuation of the human race. Running parallel to our *sex instinct* is the *love instinct* (the need to love and be loved). As we mature, these two instincts tend to fuse into a single impulse or hunger. We learn, as we grow older, that sex can represent more than just a desire to mate, that it is closely related to the esthetic impulse to love. Thus, the sex-love impulse is a psycho-biological force incorporating the idea of both the physical or biological and the psychological or emotional. This sex-love impulse becomes an integral part of everything we do.

It is impossible to overrate the importance of our sex-love instinct. Our personality, the degree to which we succeed or fail in our work, our ability or lack of ability to attract friends, every aspect of our life is influenced by the degree to which we use (or abuse) this impulse. It becomes an enormous force for good in our life when we understand it. It becomes a source of suffering when we abuse its physical aspect or neglect its emotional aspect.

Dr. Gelolo McHugh, psychologist at Duke University, described sex as a God-given force for human good, a medium for the expression of love.

On the emotional level the drive for survival can be expressed in three different ways:

1. Sex for sex's sake (sex without love)
2. Love for love's sake (love without sex)
3. Sex with love (married loved: the ideal)

We all know that we can achieve sexual gratification, release or satisfaction, whatever we choose to call it, without experiencing the emotion of love. Biological sex (sex for sex's sake) is part of human nature. Sex acts are consummated millions of times a day in the absence of love. This is *reality*.

It is also true that between two persons, a strong feeling of love can exist that does not include a desire for physical intimacy.

There is true married love (a love-sex unity) which combines the physical and emotional, an ideal amalgamation of sex and love. One complements the other. As Theodor Reik has said: "Sex and love usually go together just as whiskey is taken with soda. But the mixture of the two does not change whiskey into soda or soda into whiskey. All kinds of mixtures of both are possible."

Since the need for affection is so basic in all of us, we can conclude that the act of loving is unconsciously motivated by one's own wish to be loved. This element of self-love exists in every love relationship. We demonstrate in a physical way what we like the other person to do for us. True love is *reciprocal*. The unselfish giving and receiving of affection is essential to a state of well-being and emotional security.

chapter three

SEXUAL PROBLEMS IN MARRIAGE: PSYCHO-LEGAL ASPECTS

GENERAL CONSIDERATIONS

It is an established fact that 75% of the annual 400,000 divorces in this country are caused by sexual incompatibility. Marriage counselors, psychiatrists, lawyers, and clergymen have arrived at this conclusion from their consultations with couples experiencing marital difficulties.

In-law complications, adultery, excessive drinking, money quarrels, personality incompatibility, and jealousy are usually given as causes for marriage failure. On closer look, however, the basic underlying trouble may be an imbalance in the sex-love relationship.

More often than should be the case, the husband or wife seeks the advice of an attorney and ask for a separation or divorce. Seldom when giving the causes of their marital difficulties do they mention sexual disharmony. Usually the lawyer is well-meaning and sympathetic, but uninformed on the psychodynamic aspects of sexual problems. Without further inquiry he may accede to the desires of his client and take legal steps to dissolve the marriage. This is regrettable because:

1. It alienates two people who, having once been in love, could be guided back into love.

2. When the husband or wife leaves the marriage bed and lives apart, there is less likelihood of a reconciliation.

3. When husband or wife goes to a lawyer without the knowledge of the other, there is created an atmosphere of tension and distrust which makes it more difficult to achieve a future satisfactory solution.

It is our opinion that the *inadvertent nurturing* of divorces by some lawyers is the wrong approach and accounts, at least in part, for the ever-increasing divorce rate.

Many sex problems in marriage have psycho-legal aspects.

Some examples of psycho-legal complications: (1) A woman may consult an attorney to secure annulment of her marriage on the ground that her husband is impotent. (2) Husband or wife, suspecting the partner of infidelity, seeks advice on how to obtain evidence that would be sufficient for a court action. (3) A husband may make excessive sexual demands on his wife or may want her to indulge in practices not acceptable to her. Developing an aversion to sex, she may wonder what, if any, her legal rights may be. (4) A woman may discover that her husband has been complaining that she is unresponsive and refuses to fulfill her marital obligations.

We have discovered that many such problems in marriage could be solved satisfactorily through the combined efforts of an attorney and a psychiatrist. The authors have had opportunities to put into practice this psycho-legal approach and have been able, in the majority of instances, to save marriages which otherwise would have ended in divorce.

To our knowledge there has been no published literature whereby such a method has been tried. Our new approach was inspired by the nature of the questions asked by husbands and wives regarding their respective *sexual rights in marriage*.

Let us examine the marriage contract from the legal standpoint and see just what each partner is entitled to, sexually, and what obligations each owes to the other.

The right to sexual intercourse distinguishes the marriage contract from any other type of contract. Actually, marriage is the only status created by the law regulating behavior in sexual relations. Implied in every marriage agreement is the right of each partner to expect his or her mate to be physically and emotionally capable of consummating the sex act. Each is entitled to the exclusive sexual enjoyment of the other. These are basic legal rights and obligations in marriage. It is astonishing how few people know that the contract of marriage includes these legal aspects of their sex relationship.

WHAT CONSTITUTES NORMAL AND ABNORMAL PRACTICES IN MARRIAGE

There is considerable confusion as to what is normal in sex behavior and what is abnormal.

Every psychiatrist encounters patients, married and unmarried, who have suffered from acute states of anxiety because of indulgence in practices which they regarded as "perversions."

Lawyers are also consulted by couples where the nature of the sex relationship caused friction and marital disharmony.

Incidentally, the derogatory term "perversion" is now obsolete. It has been replaced by the more scientific term, "deviation."

One woman threatened to divorce her husband because she claimed he was a "pervert." When asked what his perversion was she replied that he liked to "suck her breasts." She felt such an act must be "unnatural and abnormal." This is merely one illustration of general misconceptions of what is normal and abnormal.

The oral-erotic impulse is present in every human being. In its more extreme manifestations, fellatio or cunnilingus (mouth contacts with the male or female genitals) are carry-overs of an infantile impulse to suck the mother's breast or the nipple of the bottle, depending upon whether we were breast or bottle-fed. If the libido is fixated at the oral-erotic level, the individual, as an adult prefers oral sexuality to coitus.

However, among the majority of persons who have achieved a heterosexual goal, certain oral stimulations practiced between husband and wife need not be construed as perverse. The mental attitude of the respective partners plays an important role.

According to Kinsey, Pomeroy, and Martin: "In marital relations, oral stimulations of male or female genitalia occur in about 60% of the histories of persons who have been to college."

They go on to say: "In nearly all of the upper-level histories which involve oral contacts, the males make contacts with the female genitalia. In about 47% of the histories, the female make similar contacts with the male genitalia."

We are told by the same authors "that these oral practices existed in every civilization in the history of the world. Pictorial evidence of these activities can be found on pottery and other objects from Greece, India, China, Japan, and elsewhere."

Kinsey and his associates in their investigations, discovered that many separations and divorces revolved around dissension over oral sex relations. They also mention that, in several instances, husbands were even murdered by their wives because of disagreements involving mouth-genital contacts.

Oral stimulation of the genitals of the opposite sex as fore-pleasure is regarded by many psychiatrists as compatible with normality, provided there are no feelings of guilt or conflicts associated with the act. They may be considered accessory forms of sexual excitation. If the individuals are enabled to achieve satisfaction from coitus by such pre-practices as fellatio and cunnilingus, these cannot in every case be labeled "abnormal."

In a happy marriage, whatever husband or wife do, within

reason, to express physical love and give pleasure to each other is normal. The term "within reason" involves the mutual attitude of the husband or wife, toward certain preliminary love-making techniques. Drs. Abraham and Hannah Stone, authors of the *Marriage Manual,* feel that there is no particular routine to follow but that "one should preferably develop one's ingenuity and skill and make sex life a mutual adventure."

Deviations are allowable as long as they lead to normal intercourse. They are usually abnormal or neurotic when they are always practiced to the exclusion of the mating that nature intended.

If the variation in love-making leads to completed satisfaction, it is better to accommodate your partner as long as the activity is acceptable to you. In fact, variations often help to restore or maintain the potency of the husband.

The late Dr. A. A. Brill, world-famous psychoanalyst, found that departure from the normal was frequently encountered in the "intimate lives of otherwise normal people." He stated: "We call them perversions only when they absolutely dominate the picture, that is when they are fixed. Occasional indulgence in these acts does not stamp those practicing them as abnormal."

The husband who inflicts pain or violence, or insists that his wife dress bizarrely, or does so himself before he can consummate a relationship, is sexually neurotic and unreasonable in his demands.

No generalities can cover what is morally or ethically right for any particular case. These things have to be decided by the individual. The psychiatrist can only educate him to the intelligent attitude, the right approach to sex. The individual must make up his own mind.

Each case of sexual variations must be judged on its own merits.

Few people know that a husband can be brought to court

for performing what is regarded as "an unlawful sexual act" with his wife or that such an act may also constitute grounds for divorce. Many of our states have written into their divorce laws the terms "unnatural acts" or "crimes against nature" as specific grounds for divorce. In other states, similar sexual acts are covered by the "cruelty" or "mental cruelty" statutes. Although the married partner is liable to criminal prosecution because of a "perverted" sexual act with his spouse, actual criminal actions is rarely resorted to.

Two recent cases were brought to our attention. In the first, a husband was performing cunnilingus on his wife in the privacy of their bedroom. One of three children in the family, unaware of the sexual activity of the parents, opened the bedroom door and observed what was going on. The child, frightened by what she had seen, ran to a neighbor with the story. The police were called and the husband arrested. He readily admitted the act and stated that he did not see anything wrong with it. He further said that the wife did not object to what he was doing and that, in fact, she encouraged him.

Armed with this confession, a conviction was obtained and the man sentenced to prison for five years.

The second case involved a similar circumstance wherein a husband performed anal intercourse on his wife with her full consent. She then reported the incident to the authorities and the husband was arrested for performing an unnatural sex act.

The authors were consulted in the following case. The wife, an attractive and educated young woman, volunteered information that her husband, a professional man of substantial standing and learning, had been demanding a type of sexual practice which she did not actually desire for several years. In seven years of married life, she had experienced normal intercourse only once. She had surrendered to his demands at the beginning through sheer sexual ignorance. Later on, she yielded thinking it was her "duty" as a wife. She stated that her husband insisted his way was "normal" and that her preference for normal intercourse showed her lack of sexual sophistication. Fraught with guilt feelings and anxiety, the wife sought psychiatric advice and legal counsel.

This woman did not actually want a divorce nor did she wish to leave her husband. What she wanted was for her husband to agree to have relations in the conventional manner. Fortunately, the husband agreed to cooperate with both the psychiatrist and lawyer and his cooperation saved the marriage. Faced with the realization that he suffered from a severe sexual neurosis, he secured the psychiatric treatment that he needed.

THE MARRIED SEX OFFENDER

In our professional experience with sexual problem cases involving the law, we have found that many sex offenders are married. Surprisingly enough, a good percentage of men charged with indecent exposure are married men, some of them the fathers of several children.

This is also true of rapists and men arrested on charges of homosexuality. It would seem that a married man with normal sexual outlets would not indulge in sexual acts contrary to the law and thus endanger not only his standing in the community but his marriage and home as well. But the courts are never without cases involving the married sex offender.

It is our feeling that many of these married men who suffer from sexual deviations which bring them in conflict with the law can be rehabilitated. Sending them to prison is considered by psychiatrists and enlightened lawyers as unscientific and pointless. In fact, incarceration without treatment often results in the offender repeating his offense after he leaves prison. Merely being behind bars does not correct the trouble nor does it serve as a deterrent to future crimes. In addition, imprisonment has the added disadvantage of making it easier for the wife to dissolve the marriage while her husband is away.

Psychiatrists and lawyers are now beginning to realize that most sex offenders are sick people. In view of this fact, we feel that wives should not act in haste and seek a divorce; rather, they should encourage their husbands to receive psychiatric help. Thus many marriages which otherwise would end in divorce could be saved by timely and constructive professional management.

CASE ILLUSTRATIONS

Case 1. A young man had been arrested for molesting women with indecent advances and obscene remarks. Since he was married and the father of two children, and never had been arrested previously, the court decided to have him submit to psychiatric treatment in preference to sending him to jail or a mental institution. After several interviews, he mentioned that he had never received any sex education and had apparently failed to satisfy his wife sexually. He accused her of being frigid. Actually, he lacked the elementary rudiments of love-making. After instruction in sex technique, and treatment that included self-analysis, he understood the psychological factors that had led to his particular sex complex.

Since completing treatment, he has been in no further difficulty with the law, and his wife reports that what seemed a disaster has proved a blessing. Her husband has become a changed man. She has been happy for the first time since they married and has no difficulty responding to his love-making.

He was so satisfied with the progress he made that he wrote us a lengthy letter informing us that he had purchased a new home, had gotten a promotion on his job, and was certain that his sex life was permanently under control.

This case represents one wherein the wife was patient and gave her husband an opportunity to be cured of his sexual aberration. If the husband is cooperative and places himself under psychiatric supervision, the wife, particularly if she has children, should give her husband a chance to be restored to normality. If treatment proves ineffective or he discontinues treatment, then she is privileged to make other plans. This holds true in all cases of neurotic sexual aberrations.

Case 2. The court recently referred a young married man, the father of a child, who was arrested for "peeping" into a ladies toilet. He would hide, bore holes into the walls of public lavatories, and observe the women entering and leaving.

On the first two occasions when he was caught, he pretended he was a plumber making repairs. However, one time a woman, seeing his eye at the peephole he had made, screamed, and he was caught and placed under arrest.

Oddly enough, the young man was extremely religious, well educated and a good provider and had never gotten into any previous difficulty with the law. His wife, who was devoted to him, was naturally stunned when told by the police that her husband was a "Peeping Tom."

Because the judge regarded this case as a "sympathetic" one insofar as there was no evidence of any criminal tendencies, the man was placed on probation with the stipulation that he avail himself of psychiatric treatment.

His sexual deviation, the technical name for which is "voyeurism," from a French word meaning "look," was traced to sex experiences in childhood and early adolescence when he had looked through the keyhole of the bathroom at his sister. This premature sex stimulation became a fixation with him, a constant secret wish to spy on women while they occupied ladies' rest rooms. Cases of voyeurism, like those of "indecent exposure," are very common. As previously stated, most sexual deviations of a bizarre character represent forms of sexual immaturity. Stekel regarded them as manifestations of "psychosexual infantilism."

Our "Peeping Tom" patient took advantage of the opportunity of learning to control his voyeuristic impulses. He read up on the subject of sexual aberrations, acquired a scientific understanding of their origin and development, and was finally able to give up what he agreed was a "senseless game of satisfying a sex urge that began in childhood." He was convinced that for a husband to consider himself sexually adequate, he first had to achieve sexual maturity. He also expressed a genuine wish to make his marriage a happy and successful one. He loved his wife and child and stated that they meant everything in the world to him.

Case 3. Another young man, whom we shall call Jim, age twenty-six, married, sought psychiatric examination after being arraigned on a disorderly conduct charge. It was discovered that, for several years he had suffered from a sexual complex, rather bizarre in nature—stealing ladies' panties from clotheslines.

During his early adolescence, at the period of sexual awakening, he had become fascinated by panties which his sister had carelessly left about in her bedroom. These stimulated him sexually, provoking fantasies of what women look like clad only in panties. This led to an interest in advertisements and displays of women's lingerie. As he grew older, he began acquiring ladies' panties by stealing them from clotheslines. This complex became his hidden secret. He felt that marriage would cure him of his affliction, but not being sexually well adjusted, he made excessive demands in his wife who developed an aversion to intercourse. His wife suspected that there must be something wrong with him sexually. He accused her of being cold, because she refused to have sex relations every night. They became more incompatible and he felt justified in returning to his old habit of panty-stealing until the law finally caught up with him. However, the court decided to give him an opportunity to avail himself of psychiatric treatment. Jim was cooperative and wished to be cured, but his wife decided to leave him and sought a divorce on the grounds that her husband was sexually abnormal. One can understand how difficult it is for a wife to tolerate a sexual aberration in a husband, particularly when the security of her marriage is threatened by the possibility of his being institutionalized.

Innumerable wives are confronted by this very problem.

Many men charged with indecent exposure, for example, are married and have children. Others are homosexual and deprive their wives of normal sex gratification. All husbands who have a serious sex aberration that brings them into conflict with the law or prevents their wives from achieving sex gratification, are sexually inadequate and are in need of help.

In the above case, we have an example of a husband who forfeited the love of his wife because of a sexual aberration that existed prior to marriage.

He is responding favorably to treatment and is developing sufficient discipline to enable him to make an adequate sex adjustment in the future.

Case 4. One patient, married and the father of a nine-year-old boy, was unable to enjoy sexual relations with his wife. He had been unable to discontinue his adolescent practice of masturbation. He also confessed to certain deviations which his wife, apparently, had no knowledge of, proceeding from sadomasochistic sexual fantasies.

He reported his sex history as follows:

"During adolescence, masturbated daily, sometimes twice a day. The act was accompanied by looking at lewd pictures or lewd thoughts about certain girls or women I knew.

"I continued to masturbate after adolescence and still do even though I'm married. In my teens, I would often attend theaters and masturbate during scenes in which women appeared lightly clad. I often felt ill effects, such as strain in the testicles after prolonged episodes of masturbation, some-times lasting two hours before reaching a climax. I would not expose myself in the theatre but would masturbate through a torn pocket.

"I would cut out pictures of women from magazines or newspapers and while looking at them would masturbate. I spoke of telephoning women. When calling strange women on the phone, I would lay these pictures on the floor nearby, masturbate as I talked to them, and look at the pictures on the floor. On reaching a climax, I would use an obscene word or ask an intimate question. In some of these calls, I gave a fictitious name, informed the woman that I was a total stranger, and then told her a lurid story of being a war casualty with special sexual needs since the nature of my injury pre-vented normal gratification. I would ask them to tell me that, at my direction, they were touching their breasts or their genitals and that this gave me sexual relief. While this con-versation was going on, I masturbated. Only two such calls brought me cooperative response, and I called the women re-peatedly and enjoyed them in my telephonic masturbation.

"In other calls, I was sharply rebuffed, threatened with police action, or smartly told off, but I enjoyed this too. When a woman quarreled with me over my use of obscene language, I seemed to enjoy it most of all and would pretend to be apologetic while I masturbated to the point of climax, and then I would make an obscene remark. On other occasions, when I had reached my climax during the conversation, I would apologize sincerely and beg their forgiveness. These phone calls left me feeling dejected and ashamed afterwards.

"During the past summer, I discontinued calling women al-together. Instead, I would walk through apartment projects looking at women as they sat on front doorsteps or sunned themselves on the lawns. In most cases they wore brief cloth-ing and I would stare at them for chance glimpses of their bare breasts or their pubic hair. If I found a vantage point where I could continue to observe them while they were unaware of it, I would masturbate through a torn pocket but seldom reached a climax. In some instances when I felt safe enough I would approach women and make remarks such as, 'You sure have a beautiful set of tits there,' or 'you sure have a lot of hair on your c—t. I'll bet you use it a lot.' When they responded angrily, I would expose myself and masturbate in front of them saying, 'How would you like to have this stuck in your —. Ain't it a beauty?'

"In some cases, when I encountered women sitting on the front step, I deliberately bent down and looked under their dresses or shorts and made some remark about all the hair they had between their legs.

"But I seldom satisfied my sexual urges by such talk and only stimulated myself further, so I looked to my evening sorties to climax my sexual desires. They took place when I peeped into windows where I could observe without fear of detection and masturbate freely and to a satisfactory conclusion.

"Sometimes I would wait near an apartment project for a woman coming home late at night, and I would follow her from the bus, making indecent remarks to her or even touching her. However, window-peeping was my main source of sexual satisfaction in the summer. There was a particular woman whom I would watch. She lived in an apartment at ground level and one window opened toward a deep patch of woods where I could watch with no chance of being caught. I knew this woman's routine, and about bedtime, I would begin to work myself up by masturbating. Then I would post myself and watch her undressing until I would reach a climax in my masturbating.

"For a short while I had stolen women's underthings from clotheslines, such as brassières, slips, and silk stock-ings. I would rub them against my penis as a preliminary to masturbating.

"On many occasions, when I was unable to see anything by peeping into windows, I would come home and masturbate into the toilet. I did this despite the fact that I could have had normal intercourse with my wife.

"I would imagine having women whom I knew and liked as captives in my fortress and making their position so desirable that they willingly stayed there as my mistresses. But the dreams and fantasies that aroused me most were those wherein some woman who had been mean and quarrelsome to me became my captive. I would build them up only to humiliate them, and then I was able to satisfy my sexual desires. As these fantasies passed through my mind, I would masturbate."

The above patient developed insight into the psychological causes of his sexual problem and responded favorably to treatment. He made a satisfactory heterosexual adjustment and successfully gave up masturbating, preferring normal sexual relations with his wife.

The above case illustrations are but a few of the many cases of married sex offenders we have encountered in recent years. A follow-up of our cases has convinced us that the majority respond favorably to proper therapy. There are, of course, many cases which never come to the attention of the authorities. In many instances, attorneys may be consulted by wives seeking release from husbands whose deviations result in sexual frustration or incompatability. Such men are potential offenders but they are also potentially normal, and psychiatric treatment can help them achieve normality.

It is our hope that attorneys who encounter such cases attempt to persuade the wife to seek treatment for her husband rather than insisting on dissolving the marriage. In many such cases, if the wife can prevail upon the husband to accompany her to the lawyer's office, it would be a big step forward. The lawyer can explain to both the husband and wife the legal problems, make recommendations, and if necessary, refer the husband to a psychiatrist.

Only through re-education and enlightenment of the public can we hope to break through the barrier of sex ignorance and begin to save married couples from separation and divorce. The married sex offender is generally a man in dire need of understanding and treatment. Placing him in prison is seldom the answer. The man must, at some time, re-enter society. Unquestionably, the best ends would be served if such a man were allowed to receive psychiatric treatment and, at the same time, were given an opportunity by his wife to become a good husband.

The Psycho-Legal Approach to Marital Problems

The authors have previously made clear their feeling regarding the procurement of quick separation and divorce. We are of the opinion that it is a mistake for any married couple to approach a problem of marital discord with divorce in mind. And this is especially true when children are involved, for not only do we believe that the sanctity and harmony of the home should be of prime importance, but the need for children to have the love and care of both father and mother is equally important.

Too often the husband or wife is sort of "pushed" into a divorce action for want of a better idea or a more intelligent approach to the real problem which has wrecked the marriage. This, of course, is not a realistic or proper approach nor should either party be encouraged to proceed with legal action until all avenues of salvation have been thoroughly examined.

We have found, in practice, that cooperation between lawyer and psychiatrist is most successful. It is our feeling that many marital upheavals are the result of emotional distress which creates problems requiring the attention of a qualified medical specialist; that it is not so easy nor is it intelligent to solve such a situation with an exclusive legalistic viewpoint; and that the lawyer is wise to make proper inquiry into the exact difficulties and then, if necessary, refer one or both of the parties to a psychiatrist.

This *psycho-legal approach,* although a new concept, has, in fact, worked in actual practice. However, it should be noted that certain courts and various jurisdictions have methods of trying to accomplish a similar end. There are, for example, "cooling off" periods or pre-trial conferences which include attempts at reconciliation before divorce is granted. Some courts have staff counselors who speak with the parties to a divorce action in an effort to effect a reconciliation, and in some states, the judge himself calls the parties into his chambers for a conference aimed at gaining a harmonious result. There are certain states which have legislated in the field of reconciliation with the aim of saving the marriage and obviating the divorce, about which more will be said subsequently.

However, nowhere do we find a strictly voluntary plan of cooperation devised by the lawyer to include the psychiatrist for the sole purpose of determining what the actual trouble is between husband and wife and then recommending a course of treatment or counseling—with full association by the lawyer—for saving the marriage.

Let us examine briefly three case histories illustrating what we mean and the results of the direct cooperative approach.

Case 1. John D., a man in his middle forties, successful in his profession, and well known in the community, consulted one of the authors. He was married eighteen years and the father of five children. His work put him in close contact with many people including young, single, and attractive girls. John D. was himself an attractive man. It is of interest to note here that John's wife proved to be an especially pretty woman, too.

John D. made the mistake of entertaining a young woman on an occasion when his wife and children were visiting her parents. Upon her return, Mrs. John D. discovered a scented handkerchief in the bedroom which she knew was not her own. Because she had previously suspected her husband of extra-marital activity, Mrs. John D. demanded an explanation and failing to get a satisfactory one, ordered the husband from the house.

"This is the end," she shouted. "I can't do anything else but get a divorce to maintain my self-respect." No amount of apology or pleading altered her position, and she was determined to consult her lawyer and begin divorce proceedings.

Fortunately, Mrs. John D. agreed to consult with Mr. Brenner, presumably to tell him all the negative things about her husband.

"Why does John act the way he does?" the lawyer asked.

"I only wish I knew," she replied.

"Have you ever asked him?"

"Oh, yes, and all he says is that he has a problem and needs to see a doctor."

This was the opening Mr. Brenner had hoped for. Upon further questioning of both wife and husband, it was determined that John D. did in fact have a problem that required proper medical care. The wife was prevailed on, for the sake of the children and that of the husband, to cooperate.

John was referred to Dr. Caprio for consultation. The wife was also called in for discussion. After a course of psychiatric counseling of both husband and wife, along with supportive legal counsel, the couple found what had caused the difficulty and it was corrected. At last report, John D. was behaving in a normal manner and his home life was once again happy. His wife never did get around to seeing her own lawyer about a divorce; actually she didn't want one in the first place. Had nothing been suggested about her husband's emotional problem, a divorce would have been inevitable.

Case 2. Mrs. C., a housewife of sixty-three, consulted Mr. Brenner and insisted on an immediate divorce. Her husband had been drinking to excess over a long period of time, and their home life became intolerable. She was reminded that a divorce for a woman of her age would be regrettable and that she would spend many lonely hours and days in the waning period of her life.

Mrs. C. broke down and cried. She said, "I can't live with him, but I don't think I can live without him. What shall I do?"

"Why don't you let me talk with him and suggest that he see a medical specialist," Mr. Benner answered.

Mr. C. was only too glad to do everything necessary to get back into his wife's good graces and readily accepted the proposal that he talk with Dr. Caprio about his problem, a problem which he admitted.

After many sessions with both husband and wife, some with all of us together, Mr. C. began to understand the feelings of his wife in a clearer light. He gained insight into his own problems and the reasons for his behavior, and he cut his drinking down to a cocktail before dinner.

Again the divorce court was cheated of a participant.

Case 3. Mrs. B.W. was treated by Dr. Caprio during a nervous breakdown, which she later insisted was brought on by her husband. Both husband and wife were in their early thirties and he was a nightclub entertainer. They had one child. Mrs. B.W. related how her husband stayed out until the early hours of every morning and how he berated her for not being as pretty as the chorus girls at the club. There came the time when he ignored her entirely. Tensions mounted and the arguments persisted until the breakdown occurred. After recovery, Mrs. B.W. moved from the home and took the child with her. She wanted a lawyer to file suit for a divorce.

The authors studied the legal and psychiatric considerations in the matter and decided that this marriage was worth saving and that, with proper counseling, it could be done. Although the parties were reluctant to listen, they finally agreed to a series of discussions between themselves and the authors; a suggestion which proved fruitful.

When last we heard from Mrs. B.W., she was making a very satisfactory adjustment, as was her husband, and the home life was back in proper balance.

It is of interest to examine, although briefly, the plan of concilation as set down by California law. This law, passed in 1939, was actually preceded by similar statutes in Michigan (1919) and Wisconsin (1933), but it is used more extensively in the State of California.

Pursuant to this law (found in sections 1730-1772 of the Code of Civil Procedure, Calif.) the County of Los Angeles established a full time Conciliation Court with a complete staff. The purpose of the court is to provide a forum where parties to a marital dispute might reconcile without the necessity of divorce.

It was not until 1954 that the Conciliation Court became really active and effective. Statistics indicate that about one hundred conciliation cases are filed in Los Angeles County each month and that the incidence of success is approximately forty-five percent. In other words, forty-three out of every one-hundred couples who seek help through this method are reconciled. Of this number, three out of four couples were reported living together after one year had gone by. In 1957, it was estimated that one thousand children were saved from broken homes through efforts of the Conciliation Court.

The basic procedures used by the Court have been designed for simplicity and expediency. They are as follows:

1. Petition filed by one of the parties, for which there is no filing fee or other charges by the Court.

2. Affidavit setting out general information regarding the parties and a list of their marital difficulties.

3. Notice of hearing sent to the parties. The Court may order the appearance of the parties.

4. Hearing conducted informally by a court-appointed Counselor.

The hearing is in a private office and may be in the presence of the lawyers who represent either of the parties or it may be just with the parties themselves. In some cases the Counselor may wish to speak with each party separately. Husband and wife are told that the Court wishes to help them but that the Court will not order them to do anything which they actually do not want to do. Each is given a written memorandum which reads:

> By way of introducing you to the work of the Court, attached is a copy of a typical Reconciliation Agreement as entered into by persons who have become reconciled in this Court.
>
> In the event that you should become reconciled, an agreement would be prepared with your help which would cover the problems of your marriage. These might include some of the matters covered in this Agreement as well as others pertaining directly to your own case.
>
> This copy has been handed to you to read because it may suggest to you matters which you may wish to discuss with the Counselor as well as to acquaint you with the general form of Reconciliation Agreements utilized in the Conciliation Court.
>
> JUDGE

At this point in the procedure, if the parties do not wish to consider conciliation, the conference is ended and the lawyers are notified. The parties are then free to pursue any course of action they desire. Those who wish to go ahead are afforded private hearings and conference, and if the conciliation procedure has been invoked prior to the filing of a divorce petition, there is a thirty-day stay on such divorce action. Even if divorce action has been commended before the conciliation attempt, conciliation may be effected at any time during the pendency of the divorce suit.

During a conciliation hearing, the Counselor discusses with the couples the typical agreement, and further discussions are had as to those particular matters and problems which appear to be causing the trouble in the instant case. If, after discussion, the parties agree to conciliation, a written agreement is entered into, which is signed by the parties and approved by the Counselor and the lawyers. The Judge then signs an Order of Court making it mandatory for each party to abide by the terms of the Agreement for a thirty-day period. This Order may be further extended by consent of the parties. At the expiration of the thirty days, each file is reviewed by the Judge who then writes a letter of congratulations and encouragement to those couples who have reconciled; those couples who feel a reconciliation is impossible are called for further conferences, and failing in this, the Agreement Court Order is terminated.

The Conciliation Agreement itself begins as follows:

> The aid of the Court having been requested to effect a reconciliation, or an amicable settlement of the controversy existing between the above named husband and wife, and a Court conference having been held thereon in which it was indicated that certain conduct is deemed necessary to preserve the marriage or to implement the reconciliation of the parties, the parties hereby agree, each with the other and with the Court as follows:

Various aspects of married life are then set forth in detail, spelling out the duties and obligations of each party. For example:

> Forgetting the past
> Division of responsibility
> The home
> Support of the family
> Welfare of the children
> Where wife works outside the home
> Husband's role in the family
> A normal married life
> Falling out of love
> Work, hobbies, etc.
> Privacy
> Mutual friends
> Religion
> Fighting
> Bearing grudges
> Late hours . . . gambling
> Nagging
> Family prayers
> Mealtime
> Children . . . care of . . . control over . . . conduct toward
> Love making . . . sexual intercourse
> Personal appearance
> Earnings, paycheck, expenses . . . budget

Details of the above and many other problems, depending on the needs of the particular case, are incorporated into the agreement. The obligations of each party to the other, in accordance with the terms of the Conciliation Agreement are thus enforceable by law.

It is our opinion that this plan, or others which have for their purpose the saving of the marriage, is good and that it merits the serious consideration of all those who work in this field, or who are interested in getting to the actual roots of marital difficulty.

The presiding Judge of the Los Angeles Court of Conciliation had this to say about the divorce problem:

"Divorce is a disease. It is contagious. And in the United States it has reached epidemic proportions. Yet no one in the Los Angeles Court of Conciliation advocates the abolition of divorce. In many cases, legal separation is the only way to preserve the health and sanity of both parties to a marriage.

"But we have found that in the overwhelming majority of marriages, divorce is neither necessary nor justified. It is in these cases that the conciliation procedure, the cooling-off period, and the Conciliation Agreement have been most effective. This procedure in various forms is now available, not only in California but in Illinois, New Jersey, Michigan, and the District of Columbia.

"In communities where it is not available, the local Community Chest can direct persons to a reputable family-counseling service. But ultimately, neither counseling nor conciliation courts are the answer to marital discord. It is up to all of us to develop a new sense of the spiritual values in marriage and rededicate ourselves to one of our most precious heritages—our homes and our children."

IMPOTENCE AS GROUNDS FOR ANNULMENT

Impotence refers to sexual inadequacy in the male. It does not mean the inability to have children nor the inability to have sex relations, although there is a type of impotence where the husband is unable to consummate the sex act. While impotence can be caused by some physical disorders, ninety percent of all impotence is the result of psychic conflict. It is a very common sexual disorder and a frequent cause of annulment and divorce.

Dr. Wilhelm Stekel wrote: "In men love-inadequacy is increasing to an alarming degree, and impotence has come to be a disorder associated with modern civilization. Every impotent man forms the nucleus of a love tragedy. For impotence makes marriage impossible or may be the cause of an ill-fated one; it also undermines the health of the woman and has an equally pernicious effect upon the married life of both husband and wife.

"The percentage of relatively impotent men cannot be placed too high. In my experience, hardly half of all civilized men enjoy normal potency."

Dr. Eustace Chesser informs us that authorities in Great Britain and America have estimated that some seventy percent of wives are mentally and physically aroused without being satisfied. Still another investigator claims that cases of unsatisfactory experiences or sexual dissatisfaction among women run into hundreds of thousands.

The right of both the husband and wife to enjoy sexual relations is so inviolate that the physical or psychological inability on the part of either to engage in sexual relations is grounds, in most states, for the dissolution of the marriage contract. This is generally accomplished by an action for annulment. In the eyes of the law, such a contract may be rescinded on those grounds and considered as never having been entered into legally.

Impotence, according to the laws in most states, must have been unknown to the complaining wife at the time of the marriage, and it must continue until the case is heard. If the wife had knowledge of the husband's sexual inadequacy at marriage, her complaint will be disregarded.

In a case decided many years ago in New Jersey, the court, faced with the problem of sufficiency of proof, applied a test which later came to be known as "the doctrine of triennial cohabitation." According to this, if the wife, after three years cohabitation with her husband, was still a virgin, he was presumed impotent, and his wife was entitled to an annulment. Another court ruled on a similar case as follows:

"In lieu or in amplification of proof, incurability may be presumed from the establishment of appropriate facts. On a showing of continued cohabitation, the wife meanwhile being apt and remaining a virgin, the husband will be presumed to be impotent and the burden will be on him to overcome the presumption of proof that he is not at fault."

In a recent case, decided just as this manuscript was being prepared, it was the husband who brought an action to annul the marriage on the grounds that he was physically incapable of consummating the marriage because of psychological maladjustment. The wife, through her attorney, concurred. She further declared that she had had no knowledge of her husband's disability when she married him, and that she had entered the marriage with the expectation of having normal sexual relations and having children. At the hearings, the husband testified that a mental abnormality made him unable to perform intercourse. This was supported by testimony of a psychiatrist who had diagnosed the trouble as psychic in origin, and found it unlikely that a cure would ever be effected. Despite the evidence, the court denied the annulment.

On appeal, however, the decision of the lower court was overruled; the ruling of the Court of Appeals included this statement:

"The Courts have long recognized the fact that impotence is frequently the result of psychogenic causes. Indeed, one medical authority states that most cases of impotence seen by neurologists are of the psychic type rather than the result of physical defects. In diagnosing such a subjective condition, the physician must necessarily rely largely on the history and symptoms described to him by the patient. Accordingly, it is proper for the physician to base his diagnosis as to the defendant's impotence upon the history and symptoms which the latter related to him and the trial justice should have permitted him to answer the questions propounded to him."

There are twenty states in which impotence is a specific

ground for annulment, and thirty states grant divorce on the same grounds. A few other jurisdictions have no statutory ground for annulments although the courts will grant annulments if they decide this to be in the best interest of the complaining parties. The wife must commence legal action within reasonable time after the impotence has been discovered; if this is not done, the court may declare that she has then "waived" any right to complain.

Because impotence is a curable condition, it is recommended that divorce or annulment on that ground should not be rushed into. Attorneys encountering such cases should seek the opinion of a qualified psychiatrist before proceeding with court action.

ADULTERY (PSYCHODYNAMIC ASPECTS)

Recent studies, including the famous Kinsey Report, have established the fact that adultery is a major cause of the ever-increasing divorce rate which has already reached the alarming proportion of one divorce in every three marriages.

The approach of society and the law to adultery is one of morality. It is considered wrong per se. Psychiatrists, however, know that adultery is often a behavior deviation, that it may stem from childhood frustrations. Infidelity may be an expression of a dormant neurosis. If we are to understand the whys and wherefores of such conduct, it is necessary to hold moral prejudices in abeyance and inquire into the motivating psychological factors.

We believe that divorce is not the only or the best solution to this problem because, if the "guilty" person received the counseling he or she needed, the marriage and the home might be saved. This presupposes, of course, cooperation, understanding, and forgiveness on the part of the aggrieved party.

It is generally a waste of time and effort for the lawyer or marriage counselor to lecture to the unfaithful party on moral grounds, nor does it do any good to damn or tear down the character of such a person. There are causes for this type of behavior which must be uncovered, analyzed, and treated if positive results are to be obtained. The psychiatrist avoids condemnation and tries to uncover the personality problem.

The authors are of the opinion that there is, in most infidelities, a combined rather than a single responsibility. Although one of the partners may be the "guilty" one, the entire blame may not be his.

A case in point follows.

Martha was married to a very immature, boyish husband. Since she was older than he, she played a somewhat maternal role in the marriage, rendering the husband emotionally dependent upon her. The result was an immature sexual relationship which angered the wife and caused her to lose respect for him.

Martha's childhood had been incomplete and frustrating because her father had died when she was a little girl. She longed for and needed a husband who was strong and mature, the embodiment of the wistful, girlhood memories of her father.

There came up on the scene an older man who was suave, well-to-do, and polished. He became friendly with both Martha and her husband. Because of the unhappy relationship between them, they both welcomed this man, who became a frequent visitor in their home. Eventually, Martha found herself enamored of this man and yielded to him.

In relating the story, Martha said that the man had surprised her by proposing that she spend a weekend with him. She accepted. It was the beginning of an affair which was sexually perfect and wonderful to her.

"Is it possible?" she asked. "I can hardly believe that it happened. I seem to be in a trance. He made me feel our love was so fine. He was more like a father to me, not at all wolfish."

The clue in her statements was "he was more like a father

to me." That phrase exposed her psychic problem. Martha had a father fixation. She was the victim of unconscious desires to fill the void of a father in her childhood. The infidelity was symbolic of her wish to find a strong, understanding father.

After the older man had gone out of her life, Martha began to have guilt feelings. She could not feel right in the presence of her husband and became neurotic and depressed. Eventually, she developed the classic symptoms of a chronic psychoneurotic which brought her to the psychoanalytic couch.

Martha was told why she had entered into the adulterous relationship and began to understand the father fixation behind it. Her husband, who cooperated willingly, was counseled into ways of being more aggressive and masculine. When he was able to assume the role of a strong man, someone Martha could lean on and respect, their marriage took on new meaning and stature.

Separation or divorce in this case would have solved nothing for either Martha or her husband. Careful inquiry and painstaking effort showed each of them the shortcomings that led to their unhappiness.

The time for a married couple to seek guidance is before the problem has reached the stage of separation or divorce, before either party does anything they may regret later. An impartial and well-trained observer can generally find the trouble and save the marriage. In every case this should be done without reservation.

The late Dr. Abraham Stone, world-famous marriage counselor wrote: "The basic conflict between biology and culture, between desire and inhibition must be resolved individually in each instance . . . Sexual promiscuity is certainly undesirable. It may bring a transient physical satisfaction, but not a deep emotional fulfillment. In spite of our changing values, a lasting union of one man with one woman is the most ideal form of human sex relationship."

ADULTERY (HISTORICAL AND LEGAL ASPECTS)

Our present-day legal concepts of adultery are derived largely from English law, although the ecclesiastical courts of the Church of England have had a certain influence as well.

Because most of the American colonies followed English common law we inherited certain deficiencies which statutory enactments have corrected to a great degree. The common-law concepts of sexual behavior were not strict, and adultery, for example, was not a punishable offense. Nor were other deviant types of sexual conduct which today we consider to be serious, then regarded as punishable offenses, as long as public decency was not breached and children were not involved. Because of this lenity of the common-law court, the ecclesiastical courts attempted, from time to time, to take over the jurisdiction of sexual offenses. For reasons outside the scope of this work, the control of the church courts was never effective, and their powers were eventually abolished by the Puritan Revolution in England. During the 17th century the ecclesiastical courts regained some of their former jurisdiction over sexual matters only to lose it again. In the latter part of the 18th century, the power was, for all practical purposes, gone forever.

However, during the several centuries of the ineffectual control over sexual offenses by the ecclesiastical courts, the common-law courts did, from time to time, out of sheer necessity, exercise jurisdiction over many sexual matters. This was especially true when rape, prostitution, sodomy, and like offenses were involved. Finally, after the Puritan Revolution, a strict code of sex crimes was set down and adultery was considered a crime even at common law, and punishable by death.

It is of interest to note that colonial American legal restrictions on sexual practices almost paralleled those of the English. For example, those colonies under the Puritan influence, such as Massachusetts, imposed strict penalties for sexual offenses, and adultery was a capital crime. In actual practice, however, it is doubtful if such extreme measures were used often. Other colonies following different common-law principles punished adultery by fine. This was the practice in "cavalier" Virginia and Maryland.

Before we examine the modern-day concepts of adultery and how it affects the marriage contract, let us briefly look into the basic differences between adultery at common law and adultery as viewed by the ecclesiastical courts because, as earlier noted, our present laws are based on elements contained in each. At common law, and Roman law, too, for that matter, adultery was defined as sexual intercourse by a man, married or single, with a married woman not his wife. The guilt was primarily on the woman; the main idea was to protect the man from the responsibility of raising a child not born of a legal union. According to ecclesiastical law, however, the state of marriage was an inviolate one; thus the concept of adultery was enlarged to include any married person—male or female—who engaged in sexual intercourse with a person not his or her lawful spouse.

Our modern statutes are not without confusion in this field. According to some state laws, if either the man or woman are married, both are guilty of adultery, while other states do not incriminate the unmarried person. Still other states rule that the woman can be charged with adultery only if she is married although the man need not be married to be so charged. The conflicting statutes lead to much confusion and strange results. Thus an unmarried person having sexual intercourse with a married person may be charged with fornication and not adultery.

It would seem that the better viewpoint in dealing with adultery is the broad one which follows the dicta set down in many courts—that sexual intercourse by a husband with an unmarried woman is as much a violation of the marriage contract and of the rights of his wife, as if committed with a married woman. And the same reasoning should be applied to the wife in her extra-marital conduct.

A distinction must now be made between adultery as a ground for divorce and adultery as an indictable criminal offense. The difference is not in the act itself, which may be identical, but in the sufficiency of proof. In a civil case, proof will suffice which, in a criminal action, will not be sufficient for conviction. Adultery as a ground for divorce is recognized in every state without exception, and in the State of New York, it is the exclusive ground. The proof required in a divorce action must, of course, be competent although, when corroborated either by the facts or the circumstances or by direct testimony of witnesses, the evidence is generally found sufficient to grant a divorce. If the defendant is shown to have been predisposed to the adultery and the opportunity was present for its commission, and the circumstances were such so as to lead a reasonable and just man to conclude that the act had been committed, there is usually sufficient ground to secure the divorce. In other words, in order to maintain a divorce action on circumstantial evidence of adultery, two points must be demonstrated. One is the opportunity to engage in the act. The second is the will to so engage in it.

But to secure a criminal conviction, the proof, as in all criminal matters, must be "beyond a reasonable doubt." In most cases of adultery, such proof is very difficult, if not impossible, to present. It is for this reason that there are few prosecutions for criminal adultery although, under the same circumstances, an action for divorce would be successful. And to further add to the already existing confusion, many statutes differ as to what constitutes adultery.

It was noted earlier that many statutes differ as to the status of the parties involved, that is whether one of them (or both) is married. Some states require an open and "notorious" relationship before adultery can be criminally proved, so that it would seem that such conduct carried on in private would exclude the participants from prosecuting. Other states require the relationship to be one of some duration—"habitual" is the favored word—so that a single act of adultery may not constitute an offense.

In any event, it is clear that adultery is a ground for divorce in every jurisdiction and, under certain circumstances, ground for criminal prosecution. There is no question that our courts consider adultery the most flagrant violation of the marriage contract and, from the standpoint of relief to the innocent party, the remedy is clear and the law well settled.

Conclusions and Recommendations

Sexual disharmony between married partners is a very serious matter and in no case should it be taken lightly. As we have pointed out earlier in this chapter, it may be the cause for other marital discord and the originating cause for divorce or separation. In addition, it may be the basis for subsequent physical and emotional disorders.

Sexual infidelity, impotence, and deviations are problems which should not be left to the amateurs; nor should these symptoms, on the other hand, be allowed to go on without competent counseling or professional treatment.

It is not implied that sex is the sole basis for marriage and that sex is a cure-all for all unhappiness. We do not believe that, just because a married couple has a satisfactory sex life, all their problems are automatically solved; nor do we wish to convey the idea that it is our belief that sexual pleasure is the only important thing in marriage.

We do feel, however, that a happy and well-adjusted sex life, expressing mutual love and understanding, goes a long way to making married life good. Sex is one of nature's way of allowing man and woman to show their love for one another in marriage. Spontaneous, happy and satisfying sexual relations between husband and wife can, by themselves, be the basis for a solid marriage, giving a feeling of security, well-being, and adulthood to each partner. There are many who maintain that all other problems which arise in marriage can and should be solved by proper use of this ultimate expression of love.

There are and perhaps there will always be, barriers which confront those who deal with and try to solve problems of marital sex. Sex seems to be a topic which few persons, even though adult and intelligent, can rationally discuss among themselves or in the presence of another. A serious discussion of sexual problems often becomes confused with wrong implications, and nothing is accomplished.

Not so long ago mental illness and leprosy were considered alike—something not to be touched. Sexual problems have much the same standing. Those of us who deal with such matters often meet with raised eyebrows and suspicious glances. It is difficult to discuss sex within the private confines of home or office and almost impossible to do so in a group. This is a most unfortunate situation inasmuch as sex should not be reserved for backroom talk. Sex and sexual behavior are realities, a part of universal human behavior, and should be regarded with respect and treated with intelligence.

If you have an attack of appendicitis, it would be foolish to arrange for a funeral before calling the doctor. If you have a problem in marriage, it is just as foolish to seek a quick divorce and make no attempt to find the cause of the trouble. A positive approach must be taken—one that has for its purpose the curing of the trouble and the saving of the marriage.

What do we recommend?

Every married person who finds himself or herself in the throes of an unhappy home situation should sit down and honestly ask if there is and has been a happy and satisfying sexual relationship. "Too tired tonight" for sex, or "Let's not act like kids," or "We better not, the children might wake up," or any other excuse for postponing marital relations may be the beginning of real trouble.

All married couples should frankly and openly discuss sex so that each may be aware of the needs and wants of the other. In that way, a harmonious relationship can be established upon which happy sexual relations can be built.

Each married partner must be understanding and respectful of the other's wishes and desires. Do not "'force" yourself on your husband or wife; on the other hand do not shy away or disregard the desires of the other.

Always be "sweethearts" and "lovers"; don't let your marriage sink to a humdrum matter-of-fact thing. Experiment, if both partners so desire, in new and interesting ways of sexual satisfaction. Do not enter into sexual activities from the basis of "duty" or "I do it because he is entitled to it."

We are of the firm opinion that much progress could be made if lawyers and psychiatrists worked in closer cooperation with each other, even to the point of sitting down with the husband and wife and advising them with regard to the psychodynamic and legal aspects of marital sex.

chapter four

THE HOMOSEXUAL PROBLEM

DEFINITION

The term "homosexual" refers to sexual relations with a person of the same sex. It is derived from the Greek prefix meaning "same." It was first used in 1869 by a Hungarian physician named Benkert. Unfortunately, Benkert was misled into believing that homosexuality was a congenital condition.

"In addition to this normal sexual urge in man and woman," he wrote, "nature in her sovereign mood has endowed at birth certain male and female individuals with the homosexual urge, thus placing them in a sexual bondage which renders them physically incapable even with the best intention—of normal erection. The urge creates in advance a direct horror of the opposite sex, and the victim of this passion finds it impossible to suppress the feeling which individuals of his own sex exercise upon him."

This concept of homosexuality, formulated almost a century ago, is now obsolete.

Many psychoanalysts, today, agree with Clara Thompson who, in an article entitled "Changing Concepts of Homosexuality in Psychoanalysis," wrote:

"The term 'homosexual' as used in psychoanalysis has come to be a kind of wastebasket into which are dumped all forms of relationships, with one's own feelings, thoughts, or repression of any of these. In short, anything which pertains in any way to a relationship, hostile or friendly, to a member of one's own sex may be termed homosexual. Under these circumstances, what does an analyst convey to himself, his audience, or his patient when he says the patient has homosexual trends! It does not clarify much in his own thinking, when he uses the term in talking with the patient; his words, instead of being helpful, often produce terror, for in ordinary speech the word 'homosexual' has a much more specific meaning, and, in addition, a disturbing emotional coloring."

Accordingly, definition, meaning, and implications of homosexuality need to be clarified and scientifically re-appraised.

WHO IS A HOMOSEXUAL

The danger of loosely characterizing individuals as homosexuals because of certain "suspicious" conduct and gestures has been pointed out by Dr. Karl H. Bowman and Bernice Engle.

"From a legal standpoint, any person convicted of carrying out a sexual act with any person of the same sex would be convicted of homosexual activity and classified as a homosexual. Some individuals so convicted may be completely homosexual in their attitude and behavior and have no interest whatever in heterosexuality.

"However, other individuals so convicted by the courts may not have really desired such a homosexual experience, may have felt disgusted at having yielded to the approaches of the other individual, may have in the past led an active heterosexual life, and may lead an exclusively heterosexual life in the future. Calling such persons homosexuals is comparable to calling a person with one-sixteenth Chinese blood and fifteen-sixteenths white blood an Oriental and not a Caucasian."

As evidence that a wide variety of homosexual and heterosexual patterns exist among human beings, Kinsey introduced the following heterosexual-homosexual rating scale:

0. Exclusively heterosexual

1. Predominantly heterosexual, only incidentally homosexual

2. Predominantly heterosexual, but more than incidentally homosexual

3. Equally heterosexual and homosexual

4. Predominantly homosexual, but more than incidentally heterosexual

5. Predominantly homosexual, but incidentally heterosexual

6. Exclusively homosexual

Persons who have had only a single or isolated homosexual experience in their entire lives cannot be regarded as homosexuals. Others have indulged in homosexual gratifications occasionally, while still others are promiscuously bisexual. They should be differentiated from those who resort to intimacies with members of their own sex exclusively.

PREVALENCE

Homosexuality exists among persons in all walks of life—the poor and the rich, the ignorant and the intellectual, the African and the Eskimo, the atheist and the churchgoer, the married and the unmarried, the young and the old.

According to John McPartland, author of *Sex in our Changing World*, "The retreat into homosexual practices of tremendous numbers of our men and women is one of the danger signs of our future."

The current percentage of homosexuals is difficult to estimate. We know that it occurs wherever groups of the same sex live together, in private boarding schools, military barracks, prisons, and dormitories.

The average citizen believes that male homosexuals are a small group, usually recognizable by their undisguised effeminacy. Actually, those who fall into that overt homosexual type—commonly called "queers"—constitute a very small percentage of the total number of homosexuals in America. The more discreet majority avoid attention both from the police or the general public. Contrary to popular belief, the largest percentage of homosexuals give an outward appearance of being well-adjusted persons.

Homosexuality is far more widespread than generally believed. In *Sexual Behavior in the Human Male,* Dr. Alfred C. Kinsey and his coauthors state that over fifty percent of males, at one time or another, have had homosexual leanings. Another writer states that one third of all American males have engaged in homosexual activity at least once in their lives. Others claim that three percent of our adult male population are practicing homosexuals.

As for the incidence of Lesbianism, which is found in both primitive and civilized societies, it is impossible to estimate its prevalence.

According to Dr. Kinsey's report, *Sexual Behavior in the Human Female*, based on 5,940 sex histories, nineteen percent of the females who gave their sexual histories admitted contact with members of their own sex.

Dr. G. V. Hamilton, author of *Homosexuality as a Defense Against Incest*, found that, out of one hundred women questioned, one-fourth admitted sexual intimacies with other women.

Katherine B. Davis, author of *Factors in the Sex Life of Twenty-Two Hundred Women,* found that homosexuality, in the sense of an intense emotional relationship for another woman, existed in half the cases with four hundred and fifty admitting "overt" experience.

Regarding the comparative prevalence of male and female homosexuality, Dr. Beran Wolfe was of the opinion that homosexuality is more prevalent among women but is less intensive. Havelock Ellis believed that homosexuality is as widespread among women as among men. He estimated that from two to five percent of a cross section of the female population are homosexuals.

It is also interesting to note that the Kinsey investigations disclosed a lower incidence of homosexual contacts among the female than among the previously studied male group (twenty-eight percent as compared to fifty percent).

As for our own opinion, we share the views of Dr. E. A. Bennet, psychiatrist at the West End Hospital for Nervous Disease in London. He maintains: "Homosexuality is probably as common amongst women as amongst men, but it is less prominent, and it has been given less attention. It may well be that female homosexuals outnumber males." Bergler seems to feel that the incidence of homosexuality among females is greater than among males. Dr. Samuel W. Hartwell, a psychiatrist and author of *A Citizens' Handbook of Sexual Abnormalities*, states, "There are probably many more homosexual women than men."

One must take into account that there are greater opportunities for women to become sexually intimate with members of their own sex, for society is less apt to frown upon a love relationship between two women. Kisses and caresses between women are more common and less immediately suspect than similar expressions of affection among men.

Then, too, while male homosexuals are subject to punishment by law, one seldom hears of a Lesbian brought into court. As a result, women have less to fear about being apprehended and imprisoned. In like manner, they are less subject to blackmail and scandals than are male homosexuals. Thus a woman is less apt to be deterred by fears and anxieties which beset the male sex.

While in Edinburgh, Scotland, one of the authors came across an article in *The Scotsman*, Scotland's national newspaper, entitled "Growing Problem of the Homosexual." The subtitle read: "Prevalence of the practice warrants more responsible concern and action." The author of the article, Graham Turner, gave the results of his investigation of the problem in the chief Scottish cities. He found that homosexual groups tend to be self-propagating, and there is a serious danger of the corruption of youth. Since this article contains relevant factual material, we wish to give the reader the benefit of Mr. Turner's report as it appeared in print. "The most controversial feature of the Wolfenden Report was its recommendation that homosexual behavior between consenting adults in private, no longer be considered a criminal offense. This recommendation aroused a great deal of bitter argument and divided the whole country on readily discernible lines.

"Unfortunately, the dispute did not persuade the general public that the question of homosexuality was of urgent concern. The evidence of a startling increase of such behavior seemed to make it all the more distasteful to many. In the absence of legislation, the matter has either been forgotten altogether or continues only on a plane which considers the law as merely an unjust restraint on the private actions of the individual.

"It needs to be lifted again to the level which Mr. James Adair, the former Procurator-Fiscal of Glasgow, raised it, in his now famous dissenting reservation to the Wolfenden Committee's recommendation. As he said in that reservation, homosexuality deeply concerns the whole 'moral, physical and spiritual welfare of public life.' In our approach to this problem we must have a constructive concern and care for the individual, and a clear vision of its relevance to the whole fabric of our national life.

"Many will reply that a man's private life is his own concern, and completely separate from the responsibilities which public office entails. Yet one of Scotland's leading psychiatrists, Dr. W. E. Miller, Professor of Mental Health in the

University of Aberdeen, told me that as a psychiatrist he knew that a man who was incapable of making moral decisions in his private life could not possibly be expected to make them in his public office.

"Others will try to draw an analogy between homosexual and heterosexual license and point out that adultery, which is not punishable by law, is equally damaging to a man's judgment. Then they draw the conclusion that it is, therefore, completely unjust to punish homosexual acts committed in private between consenting adults.

"This approach is fallacious. It ignores the fact that homosexual groups operate in such a way that they are self-propagating and owe their first loyalty to other members of the group. Nothing could illustrate this more convincingly than Mr. James Adair's revelation to the General Assembly of the Church of Scotland last year that he knew of one homosexual club in London which had at least 14,000 members with links around the world. It is a fact that homosexuals tend to promote other homosexuals.

"As the B.M.A. report on prostitution and homosexuality said in 1955: 'The existence of practicing homosexuals in the church, Parliament, civil service, armed forces, press, radio, stage and other institutions constitutes a special problem.'

"In addition to this aspect of the problem, there is the terrible danger of the corruption of youth. The danger here is that homosexual practices tend to continue for some time before they are discovered. The results of these offenses are often disastrous. I was told of one case where a school official had involved 70 or 80 children in homosexual activity and that these children were now beginning to appear before the courts on charges of sexual and other kinds of misbehavior.

"The need for a realistic and positive approach to this problem is obvious. It becomes of especial concern when a document like the Wolfenden Report says, after hearing the evidence of Scottish experts, that homosexuality is about as prevalent in this country as in comparable areas south of the border.

"My inquiries would fully support that view. Yet, if we accept this expert opinion, the police figures for prosecutions are completely unreal. For instance, in 1955, 2,288 persons were found guilty of homosexual offenses of all sorts in England as against a mere 80 in Scotland. In the three years ended March 1956, 480 persons were found guilty of homosexual offenses committed in private in England. The figure for Scotland was nine (9).

"It is perfectly obvious that police action is proving ineffective. The existing differences in Scottish and English law could not account for such discrepancies. Nothing but a lack of vigilance on the part of the police would account for the difference. In some cities I firmly believe that the police are not interested in tackling the problem of homosexual practices.

"Let us look at the evidence which is available. A well-known retired professor of psychology in Edinburgh, who has practiced on both sides of the border for more than 40 years, said that his own experience supported the view that homosexuality was as prevalent in Scotland as in comparable areas in England. He described the present situation as very grave indeed, and said that he, himself, could spend his time from morning till night treating homosexuals, had he not limited his clientele.

"Another well-known Edinburgh woman psychiatrist said there existed a very considerable problem in the larger cities, particularly in Edinburgh and Glasgow, and also in all places where there was any segregation of the sexes, such as military camps, naval establishments and schools. She said that in both the big cities there were many recognized meeting-places for homosexuals. Their haunts included hotels, public baths, cafe's, bars, and public lavatories.

"Her evidence was confirmed from other responsible sources, which said that homosexual groups foregathered every week at two hotels near to Edinburgh and later returned to that city. Tight groups of homosexuals, it added, were undoubtedly operating in the city. In several cases, as with the problem of prostitution, homosexual activity centered in particular bars.

"These facts are completely borne out by the number of homosexuals who come under the care of the Edinburgh probation officers. Though the figures represent only cases which are brought before the court, an Edinburgh probation officer told me that his office had between 30 and 40 homosexuals under its care, which represented about one third of the total case-load for all offenses. This is the highest ratio in the country.

"The picture presented by Glasgow psychiatrists—who also see only the part of the problem that is brought to their notice either voluntarily or not—is much the same as that given by their Edinburgh colleagues. The clinics I visited all treated a substantial number of homosexuals during the course of the year.

"On further investigation I discovered at least one homosexual club with 50 or 60 members in Glasgow. Another source, himself a homosexual, told me that the problem was beginning to spread to teen-age groups in the city—centering on certain record stores as meeting-points. He also said that one major hotel and one leading restaurant in the city were the present focus of activity. The problem of homosexuality becomes real indeed when one is accosted oneself on the entrance to one of the city's large railway stations.

"Yet a visit to the city probation officer in Glasgow reveals a negligible number of homosexuals under their care. There were only 30 out of a total case-load of 2600. This makes quite explicit the fact that few homosexuals are in fact reaching the courts, and is clear evidence of lack of vigilance on the part of the police. The Glasgow force is at present 240 men under strength, and this is some reason for lack of action. But I was told that there was not a great deal of interest in prosecuting for homosexual offenses, which it is true, involves long periods of observation.

"By contrast with the two great cities, Dundee has only a small problem of homosexuality. When it does occur, it is of grosser physical kind and is centered around certain of the public lavatories in the city.

"In Aberdeen, on the other hand, there is strong evidence that there exists a considerable amount of homosexuality. A police officer told me that some years ago they had really aimed to purge homosexual practices in public conveniences. By putting two plain-clothes policemen on duty at one lavatory, they caught 42 offenders in a month's thorough investigation.

"The figures for the present year show a startling increase in homosexual activity in the city. In 1957 no offenses of sodomy were recorded: last year 17 were recorded. There was also a sharp increase in lewd and libidinous practices—a rise from 29 offenses in 1957 to 111 in 1958—although several of these offenses were connected with one case. The Chief Constable's Annual Report deplores the increase in the number of crimes of a lewd and indecent nature.

"Perhaps this is because the police are less enthusiastic in their pursuit of their offenders. The town's public lavatories are given a much more cursory examination than was the case during the investigation mentioned. It is, however, well known in the city that homosexual practices are widespread among the professional classes.

"More concrete evidence of the extent of the problem in the city comes from figures provided by the probation officers. Even though the police are not investigating the problem very keenly at the moment, some 20% of the case-load of the probation office over the age of 21 is homosexual. These offenders come from all classes of the community.

"In the smaller towns, such at Perth, Ayr and Inverness, the extent of homosexuality is more difficult to discover. The strength of local opinion is often sufficient to drive activity well underground, until it breaks the surface from time to time.

"A separate problem is the extent of homosexuality in prisons. The fact must be faced that prison is essentially a homosexual environment—and when homosexuals are convicted and sent there, it can only aggravate the existing problem.

"This then is a glimpse of the size of the problem—a glimpse because it must represent only the homosexuality which actually comes to the light of day. It is certainly widespread enough to warrant responsible action."

PRESENT-DAY ATTITUDES

Many people today refer to homosexuals as "queers," "degenerates," or "perverts." But a derogatory attitude toward inverts only makes matters worse. Social ostracism or the threat of incarceration does not deter sexual inversion. Society should recognize the fact that we cannot wipe out homosexuality. But we *can* take steps to prevent homosexuality and to eliminate attitudes which discourage inverts from seeking treatment.

We agree with the Rev. James Van Venderveldt and Dr. Robert P. Odenwald, authors of *Psychiatry and Catholicism*, who write: "There is no justification for regarding homosexuals as a class to be abhorred as depraved and degenerate. They, like all sick people, deserve to be understood and to be given the same sympathetic assistance that is willingly given to other types of people. Scorn, contempt and undue severity will only increase the feeling of inferiority that predominates in many homosexuals despite an outward appearance of insouciance or defiance."

Our present social attitude toward homosexuality should be a realistic one. The importance of sex enlightenment as a necessary step toward successfully challenging the increasing incidence of sexual maladjustments is aptly expressed by Robert MacIver (Professor of Sociology, Columbia University) who states:

"We should not be afraid of the truth about human behavior. Knowledge of the facts won't cause immorality, but it will remove false fears and unwise expectations. It will show what are true dangers and what are imaginary ones. We all agree that unenlightened guidance is bad where physical health is concerned. We must learn that it is no less bad when moral health is the issue. Only through knowledge of the facts can we deal intelligently with the serious problems of personality that arise in the area of sexual relations.

"Our public assumptions are a morass of misdirection. We treat homosexuality as a crime, though of itself it is no more criminal than an endocrine imbalance. We attach the ideas of abnormality or wickedness to manifestations of the sex drive in the young that are profoundly natural. We associate their interest in sex with notions of unwholesomeness or 'uncleanness' that totally misrepresent the situation. We cannot give direction here until we first acquire knowledge."

It is only recently that the public has been awakened to the need for knowing more about homosexuality.

Despite the appalling prevalence of homosexuality in this country, there is a paucity of authoritative information accessible to the lay reader regarding the nature, cause, and curability of this particular sexual abnormality.

As for female homosexuality, very few books have been devoted specifically to this subject. More than a generation ago, Freud wrote: "Homosexuality in women, which is certainly not less common than in men although much less glaring, has not only been ignored by the law but has also been neglected by psychoanalytic research."

Yet the study of Lesbianism is no less important than the study of homosexuality among men. Lesbianism is equally capable of undermining the stability of our social structure. Much of the incompatibility between the sexes is related to this problem. Unconscious or latent homosexuality in women unfavorably affects their personalities and promotes marital unhappiness. It is responsible, in part, for our increasing divorce rate.

Most psychiatrists agree that society's attitude toward homosexuality is unenlightened and steeped in social prejudices. Referring to homosexuals as "perverts" only makes matters worse. The attitude of homosexuals toward society is also defective. We reserve the term homosexual, here, to those who lack all desire for contact with the opposite sex. Such deviants generally suffer from a paranoid mentality. They feel persecuted by society and refuse to consider their deviation as a symptom of neurosis. They argue that some of the greatest figures in history were homosexuals. They believe that homosexuality should be accepted by society and that homosexuals should be allowed to live as they please. They resist psychiatric attempts to change them, contending that many overt homosexuals are happy in their way of life. This is contrary to the facts. They cling to other misconceptions about homosexuality. For this reason society regards them as either criminally responsible for their acts, or as sick people. Many homosexuals believe there is no cure for them and that they cannot be changed. This is a rationalization for not wanting to change. They get narcissistic satisfaction in being "different." They suffer from many blind spots. They are angered when told that homosexuality comes under the same classification as other deviations, such as exhibitionism, voyeurism, and transvestism. They look upon homosexuality as an entity in itself, almost convinced of the existence of the so-called "third sex."

Incidentally, we were consulted by a motion picture company to evaluate a film produced in West Germany, entitled *The Third Sex*, for which Dr. Caprio wrote the following prologue:

"It has been reported that approximately eight to ten million of our male population and a much larger number of females have been involved in a homosexual experience. Psychiatrists believe that homosexuality is not a condition in itself but rather a symptom of a deep-seated neurosis that can be cured if the person involved wishes.

"My study of homosexual patients during the past twenty-three years has convinced me that many become involved because of doubts about their ability to function normally in heterosexual relationships. Yet the majority of these people are unaware of, or unable to evaluate, these causative psychological factors.

"I believe it important that the public be enlightened about this growing psychological and sociological situation and that it be frankly discussed as it is in this film.

"It is my understanding that the film is based on records of an actual case in Germany. While its solution of the problem cannot be considered a recommended answer for all those involved, the fact remains that homosexuality is not inborn and that a person who so desires can be conditioned into making a satisfactory adjustment."

In a radio interview following the showing of the film, Dr. Caprio stated that there is no such thing as a "third sex," and that this term was coined in now obsolete early theories that homosexuals were born that way and that they suffered from a glandular imbalance.

The film briefly concerns a young man who develops a strong attachment to a male friend, which disturbs his parents.

The mother is advised by the family doctor to have the boy associate with some girl of his own age in an effort to condition him to heterosexual relationships. The mother selects the young family maid and encourages this attractive girl to have a relationship with her son while the rest of the family is on vacation. The boy falls in love with the girl and turns away from his homosexual companion.

While such a procedure is not recommended as a solution for homosexuality, psychiatrists today believe that conditioning to heterosexual contacts promotes the successful repression of the homosexual component. However, for a homosexually inclined person to accept a relationship with someone of the opposite sex, requires considerable insight-therapy.

For homosexuals to unite and take a defensive or belligerent attitude toward society and the police department doesn't help their cause. They are defeating themselves and preventing the very thing they are trying to accomplish. If they want society to take a more sympathetic or liberal attitude toward their problem, they must, in turn, develop an appreciation of society's evaluation of it and not express hostility or contempt for anyone and everyone who doesn't understand their way of thinking and living. Psychiatrists today are trying to break this vicious circle of society rejecting the homosexual and the homosexual feeling persecuted by society.

FALLACIES AND FACTS

The amount of current misinformation regarding male and female homosexuality is amazing. This lack of knowledge makes it difficult to cope with the problem successfully.

Much misinformation has been published, adding to the public's confusion. Nevertheless, it is understandable why differences of scientific opinion exist. New theories supplant old theories. At one time doctors resorted to bloodletting for the symptomatic relief of high blood pressure. Now such a procedure is obsolete. In early times, sex offenders were either castrated or decapitated. Today they are regarded as persons suffering from a sexual maladjustment. And so with homosexuality, what we believed to be true a century ago, we know now to be a fallacy.

Let us cite a few of the misconceptions about homosexuals. There are those who believe that they are born that way; that they suffer from some glandular imbalance; that their sexual nerve centers have been misplaced by nature and are localized in certain regions of the body such as the mouth; that all homosexual men are effeminate and that female homosexuals are masculine; that homosexuals should not marry lest their children inherit the same tendencies; that so-called "queers" are physically unable to satisfy the opposite sex, as evidencd by those who become impotent when they attempt heterosexual relations; that homosexuality is incurable; and that homosexuals seldom marry.

Homosexuality is acquired; it is not congenital nor inherited. It is the behavior symptom of a deep-seated and unresolved neurosis. Homosexuals, themselves, prefer to believe they were born that way. They delude themselves into thinking that their homosexuality is caused by a congenital constitutional defect or some hormone imbalance. Dr. Clifford Allen stated quite emphatically that sexual inversion is not a congenital anomaly: "Much has been said of the congenital and endocrine types of homosexuality but there is not the slightest vestige of evidence that this condition is congenital or endocrine."

Many male sex inverts are pronouncedly masculine in physique, voice, and skin texture. Similarly, numerous Lesbians are not mannish but feminine in every respect.

It is also an error to attribute homosexuality to any physical anomaly of the sex organs. The homosexual may be virile and possess normal sex organs. Many homosexuals are bisexual, oscillating between heterosexual and homosexual activities and are capable of gratifying their sexual desires with either sex. Their homosexual cravings may be transitory in character.

There is no such thing as a "third sex."

Many homosexuals marry in order to camouflage their homosexual inclination. Some marry with the hope that marriage will solve their homosexual problem, and that as long as they have access to heterosexual relations, they are less likely to succumb to homosexual temptations.

If homosexuals want to be cured and cooperate, the results are generally favorable. Unfortunately, the overt or promiscuous type has no genuine wish to become heterosexual. If he does seek help from the specialist, he often sets up resistances which act as obstacles to his being cured.

HISTORICAL DATA

American legal concepts of homosexual conduct are derived from the English and were, as we have previously seen, influenced by the teachings of the Hebrews. In England, during the reign of Henry VIII, the punishment for a convicted sodomist was death, although the strict legal definition of sodomy was restricted to anal connections between humans or sexual contact by a human with an animal.

The word "sodomy," the legal expression for homosexual behavior, is derived from the Biblical town of Sodom, in which this type of sexual practice between males was indulged. This practice by the town's inhabitants evoked divine wrath ("Thou shalt not lie with mankind as with womankind,"—Lev. XVIII, 22), and the town was destroyed. American legal principles embody the concepts of the English common law and are developed from this and from early court decisions. These laws, although actually written down, are called "unwritten" law in contrast to statutory or "written" law enacted by legislative decree. Because of the restricted definition of sodomy in the laws of Henry VIII, many sex offenders went free. Practices such as fellatio and cunnilingus were not covered by legal prohibition and judges were reluctant to hold an offender responsible who raised the objection accordingly. But, as our communities grew and society became more complex, it became apparent that new and comprehensive laws were necessary. Today all our states have, by legislative enactment, codified sex crimes either by specific definition or by wording which encompasses offenses not covered in common law. If, however, an offense has been prohibited by statute in general terms only and without specific definition, the courts will refer back to common law, and the offender will be charged accordingly.

Pederasty is a term derived from the words "paidos" and "erastes" and means the love of boys. It was widespread in ancient times in the Orient and Greece. In Athens, public baths were places where pederasts congregated. It is interesting to note that pederasty in Rome was known as "Greek Love." Aristotle described this love for boys, and Plato refers to Socrates' relations with his students. Socrates was condemned to death for "corrupting the youth of the community."

At one time Julius Caesar was accused of pederasty and of having submitted to the pederastic advances of men who aided him in his career. His homosexual tendencies were assumed because of his allegedly effeminate interest in his physical appearance. According to Moll, Octavius was supposed to have had sexual intercourse with Caesar. Tiberius, who was notorious for his cruelty, subjected boys to immoral sexual practices. The same was true of Caligula, his successor. Nero was another who loved young boys and embraced them in public. The poet Horace was accused of homosexuality. Mentegazza asserts that Virgil also was a pederast. Male prostitution was quite prevalent in the Roman Empire.

The French blame the Italians for introducing male sexual

inversion to their country. Moll informs us that homosexuality has always been more widespread in Italy than in any other country in Europe. But its occurrence is universal in the East and West and in primitive and civilized societies.

According to Schopenhauer, if old men were able to procreate, there would be a physical degeneration of the human race. This is a philosophical explanation of why old men turned to sexual aberrations, avoiding heterosexuality in an instinctual urge for race preservation.

In Mexico, Central, and South America there are houses of male prostitution. The men in these houses assume the roles of women. Such establishments also exist in the Orient and in certain countries of Europe.

Among historical figures of recent history alleged to have possessed homosexual tendencies are Michelangelo, Shakespeare, Oscar Wilde, Byron, Whitman, Tchaikowsky, Cellini, Rosa Bonheur, Leonardo da Vinci, Francis Bacon, Alexander the Great, Queen Anne of England, Heinrich Heine, Frederick the Great, Queen Christina, Charles XII of Sweden, Catherine the Great, Queen Hatshepsut (of ancient Egypt), William Orange, and many others.

Queen Hatshepsut had herself sculptured in masculine costume and wearing a false beard.

George Sand, the French novelist, dressed in men's clothes and occasionally smoked cigars. She was nicknamed "Monsieur Sand."

Female homosexuality (Amor Lesbicus) was well known in Greek antiquity. Sappho, a famous poetess of the Greek island of Lesbos (whence the term "Lesbian") is alleged to have founded the cult of Lesbian love. According to the historians of her time, she was a woman lover. Her name has been associated through the ages with the traditional sex practice known to sexologists as "Sapphism" (cunnilingus).

The name Sappho means "clear-voiced" or "bright." Sappho was brilliant indeed, for her poems became world famous.

Lesbian practices have been known to girls of the Orient as well as to the women of Europe. In ancient China, Sapphic seductions were quite prevalent.

In his study, *Sexual Life in Ancient India,* Johann Jakob Meyer cites a document on Lesbian practices in Indian harems.

Edward Westermarck, the noted anthropologist, points out: "In Zanzibar there are women who wear men's clothes in private, show a preference for masculine occupations, and seek sexual satisfaction among women of like inclination, or normal women who are won over by presents or other means."

CONTRIBUTING INFLUENCES

Parents are responsible, either knowingly or unknowingly, for a large percentage of the cases of homosexuality. Stekel found from his professional experience that parents of homosexuals invariably showed abnormal character traits. Many homosexuals had fathers who were psychopathic, alcoholic, or neurotically strict.

Many occupations are conducive to the development of homosexuality. The theatre and night club world, for example, seem to provide a type of environment conducive to "homosexual friendships." Some theatre people regard themselves as different from ordinary people and entitled to a special "way of life." They run the gamut of the unusual and the bizarre. In their sexual relations, which are sometimes of a promiscuous nature, a trend toward homosexuality often begins as a search for the bizarre and unusual.

Another factor is the existence of a strong, narcissistic drive in people in the limelight.

A slavelike devotion to a career which rules out the responsibilities of married life strengthens the trend toward a homosexual way of living. Finally, a life characterized by loneliness among strangers, by frequent change of environment, and the necessity for sharing living quarters with members of their own sex, increases the susceptibility to homosexual gratifications.

Dr. Bernard A. Bauer writes: "It is absolutely proved that homosexuality appears wherever persons of the same sex are compelled by external conditions to live in close contact with one another in the absence of members of the opposite sex."

Dr. Rustam Mehta attributes the increasing incidence of sexual aberrations to the speeding up of the tempo of modern life. He claims that "the present-day craving to enjoy life to the very full, the desire for new and still newer sensations, the low economic threshold have drawn countless millions into the whirlpool of unnatural desires."

War has also had its effects. War widows and wives who are sexually deprived of their husbands have a problem of adjustment. Homosexuality, particularly among women, undoubtedly is influenced by wars. Then, of course, there is the factor of homosexual seduction. As far back as 1886, Professor Benjamin Tarnowsky showed that homosexuality and other aberrations of the sexual instinct were sometimes caused by seduction. In 1889, Dr. K. Kautzner substantiated that viewpoint in his study of homosexuality, published in Germany, by emphasizing the important role which seduction plays in sexual inversion.

PSYCHODYNAMIC FACTORS

Homosexuality often develops as a result of a son's strong attachment to his mother—what Freud calls the "Oedipus Complex," and in the case of female inversion, of a daughter's overattachment to her father—the "Electra Complex." A male child may develop feminine traits because he identifies himself with his mother or sister and imitates them. The opposite is true of the female child who chooses to be like her father or brother. Parents sometimes encourage these identifications with the opposite sex among their children not realizing the possible consequences to their sexual development. Regarding homosexual patterns in children, Clara Thompson informs us: "A very important determining influence in the development of homosexuality is the child's awareness that his sex was a disappointment to the parents or to the more important parent, especially if their disappointment leads them to treat the child as if he were of the opposite sex." Other mothers are guilty of infecting their sons with too much "momism" to use Strecker's term. These oversolicitous "Moms" fail to appreciate that excess love showered on a male child is equivalent to too many sweets. Boys rebel against mothers who try to make husband-substitutes out of them, which exposes them to contempt among other boys, as "mama's boy" or "sissies." Often a basic feeling of inferiority in the male child is fostered by a mother who means well but thereby sets off a homosexual trend in the son's adolescence and adult life.

There is a residue of the abnormal in sex in all of us. If the sexual instinct or "libido" reaches its highest goal of development—heterosexuality—then the individual may be regarded as "normal." However, if for various psychological reasons, the sexual instinct fails to mature, the person is more apt to seek a sexual gratification in keeping with his immature sexual development. For this reason the majority of psychiatrists consider homosexuals, for the most part, to be neurotics—children emotionally love-starved and frustrated. Homosexuals are inclined to fear the opposite sex. They are not considered "normal" only in the sense that their sex behavior represents a regression to childhood, an escape from the biological responsibilities assumed by heterosexuals. They are narcissistic (in love with themselves) insofar as their own pleasures come first, irrespective of what others think about their conduct. Many have no scruples about seducing adolescents whose lives may be seriously affected by a single homosexual experience. An analysis of their methods of gratifying their sexual desires reveals the extent of "child-play" in their behavior. They like to dress differently, enjoy mimicking the opposite sex, and indulge in emotional tantrums. In groups, they manifest symptoms characteristic of a neurotic child. Psychiatrists refer to such behavior as "psychosexual infantilism." In other words they attempt to gratify the erotic cravings of their childhood. Many have what we might call a "nipple complex"—never having been psychologically weened from the mother's breast or the nipple of the bottle if they were bottle fed. Bergler uses the term "oral eroticism" to designate this phenomenon. It explains why so many neurotics are addicted to mouth-pleasures such as overeating, excess smoking, and drinking.

Homosexuals do not understand their "unconscious." Hence, they find it difficult to discipline themselves successfully. Many "overt" homosexuals deny experiencing guilt feelings, but they suffer from a multiplicity of neurotic ailments for which they seek medical aid. They complain of headaches, fatigue, insomnia, digestive disturbances, pains around the heart, fainting spells, and dizziness. They go to their physician for relief not appreciating the role of anxiety and guilt over their homosexuality in the development of their symptom complaints. In numerous instances, when homosexuality is practiced over a long period of time, it produces a severe neurosis or even a psychosis. Reason enough why homosexuals need psychiatric treatment.

In an attempt to overcompensate for their feelings of inferiority, they develop a pseudo-narcissism (false sense of superiority). Many of them are among the pseudo-intellectuals who live in urban Bohemias and dabble in art and literature. While some are quite talented, there are many who never achieve any degree of success because of their underlying chronic frustration. They rationalize their homosexuality by claiming that some of the world's greatest artists and writers have been homosexuals.

Most homosexuals suffer from strong reactions of jealousy, sadomasochistic trends, guilt feelings, and a deep sense of insecurity. It is surprising how many major crimes are committed which can be linked to homosexuality. The ones who are strongly masochistic, who become depressed and develop feelings of inadequacy and self-pity, often decide to commit suicide. Homosexuality, therefore, is a serious problem.

A valid modern concept of homosexuality is advanced by Albert Ellis in an article entitled "Recent Views on Sexual Deviations." He makes a distinction between persons who are exclusively homosexual and those who are predominantly heterosexual but occasionally indulge in a homosexual experience. He feels that persons who absolutely cannot or will not engage in heterosexual acts are suffering from at least one of the following four, distinct, neurotic symptoms.

1. A sexual fixation on members of their own sex from which they cannot escape.

2. A specific phobia in regard to members of the other sex which prevents them from having satisfactory heterosexual relations.

3. An obsession about members of their own sex which drives them toward homosexual acts or an obsessive interest in members of the other sex which drives them toward assuming a role of that sex.

4. A distinct compulsion toward having exclusively homosexual affairs.

He adds: "One degree or another of ambisexual activity is the biological norm; and it is only cultural customs which cause most individuals to become mainly or exclusively heterosexual."

We feel that clinical evidence substantiates the important role which narcissism plays in the development of homosexual patterns. The need for narcissistic gratifications (neurotic self-love) arises out of a feeling of insecurity, and represents an attempt to overcompensate for a thwarting of our instinct of self-preservation. It corroborates Karen Horney's idea of a "basic need for affection" in all of us. One explanation for sexual inversion, therefore, is to be found in certain manifestations of our self-preservation instinct. Sex is a symptomatic expression of man's desire to survive, to love and be loved, to experience lasting pleasure, and to share it with someone else. Sex serves a dual purpose—procreation and pleasure. The former accounts for the perpetuation of the human race, and the latter serves to make the struggle for existence more endurable and enjoyable.

Homosexuality is an extension of autoeroticism (it is co-operative masturbation). Pointing to this interrelationship between masturbation and homosexuality, Stekel wrote: "In truth every indulgence in masturbation is a homosexual act as a means for releasing the never absent homosexual trends."

A child wishes to be loved by both parents. This need for biparental love partly explains why some bisexuals seek the love of both sexes. However, society will not permit us to live a bisexual existence. Because of cultural taboos, homosexuality must be repressed. The so-called normal person manages to sublimate his or her homosexual component successfully. The neurotic, however, represses his or her homosexual desires and becomes a prey to inner conflicts. Or he gives way to homosexual gratification only to suffer states of anxiety associated with conscious or unconscious feelings of guilt. Many homosexuals enter into a homosexual way of life because of anxiety over their ability to function as an adequate sexual partner in a heterosexual relationship.

Some homosexuals admit to their women friends that they

are homosexuals. In this way, they seek excuses for not being sexually aggressive in their heterosexual relationships. They achieve immunity from the effort they dread by believing themselves impotent with women. They attribute this to something "inborn." But such impotence is self-induced, a form of autocastration. Some homosexuals claim that the idea of having sex relations with a woman is revolting, yet have no aversion to sexual acts on their own sex. This, of course, is a defense mechanism for not being able to accept a woman as a sexual being—an unconscious wish to idealize womanhood. One homosexual patient stated that the thought of his mother ever having had intercourse revolted him. It explains why many homosexuals enjoy a sexless companionship with elderly women (mother surrogates or substitutes).

Men who have doubts about their masculinity sometimes develop a condition known as "Homosexual Panic"—exaggerated fears that they are homosexuals. This anxiety state exists not only among men who are self-conscious about their effeminacy but among so-called "he" men. These people are consoled when they learn that a certain amount of latent homosexuality exists in everyone. Freud once wrote: "I have never come through a single psychoanalysis of a man or a woman without having to take into account a very considerable current of homosexuality."

Such individuals need to convince themselves that masculinity is not a matter of biceps or hair on their chests. It is a matter of emotional maturity.

CASE HISTORIES

Case 1. A young college student was referred for a psychiatric examination. He had been arrested for making advances toward a man sitting next to him in the theater who turned out to be a plain-clothes police officer. This young boy came from a religious and respected family. His college career was at stake. He did not regard himself as a homosexual and claimed he was merely trying to find someone who would masturbate him. His marked feelings of inferiority during childhood and adolescence because of being cross-eyed and his shyness toward the opposite sex contributed much toward the development of an introvert type of personality. Since he was religious, he experienced acute conflicts between sex and religion. He was torn between the desire to obey and the compulsion to rebel against moral teachings.

The case is interesting for its revelation of the interrelationship between feelings of inferiority, heterosexual inhibitions, religious conflicts, and latent homosexual component.

He described his feelings of inferiority associated with his strabismus (cross-eyes) as follows:

"My eyes developed into a crossed condition at the age of six. Despite all remedial measures, the condition grew worse until I was eighteen. They finally became cosmetically straight after surgery and eye exercises.

"When I went to high school, I was painfully self-conscious of my eye condition. I always entered the classroom with my head down. I would never look anyone in the face. I walked back and forth from school looking at the pavement. I had a dread of mirrors. I avoided all contact with girls for fear they would stare at me. I also kept away from boys as much as possible. They either laughed at me or pitied me, and I could stand neither of these reactions. I had very little to do with my family. I felt everyone was staring at my eyes.

"From time to time I remember being struck by some girl's beauty, but I was so shy that I didn't know what to do about it, and so missed the boat."

He recalled that he began masturbating at the age of twelve. Once his father caught him in the act and exclaimed, "Don't play with that thing!" However, he continued to masturbate, but church attendance led to conflicts due to guilt feelings.

His guilt expressed itself in such psychomatic reactions as dizziness, pains on the top of his head, and a feeling that he was going to faint.

He further recollected that, while sleeping with his brother around the age of puberty, he became sexually sensitive but did not have sexual contact.

His antisocial offenses represented his ambivalence toward his religion. His ambivalence toward his father for reprimanding him about masturbation at a time when he did not understand the significance of the act made him project the same ambivalence toward God. His latent homosexual component was accentuated as his strong feelings of inferiority made him more introverted. Making advances to strangers in a theater symbolized, in part, an attempt to be accepted by his own sex, since he felt rejected throughout his childhood and adolescence because of his eye defect.

Case 2. A university graduate, son of a prominent architect, and a man who had never been in trouble with the authorities, was discharged from military service because of "alleged homosexual advances." There was no history of any sexual disorder during his developmental years, and the evidence indicated that he had made a good social adjustment.

He was interviewed following the administration of three grains of sodium amytal (truth drug). He related that one day, while driving toward the military base, he stopped to give four soldiers a "lift." One of them accused him of having tried to touch his sex parts. They asked him to stop the car and proceeded to beat him up. His head was badly battered. On one side, his jaw was fractured, and he had a gash on the side of his head.

Threatened with the possibility of a court-martial, which he wished to avoid as it would reflect on his family's reputation, he agreed to separate from the service and accept an undesirable discharge.

Because the nature of his discharge would handicap his chances for a good position in civilian life, he decided to engage the services of an attorney and appeal for a hearing before a Review Board for the Correction of Diagnosis.

An investigation of the four soldiers disclosed that two of them had been in numerous difficulties and had psychopathic personalities. There was considerable doubt as to whether these four accusers were capable of making truthful statements.

The psychiatric report was supplemented by the findings of another psychiatrist who made an independent study of the case. We concurred that the subject was not a homosexual nor did he possess "homosexual tendencies" (a term used in military regulations). The case has not yet been finally settled and is being re-evaluated in view of the psychiatric testimony.

The following is a fragment of the psychiatric examination submitted:

"He has never given his family any reason to suspect any sexual difficulty of any kind. He has had a normal childhood, has made good at various jobs during summer vacations from college, and has had a normal interest in the opposite sex. His heterosexual experiences convince me beyond doubt that he is not a homosexual. I believe that he is a victim of unfortunate circumstances and that he was unjustly accused by the soldier who assaulted him. Any statement he agreed to sign was motivated by a desire to bring to an end the entire unpleasant episode, fearing it might reflect on members of his family. It is not uncommon for persons in military service, who find themselves in such a predicament, to sign statements to something that they have not done only because it appears at the time to be the best solution. They are often ill-advised to resign for the good of the service, and they feel that they do not possess the emotional stamina to withstand a court-martial hearing.

"I have had occasion to examine numerous cases of this

kind and have observed that it is not uncommon for an individual to be innocently accused of having made homosexual advances by persons whose integrity is questionable. Psychiatrists have discovered that persons who assault a suspected homosexual are generally suffering from homosexual conflicts within themselves and are considered 'trouble makers,' eager to register a false complaint against someone as a cover-up for their own psychopathic traits.

"In all fairness to his family, to himself, and to his future welfare, I trust that this case will be reappraised in the light of the above information."

Case 3. This man, age forty, was arrested by a member of the sex squad in civilian clothes. He claimed he mistook the policeman for a "queer" while in the lavatory of a theater. He further contended the officer looked at him "funny" and said "Do you take it?" The officer stated that, during the conversation, the subject had a semi-erection and that he was stroking his penis. The man was arrested and the matter referred to the military police inasmuch as he was a member of the armed forces.

When questioned about any past homosexual activities, he admitted that, on several occasions, he had been approached by homosexuals and had assumed a passive role. He denied ever having accosted anyone or ever having indulged in any active homosexual act. He also stated that he had always preferred sexual relations with the opposite sex, had been married, and had never considered himself as having "homosexual tendencies."

He said that he didn't know the significance of the active and passive role until he read the military regulations. He had always been under the impression that only the person who took the active role was a homosexual. Consequently, he did not think of himself as a homosexual. Because of his admission to past intimacies, he was asked to resign. The attorney managed to get him a hearing before a military board, at which time psychiatric testimony was presented.

Because of his ignorance of homosexuality and the military regulations concerning it, his excellent record in the service, and his honesty in volunteering to tell the truth about his past sexual activities, the board accepted the psychiatric evidence that he was not a homosexual and decided to retain him in the army.

At the Board meeting, Dr. Caprio suggested that it would be wise for the medical officer or some administrative officer to give a lecture to the men regarding the part of military regulations concerning homosexuality and its various classified categories. At least the men would be properly informed, and there would be less cases of this kind in the future.

Shortly before the Board made its decision, Dr. Caprio received the following letter from the accused man.

"Dear Doctor:

"I would like to thank you for appearing in my behalf and your excellent testimony. What I would have done without you and my lawyer, I do not know. It is gratifying to know that there are such men as you in this world.

"I know you will be pleased to know that, because of your testimony, at least one man is taking your advice. My commanding officer, Major —— is giving a lecture to the men in the squadron on AF Regulation 35-56; if the rest of the commanders follow suit, then a major step will have been made in helping others.

"Again, let me thank you.

"Sincerely,

                                        ——"

Case 4. The following information was furnished by a patient who regarded himself as having a "homosexual problem." He felt it would be helpful in his analysis to jot down some of the factors that he felt had some significance in the development of his sexual difficulties. It is only by examining the thinking of the homosexual that psychiatrists are able to achieve a psychodynamic understanding of homosexuality. This particular young man, age twenty-four, admitted that he could not fully comprehend the sexual conflicts which troubled his attitudes toward love, sex, and marriage. However, his "thoughts on paper," as he labelled the material, reveal psychogenic and traumatic factors that contributed to his confusion. His father had made it clear that he wanted a girl, inferring that he was disappointed that the boy came into the world. At the age of ten, an older boy initiated him into oral sex relations. Relations at home suffered from incompatibility of the parents. His mother became interested in another man and threatened to divorce her husband. After graduating from college, he was drafted into the Army but received an undesirable discharge because of homosexuality. Following several consultation interviews, he decided to write down some thoughts about himself.

"At present, although there is one major reason why I believe that I can use some psychiatric aid, I also feel that there are aspects of my present beliefs which cannot be considered normal.

"I do not know whether this is the result of happenings during the past fifteen years, but I feel that I do not know what 'love' is. I feel no great attachment at present to my parents, although I do feel obligated for the sacrifices which they made to put me through college. It is my belief that I would not want my children raised in the same atmosphere. I do not feel that any child should be asked such questions as my mother asked me, or to hear her repeat that she was staying with my father for the sake of my sister and myself.

"I have probably been closer to my mother than to my father. His main preoccupations have always been in sports in which I have had little interest.

"For the foregoing reason, and also due to my homosexual tendency, I have been fairly leery of marriage. I have been going with one girl off and on, but I don't feel that it would be fair to marry her.

"I have always felt happiest when continually 'on the go' and have something to do. I also like to do what I want to do when I want to do it. Most of my tastes are rather set, and I feel that I have already gained a degree of independence.

"I have never realized the close relationship between the sexual aspects of life and the ability to love and to be loved. I am not sure that I have an understanding of what true love is.

"I feel that my present inability to define love, to feel what it is, and also the development of my present sexual characteristics have been mutual and intertwined. Though I can begin to understand what love is, or should be, and what normal sex relationships are, how can I change my present attitudes to conform to same?

"There was extreme parental disagreement during the first ten years of my life. Was this a large contributing factor to my present feelings of insecurity?

"Sex discussions, such as they were, were with mother. I remember being quite embarrassed at the time. During my early teens I was extremely modest, probably from feelings of physical inferiority. Although, today, I can talk to mother on the subject, or with other women, I have never had any discussion on this topic with my father.

"I frequently saw my parents nude, although I can't remember that this had any effect on me one way or the other.

"I remember being shy, introverted, and extremely moody up through my middle teens. I started masturbating at eleven or twelve. Can this be traced to feelings of insecurity and inferiority at that time?

"I have never felt particularly homesick at any time that I was away from home. From the time I was thirteen or fourteen, I have spent periods away from home.

"Homosexuality was never mentioned in the sex discussions that I had with my mother, although I probably realized what it was and that it was wrong.

"I can remember that obedience to father came mostly from fear and not respect.

"Although in many ways I have been allowed to do what I want to do, particularly since I entered college, mother still tries to exert influence in ways I don't particularly care for such as 'save money, get your sleep,' etc.

"At present, I question more than ever both my own attitudes on marriage and any impulses I may feel to get married now or in the near future. Without a fuller and more correct understanding of love and a fuller capacity to carry on normal sexual relations, I do not feel that it would be fair to marry anyone.

"At present, I can care for most of my own needs, cook my own meals, and, on the whole, am quite independent, but I do feel a desire for companionship.

"Is it possible that the past improper mother-son relationship, undoubtedly complicated by the incorrect father-son relationship, has been a cause of my prseent feeling of insecurity and emotional conflict?

"Probably the chief reasons for my thinking of marriage at present are the pressure of society and the desire for companionship which are not exactly the basis for a lasting marriage.

"I have a desire at intervals to talk about my troubles, my emotional disturbances. Is this basically a desire for pity or a desire to correct them?

"During my college years there was little or no outward homosexual manifestations with the exception of masturbation. With several women, in particular one, whom I have gone with for a period of three years, I felt that I could carry on normal sexual relationships. I experienced erection during necking sessions, and sex in itself with women had no particular repulsion. After the events of last summer and my discharge from the Army, I have found it almost impossible to attain an erection in any kind of association with the opposite sex. I have shied away from any necking sessions as they no longer mean anything. Outwardly, I don't feel any different than I did two or three years ago, but some internal block seems to have formed and changed the course of my emotions.

"The biggest problem is living with myself. I am probably selfish and materialistic. How at this stage can I change myself to the required extent?"

Case 5. A young man who had been discharged for military service because of homosexuality decided to avail himself of psychiatric treatment. He was given three months of intensive psychotherapy consisting of four sessions per week. The treatment also included hypnoanalysis followed by post-hypnotic suggestion and narcoanalysis. The case is worth recording as it represents clinical evidence of a favorable response to short-term therapy.

The attorney had referred the case for treatment with the understanding that he would be given interval reports on the patient's progress.

As a child, Joel was highly sensitive and emotional. He suffered from deep-seated feelings of insecurity and rejection, the result of a broken-home situation. He was sent to a private school where, he claims, he was exposed to homosexual experiences. Not only did many students engage in homosexual activities, but several of the tutors had such relations with the boys. Joel's effeminate mannerisms as a growing boy made him very self-conscious. His relationship to his divorced parents was a frustrating one. Never having had a close relationship to them, he suffered chronic loneliness. Deprived of an opportunity to develop a father-son relationship, he sought an outlet in companionships with his own sex. This served to block the development of normal, heterosexual relationships. He feared his father who was stern and strict, and he claimed that his mother never gave him a sense of being wanted or loved. His effeminacy resulted from his identification with his mother. Having been exposed to further sexual experiences of a homosexual nature in military service, he became more and more conditioned to this way of life.

The treatment consisted of three phases: (1) The phase of catharsis, during which period he was given an opportunity to tell the story of his life and unburden his emotional conflicts; this in itself proved beneficial. (2) The second phase consisted of insight-therapy, during which time, he was helped to see those factors that were responsible for his sexual neurosis; in this way he acquired a better understanding of himself. (3) The third state of treatment consisted of applying what he had learned, what might be referred to as the self-discipline phase of therapy.

He proved able to exercise control over his deviant sexual impulses and began making plans for a constructive future. All during treatment, he manifested an earnest desire to be helped. His father was advised to be more sympathetic and understanding and to abandon his former harshness and condemnation. After treatment was terminated, I learned that this patient was dating girls and felt less fearful in their presence. He did not believe that he would ever again become involved with his own sex.

During hypnoanalysis, he recalled that, at the age of seven, he indulged in mutual fellatio with another boy. It was repeated approximately ten times. It was at this stage that he began to develop crushes on other boys, particularly, those who were good in sports, and toward whom he felt inferior because he was not himself athletic. When he was sent to private schools, he felt rejected and wanted to return home. During puberty, he was teased by other boys because of his effeminate ways. He was told, for example, that he threw a ball like a girl. Most of the boys at school indulged in mutual masturbation. He hated the schoolmaster who conducted religious services yet had sexual relations with some of the boys.

While in the service, he made an attempt to have relations with a prostitute but could not function with her because of his repulsion. When a second attempt ended the same way, he thought he was different from other men.

He stated that, as he grew up, he was always frightened by his father who was never affectionate. "My father never showed any interest in me. He didn't know how to be a father. There was constant bickering between my parents. Mother sometimes petted me, but at other times, she was as cold as ice."

The case above further illustrates that the development of the homosexual pattern cannot be attributed to one single psychodynamic factor. It does indicate, however, that feelings of inferiority, insecurity, and rejection may constitute a common denominator in hundreds of cases of homosexuality.

Case 6. The following represents free-association information supplied by a patient who sought psychiatric treatment because he "no longer wishes to be a homosexual."

"My father was a poor provider. We were very poor. I was given the name of 'Percy' and the school kids teased me about it. They said it was a sissy name. I resented people who had lots of money. I always had contempt for my father. He was a shiftless drunk. I always tried to be perfect. My sister left home. She never wants to get married. We were all unhappy at home. There was always quarreling. I once saw my sister in the nude. I was twelve years old. It has always been on my mind. Dad would urinate in the sink. I would see his penis. He had no modesty. It disgusted me. I'd walk out and slam the door. He once urinated in a milk bottle. He was filthy. My mother was a devout Catholic. Dad was always going to bars. Mom showed no love to my sister or me. Everything centered around pleasing my father. He never paid any attention to us. He never told Mom how much he earned. I always feared Dad. His immodesty was sickening. He'd get so drunk he'd sleep on the couch with empty beer bottles around him. There was so much selfishness in Dad. He was like an animal when he ate. He would be completely nude in front of my sister. I built up so much hatred of him, I'd wish he were dead. My sister became a nervous wreck. Mom would get fainting spells. I think my sister got kicked out of military service because of Lesbianism. I also was discharged from the service because of homosexuality. Later my sister got her discharge changed with the help of a congressman.

"My sister and Dad hated each other. I wondered how Mom ever stood my father. I just had to get away from home. He wasn't even a citizen of Ireland. He finally became an American citizen. My father lost many jobs because of his drinking. Mother once had to scrub floors in a rooming house to support us. The priest told her to stay and not leave my father and to say prayers. I think she should have separated. Our lives became wrecks."

It is an unusual case insofar as both the patient and his sister were subjected to the same traumatic influences of an unhappy home, and both developed a homosexual problem resulting in separation from military service.

In a letter, following a course of psychotherapy, he wrote:

"I wish to extend my appreciation for your sincere interest in my case. I can assure you that with always a religious prayer and correct moral thinking, I will not allow myself to again enter into the activities that caused my separation from military service. True, a desire may again arise, but through prayer and strong will power, a temptation can always be overcome regardless of how strong it is. Each morning, when I attend Mass, I feel strongly my discharge from military service was the best thing that happened. Since then, I have not committed another act and feel strongly that I could overcome any and all temptations to do so. I am enjoying peace of mind as far as that problem is concerned. I now accept my problem for what it is, a symptom of my original emotional sickness. Thanks sincerely for your past assistance."

LESBIANISM AND THE LAW

In legal codes throughout history, the provisions covering male homosexual relationships have differed sharply from those affecting female homosexuals. The ancient Hittite Code, for example, condemned only male homosexuality and contained no reference to homosexual relations among women. In the Bible and the Talmud, references to homosexuality are primarily to the male; the Talmud, in fact, characterizes female homosexuality as a "mere obscenity" which disqualifies a woman from marrying a priest. Although the Catholic codes specifically condemn both male and female homosexuality, penalties were enforced only against the male. In medieval Europe, when the authority of the Catholic Church was still unchallenged, the death sentence was frequently imposed for male homosexuality. There are few recorded cases of similar action against females.

In modern times this difference in attitude continues in the laws of England and of most European countries. Only in Austria, Greece, Finland, and Switzerland are there specific statutes against female homosexuality. Elsewhere, the law applies only to males.

The situation in the United States is not so clear. The laws against homosexual activity are so loosely phrased as to render them applicable to both male and female homosexuals. Thus, in prohibiting specific kinds of sexual behavior as crimes against nature, most state laws make no distinction of sex. There are some states—Connecticut, Georgia, South Carolina, Wisconsin—where such laws do not seem to apply to female homosexuality. In four other states—Arkansas, Colorado, Iowa and Nebraska—the status of female homosexuality is unclearly defined. In nearly every other state, however, the statutes are so worded as to apply to female as well as to male homosexuality.

Nonetheless, statutory condemnations of female homosexuality are significant only in a theoretical sense, being rarely enforced. Dr. Kinsey and his associates write:

". . .practically no females seem to have been prosecuted or convicted in the United States under these laws. In our total samples of several hundred females who had had homosexual experience, only three had minor difficulties and only one had more serious difficulty with the police, and none of these cases had been brought to court. We have cases of females who were disciplined or more severely punished for their homosexual activities in penal or other institutions or while they were members of the Armed Forces of the United States, and we have cases in which social reactions constituted a severe penalty, but no cases of action in the courts.

"Our search through the several hundred sodomy opinions which have been reported in this country between 1696 and 1952 has failed to reveal a single case sustaining the conviction of a female for homosexuality. Our examination of the records of all the females admitted to the Indiana Women's Prison between 1874 and 1944 indicates that only one was sentenced for homosexual activity and that was for activity which had taken place within the walls of another institution.

"Even in such a large place as New York, the records covering the years 1930 to 1939 show only one case of a woman convicted of homosexual sodomy, while there were over 700 convictions of males on homosexual charges and several thousand cases of males prosecuted for public indecency or for solicitation or for other activity which was homosexual. In our own more recent study of the enforcement of sex laws in New York City, we find three arrests of females on homosexual charges in the last ten years, but all of those cases were dismissed, although there were some tens of thousands of arrests and convictions of males charged with homosexual activity in that same period."

Our own investigation and experience in Washington, D. C. confirm the above conclusions. According to authoritative sources, no cases of female homosexuality which came to the attention of the police were prosecuted. The usual practice has been to dismiss the incident as "misbehavior," the parties involved merely receiving a verbal reprimand.

By contrast, male inverts apprehended by the Washington police are prosecuted in practically every instance where guilt is admitted. Especially has this been the case after the presence of homosexuals in the federal government offices was given publicity in the newspapers.

Dr. Kinsey and his associates list eleven reasons to account for "such differences in the social and legal attitudes toward sexual activities between females and sexual activities between males." Among them are: (1) the fact that, in ancient society, less importance was placed on the private lives of women who were regarded as inferior to the male sex; (2) the fact that, in the majority of instances, male homosexuality is associated in the minds of the public with such acts as fellatio and rectal intercourse which are repugnant to the average person, whereas Lesbianism is incorrectly associated with kissing and embracing, with emphasis on the emotional aspects of the relationship; (3) the fact, as Kinsey puts it, that the "Catholic Code emphasizes the sin involved in the wastage of semen in all male activities that are noncoital; it admits that female non-coital activities do not involve the same species of sin"; and (4) the fact that male inverts tend to be less discreet and attract attention by overt solicitation in public places, thereby creating situations which make society feel that police action is necessary.

An important factor in the distinction between the legal treatment of male and female homosexuals is the fact that the male ego is reluctant to acknowledge that women may secure sexual satisfaction without a man. The tendency for judges not to prosecute female homosexuals, perhaps, is an unconscious denial of woman's being able to do without a man. Psychoanalysts call this mechanism of denial of unacceptable facts, "psychic annulment."

The significant report drawn up by a government commission in Sweden in 1941, to revise the penal code in relation to homosexuality, is worth full-scale citation.

The Commission proposed, in a report to the Department of Justice, certain important revisions of the paragraphs of the Code which then imposed penalties for "fornication against nature." The Commission had been charged with the study of the whole problem of the legal control of the "socially dangerous manifestations of homosexuality" for the purpose of limiting criminal prosecution to cases where such "socially dangerous manifestations" were evident. The Commission recommended the repeal of the antiquated prohibition of "fornication against nature," and this change in the law was subsequently made in 1944. As a result, homosexual intercourse, as such, is no longer punishable as a crime in Sweden. On the other hand the Commission was careful in drafting its proposed amendments to the Code, to provide adequate protection against the seduction of minors and wards, for which the

Code retained penalties. In the course of its investigations, the Commission turned to the problem of female homosexuality and made the following observations:

"Chapter 18, Sec. 10 (of the Penal Code) makes no distinction between the sexes; female and male homosexual relations fall equally under the rubric "fornication against nature" (otuki mot naturen). Nevertheless, there is a widespread opinion that this is not the case, and that only male homosexuality is punishable. The reason for this opinion is probably that there have been practically no prosecutions of women in Sweden for homosexual acts. Besides, female homosexuality is not so well known and is withdrawn from the public discussion of the problem. It is undoubtedly true, however, that homosexual patterns and activities are as prevalent among women as among men. But there is a difference in the outlets which homosexual tendencies take in sexual and related activities. These differentiate men and women, and are due partly to social circumstances which in turn have probably resulted from these differentiations. The female nature is less reticent with such signs of affection as embraces, kissing, etc., which if they occurred between men, would be regarded as homosexually colored. Female homosexuality is accordingly less easily discerned by others or by the men, themselves, who may be quite frequently wholly unconscious of their homosexual characteristics. Moreover, female homosexuality probably involves nongenital contacts to a far wider extent than is the case in male homosexuality; in what appear to be innocent caresses, the sexual element is hard to discover. The manifestations of homosexuality among women are thus less offensive and arouse no particular interest among public authorities from the standpoint of law and order and public decency. It is certainly very seldom that female homosexuality assumes a form in public places that could be interpreted as abnormal. Nor is female homosexual prostitution at all as prevalent as male. In any case, female street prostitution is as good as unknown; women who are willing to accede to homosexual advances for economic gain of one kind or another visit restaurants and similar places that homosexuals frequent. But even this form of prostitution is very limited and found only in large cities. It is hardly surprising, then, that female homosexuality is able to find a certain outlet in activities that are more or less tolerated by general acceptance, and, therefore, are less a matter of hunting after the sexual object, which is the cause of prostitution.

"As a result of the infrequent occurrence of female homosexual prostitution, blackmail of female homosexuals is rare. The generally held view that homosexual relations between women are not punishable contributes, of course, to this situation. But, though direct monetary extortion is an exceptional occurrence, other kinds of persecution are not altogether rare. Thus it is said women in subordinate positions, to whom homosexual advances are made by their superiors, sometimes usurp favors for themselves in various forms and in ways which are fully comparable with blackmail.

"According to medical experience, female homosexuality seldom leads to conflict situations, even when it is regarded as such by those involved, as does male homosexuality. There are relatively few cases where a doctor is consulted for homosexuality by a woman. It is usually in some other way that the doctor becomes aware of the presence of female homosexuality in the patient. Diverse nervous disorders may have their roots in homosexual tendencies which leave the woman dissatisfied with normal intercourse. Frigidity in marriage is thus at times held to be related to homosexual inclinations.

"Female homosexuality probably occurs at all age levels of sexual maturity, though apparently most significant among the more mature and among very young girls. As to the former, it is said that a more conscious homosexual character is to be reckoned with, which is expressed in the establishment of firm ties through living together with a woman friend, etc. The occurrence of homosexual activities among young girls, as among young boys, on the other hand, is ascribable most commonly to the first awakening in the field of sexual life. The custom abroad (more than in Sweden) of sending children to boarding schools, convents, etc., may have some significance here. Even when the bond of friendship between young girls takes an obvious sexual form as, for example, in mutual masturbation, this is usually a purely transitional phenomenon, which in no way prevents a later development into fully normal heterosexuality. There is no reason to fear any lasting consequences of such activities.

"What has just been said, however, applies only to relations among the very young girls themselves. Homosexual intimacies and advances by an older person, for example a teacher, may bring about psychic shock with serious consequences. Whether there is a risk that such activities with a young girl will lead to a reorientation of her sexual impulses toward homosexuality, it appears to be unjustifiable to assume that such a reorientation can be induced, at least where a latent homosexual inclination exists. Nevertheless, the Commission does not find that female homosexuality is any problem for pedagogical authorities, though occasionally there may have been intervention to deal with homosexual teachers.

"Homosexual relations between women seem to occur to a certain extent within certain vocational categories, where the nature of the work isolates them from contacts with men that would lead to heterosexual relations. To the extent, in such situations, that the differences between superiors and subordinates is marked, this can lead to an abuse of authority on the side of the superior. It is not impossible that abuse of authority occurs in a form in which the inmates of female institutions are used by the female officials for sexual purposes. Homosexual intimacies with officials by inmates, and homosexual activity among the inmates are always reasonably to be reckoned with to a certain extent, just as they would be with men in the same situation.

"The conditions referred to here briefly, indicate that as to female homosexuality there is not a social problem of the same kind as with males. However, it appears to be unnecessary to exclude female homosexuality from the penal code. When punishable offenses have been limited to those cases indicated in the Commission's proposed amendments, there would appear to be no reason why the relevant clauses should apply only to men, even though in practice, it is only men who have hitherto been prosecuted. Flagrant cases, to take an example, of abuse of authority by a superior in order to have sexual intercourse with young girls, if such cases should occur, should certainly be punishable in the same way that a corresponding encroachment by a homosexual male superior would be. Because of the woman's earlier sexual maturity, it might be questioned whether the age limit for punishable intercourse ought not to be set lower than for male youths, but there appears to be no practical necessity for doing this. As to cases of homosexual intercourse covered by the proposed amendments, paragraphs 2 and 3 of Chapter 18, Sec. 10, there is obviously no reason for distinguishing between the sexes. (These paragraphs would prohibit homosexual conduct directly by officials toward inmates of institutions, and would also prohibit solicitation and exercise of homosexual intercourse as to 'cause public offense.') The Commission has accordingly drafted the language of these amendments so that all homosexual intercourse therein described is legalized, whether these acts are committed by men or by women."

THE WOLFENDEN REPORT

The British Government established, in 1954, a committee to study homosexuality and prostitution. It was specified that in the case of homosexuality the Committee consider not only the practice and resulting offenses but also the treatment of persons convicted of such offenses.

The Committee was comprised of fifteen members, including two judges, two doctors, two lawyers, two ministers, two members of Parliament, and three women. Sir John Wolfenden, Vice-Chancellor of Reading University, was named Chairman of the group.

After more than three years work, much of which was devoted to the oral examination of "witnesses," the Committee submitted its findings to Parliament. Thus, in September, 1957, the so-called "Wolfenden Report" was published. Certain recommendations were made regarding the law and its application to homosexuals and prostitutes.

The following represents, in our opinion, the most important of these recommendations insofar as homosexuals are concerned:

"We accordingly recommend that homosexual behavior between consenting adults in private should no longer be a criminal offense." (paragraph 62)

"We should expect that the question whether or not there has been 'consent' in a particular case would be decided by the same criteria as apply to heterosexual acts between adults ...our words 'in private' are not intended to provide a legal definition. Many heterosexual acts are not criminal if committed in private but are punishable if committed in circumstances which outrage public decency, and we should expect the same criteria to apply to homosexual acts." (paragraphs 63 and 64)

"We...recommend that for the purpose of the amendment of the law...the age at which a man is deemed to be an adult should be twenty-one." (paragraph 71)

"There is a case for requiring the courts to obtain a medical report in respect of every young person convicted for the first time of a homosexual offense....We accordingly recommend that a court by which a person under twenty-one is found guilty of a homosexual offense should be required by law, before passing sentence on that person, to obtain and consider a psychiatric report." (paragraph 187)

"It seems to us that the academic question whether homosexuality is a disease is of much less importance than the practical question of the extent to which, and the ways in which, treatment can help those in whom the condition exists." (paragraph 191)

"We therefore recommend that the appropriate body or bodies be invited to propose a program of research into the aetiology of homosexuality and the effects of various forms of treatment. The actual carrying out of such research would necessarily be in the hands of those directly concerned with the treatment of the homosexual, since it is only from observation carried out over long periods by doctors treading individual cases that results can be established. These should include both prison doctors and psychiatrists working outside prisons." (paragraph 216)

Much has been written about the Wolfenden Report, both pro and con. It seems to us that the recommendations concerning a change in the law whereby consenting adults not be prosecuted for homosexual behavior is a step in the right direction. It remains to be seen, however, if such change will be made, either in England or elsewhere, and just what the result would be.

HOMOSEXUALITY AND CRIME

Too little research has been done in the clear relationship between homosexuality and crime. In numerous cases that come to the attention of the courts, a certain type of homosexual (the psychopathic type) may be accused of blackmail or the commission of other crimes. Newspapers often report murders of individuals for alleged "improper advances." Many homosexuals are robbed only because some men feel justified in taking advantage of them, knowing that fear will keep the victims from pressing charges. Occasionally a male homosexual or a Lesbian may murder a partner out of jealousy. In addition to such obvious crimes where homosexuality is a factor, other serious crimes are committed in which what is classified by psychiatrists as "latent homosexuality" is a factor. Latent homosexuals experience strong reactions at an unconscious level, unaware that they are reacting as a defense against their own unconscious homosexual drives; such latent homosexuals give way to compulsions to assault a homosexual in order to prove to themselves that they do not possess homosexual inclinations. Many men boast that they would "kill" another man who made homosexual advances to them. Psychoanalysts agree, as noted above, that such assaults are a defense mechanism against latent homosexual inclinations. Attacks on homosexuals are never warranted. After all, a normal, well-adjusted man can simply inform a homosexual that he does not care to become involved. Most homosexuals will desist on learning that the other person is not interested.

There are men who singly, or in groups, will pretend to accept advances of the homosexual, go to his residence or some other designated place, and sometimes allow a physical act to take place; then they beat and rob him. Normal men just don't handle a homosexual situation in this manner. One suspects men who take a sadistic delight in seeking out homosexuals, only to assault and rob them. What is there in their personality that makes them want to express this sadistic aggressiveness against homosexuals?

In many instances, an assaulted homosexual is found in some public place by a passing pedestrian who calls the police. If the police succeed in apprehending the assailants, they de-

fend themselves by charging that the victim had made indecent advances, as if this justified their violence. They will claim
to have acted in self-defense. The law is unsympathetic toward
the homosexual, considering that he had no right to make a
sexual advance. Few judges appreciate the fact that homosexuality is a sickness, that the compulsion to solicit is just as
much a symptom of a sickness as is found in the man who
has a compulsion to exhibit himself before the opposite sex,
or in the man who molests children sexually, or in the man
who obtains sexual gratification in obscene telephone conversations with strange women. Society still regards homosexuals
as criminally responsible for their acts.

Psychiatrists testifying in sex cases are very often accused of
defending homosexuality as though they approved of it. But
they are merely attempting to point out to society and the
legal profession that homosexuals are sick individuals in need
of treatment. Sending a homosexual offender to prison only
makes matters worse in most instances.

A murder case was brought to our attention recently for
psychiatric evaluation. The testimony indicated that the victim was a homosexual. Briefly, the case involved three university students who boasted that they were going to a particular
night club in order to confront homosexuals. One of the three
expressed the desire to "roll a queer." In the night club, he
became involved in a conversation with someone presumed to
be a homosexual, while the other two waited outside. Walking
to an alley with the person he had been talking to, the presumed homosexual was assaulted for having made alleged indecent advances. One of the three robbed the homosexual of
his wallet, and they left their victim dying in the alley. Found
and rushed to a hospital, the victim died of his injuries. The
three were indicted for first-degree murder. The jury acquitted
them.

Such a case illustrates the homicidal prejudice that exists

today regarding homosexuals. We feel sure that the three university students did not understand anything about latent homosexuality and how it operates in an individual. They did not know what motivated them unconsciously in wanting to "roll a queer." Why is it that the hundreds of other students had no such abnormal desires? Why did it have to be these three particular students? What was there about their individual make-ups that drew them into committing this murder? Naturally, their lawyers wanted to defend them. But how much did the jury understand about the psychodynamics of homosexuality? Who is to blame in a murder of this kind? Does homosexuality justify robbery and murder? If men feel they will be absolved in assaults against homosexuals, how many murders can we anticipate in the future? Can you imagine what would happen to our homicide rate? There would be murders committed every day. Is society to blame? Are the parents of these three boys to blame? Is there anything that can be learned from a case of this kind? Can we simply ignore it and hope that such cases will not recur?

One cannot condemn the legal profession because most judges and lawyers still evaluate such matters on the basis of inapplicable moral standards or legal considerations, such as whether the individual is mentally capable of conferring with counsel, or whether or not he was of unsound mind at the time of committing the crime. More than such legalistic evaluations are necessary. Psychiatrists should be called in to evaluate whether or not the crime was the product of a mental illness. But psychiatrists are not always consulted in such a case, and it is then judged without the benefit of psychiatric evaluation. It becomes a battle between the prosecution and defense lawyers as in the case just cited. When this happens, the psychiatrists know that the jury will decide the case according to public opinion and personal prejudices.

HOMOSEXUALITY IN PRISONS

Although this is given too little thought by too few people, including prison officials, the sex life of the average person confined in prison is a major problem. The sexual urge, being instinctive and basic, is not smothered by prison walls. The urge persists, emotions become heightened, and tensions mount. Male and female prisoners are separated from each other, and visits by wives or girl friends, or by men in the case of female prisoners, are limited and so conducted that personal contact is impossible.

The inevitable result is sex-gratification by contact with someone of the same sex, or masturbation.

Some prisoners are able to maintain their sex balance and do not succumb to homosexual practices. Such persons must call upon all their resources of self-control, but these seldom endure through a long prison term. As the confinement drags on, deprivation creates tensions and unhappiness and the prisoner is left with these choices: he may either resort to masturbation, usually coupled with fetishisms; or he may turn to homosexuality.

Consequently, some form of masturbation or homosexuality, both considered "abnormal" in the adult, is found in all types of confinement institutions. Most prisons are overcrowded; many prisoners share their cell with two or more mates; and in some of the more "progressive" institutions a dozen or more persons sleep in dormitory-type rooms in close physical proximity. This is true of both male and female prisons.

What more could be done to foster homosexual relationships?

The hardened criminal, probably turned into a sexual deviate by previous prison terms, simply goes on in this pattern. And the first termer, as yet unindoctrinated in the ways of unnatural love, often becomes his prey. The new prisoner may want to hold on to his ideals and resist homosexual practices, but this is difficult and often dangerous. His life may be threatened by the "elders," and his prison conditions may be made quite intolerable.

Furthermore, the artificial and stifling prison environment nurtures tyrannical personalities, psychotic behavior, jealousies, hate, and other personality abnormalities. Such an emotional atmosphere fosters unnatural sexual love.

We do not know of any measures taken in our prisons to curb these practices other than punishment of those offenders who are caught in the act. Officials simply accept homosexual activity as a fact of prison life. They are either reluctant to do anything about it, or perhaps there is actually nothing constructive that they *can* do.

Some countries, such as Mexico, Turkey, and Sweden, have experimented with this problem by providing private rooms for visits by wives of prisoners in an effort to allow for the release of sexual and emotional tensions. In Mexico, for example, conjugal visits are permitted on Thursdays and Sundays, with seventy percent of the inmates participating. In Turkey, the rules provide for very short visits, while in Sweden, some prisoners are allowed "home leaves." The State of Mississippi has had a system of conjugal visits in effect for about ten years and reports good results. Such visits, restricted to married male prisoners, have been made a matter of "right" in Mississippi.

In December of 1959, the American Association for the Advancement of Science held its annual meeting in Chicago. Dr. Clyde B. Vetter, Professor of Sociology at Northern Illinois University, reported to the Association on his study of prisoner-visiting rights throughout the world. Dr. Vetter, in commenting on the Mississippi system, said the conjugal visits result in less tensions among the prisoners, less homosexuality, fewer escape attempts, and other disciplinary problems. Further, the family structure is thus maintained and divorce minimized.

Dr. Vetter admitted that "conjugal visits in prisons are not compatible with the mores of the United States" but added that there was no valid basis for this feeling inasmuch as he could find no religious restriction against legally married persons enjoying marital rights either in or out of prison.

There remains, however, the problem of those prisoners who are unmarried. Unrest and jealousy can arise, creating a new though lesser problem.

A rather eye-opening account of confinement in a woman's prison was given by the well-publicized Virginia McManus, call girl extraordinary, who spent seventy-five days in the New York City Women's House of Detention in the spring of 1959. Writing in the September, 1959, issue of *Confidential* Magazine, on "My Experience With Homosexuals in Women's Prison," Miss McManus begins her account by stating: "The prison was a breeding ground of homosexuality for the uninitiated, a Utopia for Lesbians."

About half of the six hundred inmates, she believes, were confirmed Lesbians and close to that percentage engaged in homosexual contact during their stay in prison. Although the most minute precautions were taken to prevent male-female contact, the female inmates were encouraged to dance together, dress up for each other, go to movies in pairs, and associate in other intimate ways.

She tells of young girls being initiated into the practice of Lesbian love and becoming confirmed homosexuals, of the middle-aged married women resorting to Lesbianism as a sexual substitute for their husbands; and of those who were homosexuals to begin with.

Miss McManus described how certain inmates cover for others engaged in homosexual activity in an empty cell, how much of this practice goes on right under the eyes of the prison guards who do nothing to prevent it or, as she comments: "I came to understand that the guards didn't want to see."

This first-hand account was especially interesting inasmuch as the author, although a convicted call girl, is a college-trained psychologist.

Dr. Charles E. Smith, Assistant Medical Director, Bureau of Prisons, conducted an exhaustive study of homosexuality in prisons with on-the-spot observation of sixty-one male prisoners at the Medical Center for Federal Prisoners, Springfield, Missouri. Dr. Smith published his findings in an article in the *Journal of Social Therapy*, Vol. 2, No. 1, 1956.

The subjects were of various ages but approximately two thirds were under thirty. Twelve of the sixty-one refused to cooperate, insisting that they were not homosexuals, although their records disclosed a long history of homosexuality.

Prisoners at the Springfield institution who are diagnosed as homosexual are segregated, each occupying a separate cell and kept under strict supervision to prevent physical contact with other inmates. Dr. Smith observes that some are segregated as homosexuals who should not be, and others who should be are not.

This study was undertaken to test the validity of the diagnosis and classification criteria used in dealing with homosexuals, and further, to query the individual prisoner on his homosexual behavior and the prison program to which he is subjected. This was done by written questionnaire and personal interview.

These are Dr. Smith's conclusions:

> The results of this study suggest the following outstanding problems in the institutional management of the homosexual:
> 1. Some of the criteria most frequently used in the diagnosis of homosexuality are found to be inadequate, because they are not universally applicable. It is suggested that if

more absolute and irrefutable diagnosis criteria were available, it might lessen the incidence of complaints from individual homosexuals that they have been improperly diagnosed and classified.

2. Effeminacy, as manifested by professed disinterest, or even antipathy toward pornography, is suggested as a possible new lead in establishing the diagnosis of homosexuality.

3. The validity of classifying homosexuals as either active or passive is questioned by the findings in this study.

4. In assessing the attitude of the homosexuals in this group toward their deviation, there is not much indication that they are influenced by social disapproval. For the most part, these individuals appear content with ther deviation and show little desire to change.

5. Although there is no doubt that the present method of segregating homosexuals offers the best answer to the administrative problem of handling them in the prison situation, this study suggests that the method is not without its shortcomings. In particular, there are indications that segregation creates a situation in which homosexuals are placed in close proximity to potential sexual partners, and therefore may result in increased sexual tensions among members of the group. In turn, these increased sexual tensions may be projected into grievances. These tensions can be relieved to a great extent by insuring that the personnel charged with the supervision of these individuals have a humane understanding of the problems involved.

6. Lastly, the results of this study suggest that constructive efforts should be made to overcome the feelings of many of these homosexuals that they are treated with prejudice by courts and parole boards.

Peter Wildeblood, British author, sentenced to eighteen months imprisonment for homosexual offenses in the sensational Montagu case, wrote of his prison experiences in a book entitled *Against The Law*. He found three distinct types of homosexuals in prison, the first of which he classified as the strictly feminine type, who were "in fact women in everything but body," using make-up and perfume and calling each other by girls' names. The second type were those whose crimes were against small boys. The third, he says, were like himself—men convicted of homosexual conduct with other adults.

This case stirred a great deal of controversy since it involved prominent people. It was probably responsible for British governmental inquiry into the entire question of homosexuality and the relevant laws.

The authors, who have, in their respective practices, encountered many forms of homosexuality, are of the opinion that prison homosexuality can be treated like those which occur in civil life. But there is little opportunity today for the average prisoner to receive competent psychiatric treatment. Our present prison system fosters homosexuality, inadvertently causing young and inexperienced inmates to become homosexuals and making certain that those already indoctrinated remain so. In December, 1960, Federal Prison Director James U. Bennett stated that only six of the federal prison system's thirty-one institutions have full time psychiatrists.

So long as our convicted offenders are thrown together for prolonged periods without the benefit of psychiatric evaluation, treatment, and care, "unnatural" sex practices will persist.

LEGAL PRINCIPLES USED IN THE HANDLING OF HOMOSEXUAL MATTERS

An examination of recent cases and a study of state codes indicates certain general principles followed by the courts in the consideration of homosexual offenses. We find the legal provisions and measures inadequate, contradictory, and unclear.

¶ Homosexual behavior is legally considered under the heading of sodomy, which is loosely defined as sexual intercourse between one human being and another against nature and regardless of sex, or by a human being with an animal or bird. In this sense, it includes sexual intercourse in or through any opening of the body other than the human female vagina.

¶ In its narrow meaning, in strict compliance with the common-law principles, sodomy means sexual intercourse between one human being and another by anal (or rectal) connection, or by a human being with a beast in any manner.

¶ Because of the variance in the laws of the different states, it is necessary, in any given case, to determine whether the state law applies or whether common-law provisions are applicable. Most states seek to cover, by specific definition, all incidents of "unnatural" sexual intercourse be it with human being or beast. But there is often a question whether a statute not specifically clear in meaning and intent is limited by the applicable common-law definition.

¶ It is not necessary that the crime of sodomy be accompanied by force, compulsion, or violence. Thus two willing partners are chargeable, and consent is no defense. However, depending on the age of the consenting person, he may be charged as an accomplice (one who knowingly, voluntarily, and with common intent with the principal offender joins in the commission of the crime). It is generally held that a child of tender years, under the age of puberty, is not legally able to consent to the commission of a crime and, therefore, cannot be charged as an accomplice.

¶ Penetration, no matter how slight nor through what orifice, is generally sufficient—both at common law and by statutory decree—to constitute the crime of sodomy. But it is not necessary that an emission take place.

¶ Corroborative testimony is generally necessary if the crime involves a willing partner, that is, an accomplice, although such corroboration is not held necessary in the case of a non-accomplice whose participation was unwilling.

All of our states have statutes prohibiting sodomy, although two of them, New Hampshire and Vermont, do not define the offense as such. According to the New Hampshire statute called "Lascivious Acts" no one may perform an unnatural or lascivious act with another. In Vermont, "An Act Relating to Sexual Perverts" prohibits copulation by mouth. The Maryland law specifically mentions both males and females: "Every person who shall be convicted of taking into his or her mouth the sexual organ of any other person or animal, or who shall be convicted of placing his or her sexual organ in the mouth of any other person, or who shall be convicted of committing any other unnatural or perverted sexual practice with any other person or animal...." The Iowa code prohibits sexual intercourse in any orifice other than the human female vagina.

Several states, New York, Minnesota, and North Dakota among them, have comprehensive sodomy statutes specifically defining unnatural sex acts, such as carnal knowledge by or with mouth of man by man, the mouth of man by woman, the mouth of woman by man or woman, the anus of woman by man, or of man by man, or of any animal or bird by man or woman, and also sexual intercourse with a corpse.

California has separate statutes for sodomy, which encompass the common-law definition of the crime, and for fellatio and cunnilingus. It is of interest that the penalty for the latter crime is greater than for the former. Arizona also has two separate statutes though the penalty is the same. A few states, Indiana and Wyoming among them, include masturbation in their sodomy statutes. Michigan law prohibits acts of "gross indecency" in public or private, and New York has a separate statute covering loitering about any public place to solicit men to commit a crime against nature or other lewdness. In the District of Columbia, homosexuality is included under a general-assault statute. The District of Columbia also has a statute specifically covering sexual crimes. The state of Georgia, which imposes the severest penalty for sodomy, distinguishes that crime from the crime of bestiality.

Penalties imposed on those convicted of sodomy vary as

greatly as the definitions. In Georgia, the sentence is life imprisonment at hard labor. Maximum sentence in New York, where the crime is a misdemeanor, is one year when it has not been done against the will of the partner and such partner is over eighteen. However, if the act was carried out against the will of the victim, a maximum prison sentence of twenty years may be imposed. The Connecticut maximum is thirty years. In North Carolina, the minimum term is five and the maximum sixty years. Kansas, Oklahoma, Mississippi, Iowa, South Dakota, and Washington have a fixed maximum term of ten years, and Ohio, a term ranging from one to twenty years. New Mexico, which sets a minimum penalty of a year, allows the sentencing judge to fix a maximum at his own discretion. Virginia has a one-year minimum and a three-year maximum. The penalty in other states, including New Hampshire, Delaware, and Louisiana, is a money fine or a term of years.

PUNISHMENT FOR SODOMY

Life imprisonment at hard labor	Georgia	
	Conn.	30 yrs.
	Fla.	
	Mass.	
	Minn.	20 yrs.
	Neb.	
	N. Y.	
Imprisonment with a fixed maximum term	Mich.	15 yrs.
	Iowa	
	Kan.	
	Miss.	
	Okla.	10 yrs.
	S. Dak.	
	Wash.	

N. Y. The penalty named is for first-degree sodomy, "against the will" of the victim; second degree —male or female under 18 yrs. not amounting to sodomy, 10 yrs.

Wyo.	5 yrs. or 12 mos.
R. I.	7-20 yrs.
Nev.	5-life
N. C.	5-60 yrs.
Ark.	5-21 yrs.

max.; an act not amounting to first or second degree, is a misdemeanor.

Mich. Solicitation to sodomy by male over 15 yrs. of a boy under 15 yrs., 5 yrs. max.

Cal. with mouth, 15 yrs. max.

Md. with mouth, or any other unnatural act, $1000 max. and or 10 yrs.

Ariz. same penalty for fellatio and cunnilingus.

Mont. child under 14 cannot be an accomplice.

Pa. solicitation to commit, $1000 max. or 20 yrs. max.

D. C. with person under 16 yrs. $1000 max. or 20 yrs. max.

Tenn.	5-15 yrs.
Utah	3-10 yrs.
Tex.	2-15 yrs.
Ala.	2-10 yrs.
Ky.	2-5 yrs.
Colo.	1-20 yrs.
Ohio	1-20 yrs.
Ore.	1-15 yrs.
Cal. Ill. Maine N. Dak. W. Va.	1-10 yrs.
Ariz.	1-5 yrs.
Vt.	1-5 yrs.
Wis.	1-5 yrs.
Va.	1-3 yrs.
Ida.	5 yrs. min.
Mont.	5 yrs. min.
N. M.	1 yr. min./$1000 min.
Mo.	2 yr. max.
S. Car.	5 yr. &/or $500 min.
Ind.	2-14 yr./$100-1000.
Md.	1-10 yrs.
Pa.	$5000 &/or 10 yrs.
La.	$2000 &/or 5 yrs.
N. J.	$1000 &/or 21 yrs.
D. C.	$1000 &/or 10 yrs.
N. H.	$1000 &/or 5 yrs.
Del.	$1000 &/or 3 yrs.

INADEQUACIES OF THE LAW

It is made clear in Kinsey's *Sexual Behavior of the American Male* that sex laws are motivated by emotions operating at the unconscious level. Kinsey's statistics on the incidence of sex acts considered illicit but which do not come to the attention of the courts demonstrate that our present sex laws are unrealistic and inadequate.

This is what Kinsey and his co-workers conclude:

"It is ordinarily said that criminal law is designated to protect property and to protect persons, and if society's only interest in controlling sex behavior were to protect persons, then the criminal codes concerned with assault and battery should provide adequate protection. The fact that there is a body of sex laws which is apart from the laws protecting persons is evidence of their distinct function, namely, that of protecting custom. Just because they have this function, sex customs and sex laws seem more significant, and are defended with more emotion than the laws that concern property or person. The failure of the scientist to go further than he has in studies of sex is undoubtedly a reflection of society's attitude in this field.

"It will be recalled that 85% of the total male population has premarital intercourse, 59% has some experience in mouth-genital contacts, nearly 70% has relations with prostitutes, something between 35 and 40% has some homosexual experience, and 17% of the farm boys have animal intercourse. All of these and still other types of sexual behavior are illicit activities, each performance of which is punishable as a crime under the law. The persons involved in these activities, taken as a whole, constitute more than 95% of the total male population. Only a relatively small proportion of the males who are sent to penal instiuttions for sex offenses have been involved in behavior which is materially different from the behavior of most of the males in the population. But it is the total 95% of the male population for which the judge, or the board of public safety, or church, or civic group, demands apprehension, arrest and conviction, when they call for a cleanup of the sex offenders in a community. It is, in fine, a proposal that 5% of the population should support the other 95% in penal institutions. The only possible defense of the proposal is the fact that the judge, the civic leader, and most of the others who make such suggestions, come from that segment of the population which is most restrained on all types of sexual behavior, and they simply do not understand how the rest of the population actually lives.

"The judge who is considering the case of the male who has been arrested for homosexual activity should keep in mind that nearly 40% of all the other males in the town could be arrested at some time in their lives for similar activity, and that 20 to 30% of the unmarried males in that town could have been arrested for homosexual activity within that same year. The court might also keep in mind that the penal or mental institutions to which he may send the male has something between 30 and 85% of its inmates engaging in the sort of homosexual activity which may be involved in the individual case before him.

"On the other hand, the judge who dismisses the homosexual case that has come before him, or places the boy or adult on probation, may find himself the subject of attack from the local press which charges him with releasing dangerous 'perverts' upon the community. Law-enforcement officers can utilize the findings of scientific studies of human behavior only to the extent that the community will back them. Until the whole community understands the realities of human homosexual behavior, there is not likely to be much change in the official handling of individual cases."

The laws of the various states are so confusing and irregular on this subject that it is almost impossible to generalize as to what constitutes homosexual behavior, who is chargeable with homosexual conduct, what the penalty is for conviction, and how the homosexual is managed. Karpman says: "The penal codes of the various states present the most absurd discrepancy with respect to the penalties for sodomy," while Judge Ploscowe points out that, although homosexual behavior or conduct violates some statutes in all our states, some types of sexual behavior, ordinarily regarded as homosexual in character, such as fellatio, cunnilingus and sodomy, need not be confined to action between male and male or female and female. The practices may, of course, be indulged between heterosexual persons as well, married or single. To add to the already confusing picture, many and varying terms are used in the different states to define homosexuality and homosexual conduct, some of which are: crimes against nature, buggery, bestiality, fellatio, cunnilingus, sodomy, lewd conduct, lascivious conduct, etc.

We are of the opinion that the following sixteen guide posts should be followed by lawyers, psychiatrists, and community leaders when dealing with problems involving homosexual matters.

1. The law must recognize that the homosexual is not a person with a "criminal mind" but an emotionally sick person who needs help and understanding from society and the law, and treatment by competent medical specialists.

2. Law enforcement officers, lawyers, and judges should be so trained that they have knowledge and understanding of the problem of homosexuality and can make proper inquiry into the underlying factors and psychosociological background of each offender.

3. Each case involving a homosexual must be studied individually so that "types" are eliminated and standardized management done away with.

4. The law should eliminate as crimes, offenses which are carried on by adult people within the confines of their own residences, or if they are done with the consent of two adult partners and do not create an atmospehre offensive to society, or if two married people desire sexual relations in any manner gratifying to them. This would eliminate the concept of "assault" as an element of homosexuality when consenting adults indulge in this practice.

5. The law should differentiate between those homosexual offenders who are adults and whose acts do no actual psychological or physical harm and those offenders whose victims are children, defective persons, and the like. The law should also differentiate between offenses which are harmful and those which are not.

6. Present-day police methods of entrapment, involving "planted" police officers in public rest rooms, parks, bars, and other places should be eliminated so that a person who otherwise would not be prone to a homosexual act is not placed under temptation. Elimination of these methods would cut down the incidence of homosexuality.

7. Every apprehended homosexual offender should be given a thorough psychiatric examination and evaluated as to prognosis of recovery. This report should be made available to the judge and prosecutor as well as the defense counsel before trial or sentence. Procedures should be established permitting the psychiatrist, the lawyers, and the judge to discuss each case so that there is no misunderstanding of the causes of the act and so that an intelligent approach to the treatment of the offender can be made.

8. A uniform penal code covering sexual crimes should be established eliminating the disparity between legal definitions found in the various state laws and the confusion that results therefrom.

9. Medical Associations and Bar Associations should initiate a program of cooperation between their members active in this field so that lawyers and doctors, the country over, will become better informed and better able to handle the homosexual problem.

10. Doctors and lawyers should, at the community level, devise a program of educating the community to a better understanding of the homosexual. Children should be made aware of this problem. The afflicted homosexual should not be regarded with scorn and loathing and called epithets such as "fairy," "sissy," "pervert," "queer," and the like. Such name-calling does great harm.

11. Every prison and institution of detention should conduct a program of sex education and professional counseling. Activities in these institutions should be devised to divert the

attention of the inmate and lessen opportunities for homosexual contacts. This applies to female inmates as well as male.

12. There should be carried on, both at the local and national levels and beginning with the study of small children, constant research into the sociological, psychodynamic, and physiological aspects of homosexuality, with findings made available to the public along with recommendations for remedial measures.

13. Legal and medical groups should revise and simplify their definitions so that both can use a common set of terms. Because doctors and lawyers differ on the meanings of terms even among themselves, it is almost impossible to reach a proper and intelligent handling of a case.

14. Psychiatrists who are specially trained or who have special knowledge in the field of homosexuality should contribute to community education so that their knowldege can serve everybody. The general practitioner should always be careful to evaluate his patient, and if necessary, refer him to the proper specialist for treatment.

15. The law should differentiate between the admitted homosexual, whose history of such behavior is long and continuous, and the person who is guilty of an isolated homosexual act and whose experience may be the result of a temporary emotional problem which could, with understanding, diagnosis, and treatment be cured.

16. Because it is a generally accepted fact that long prison terms reduce the chances for rehabilitating the homosexual, emphasis should be placed on treatment and counseling. If imprisonment is deemed necessary, it should be a short term, with release conditioned on the mandatory continuation of proper treatment by a qualified psychiatrist, and the regular reporting of progress to the court.

HOMOSEXUALITY IN OTHER COUNTRIES*

Austria

All forms of "indecency vs. nature" committed with persons of the same sex, male or female, are punishable. The law does not distinguish between buggery and other homosexual acts, and "indecency vs. nature" has been defined by the courts as "any act which is designated and appropriate for seeking and finding sexual satisfaction from a body of a person of the same sex."

The penalty is imprisonment at hard labor up to a maximum term of five years. If, however, the acts are commited by the "application of dangerous threats or actual physical violence or ruseful stupefaction of the other partner as to render him unable to offer resistance," the punishment is penal servitude up to ten years; and if one of the parties suffers serious injury to health as a result of violence, the sentence may run to twenty years. If death results, the penalty may be execution.

In practice, first offenders do not receive more than three to six months imprisonment unless there are aggravating circumstances, and probation is frequent.

Minor acts of indecency not amounting to "indecency vs. nature," as defined by the courts, are punishable by detention for periods between eight days and six months.

Belgium

Homosexual behavior, as such, is not punishable, and a homosexual act is punishable only if it involves indecent assault, an affront to public decency, etc.

Consent is no defense in a charge of indecent assault if the victim is under sixteen. If the offender is one of the victim's parents, consent is no defense if the victim is under twenty-one

* From Berg and Allen Appendix.

unless he is married, in which case, consent is a defense if he is over sixteen.

The maximum penalty for indecent assault is fifteen years imprisonment if the victim is under sixteen; ten years if the victim is over sixteen but under twenty; and five years in other cases.

The maximum penalty for outraging public decency is one year imprisonment and a fine of 500 francs; or three years imprisonment and a fine of 1,000 francs if a child under sixteen is present.

Denmark

Homosexual acts committed with a child under fifteen years are punishable by imprisonment up to a maximum of six years, as are homosexual acts procured by force, fear, threats, fraud or drugs. Offenses against inmates of certain institutions, such as orphanages and mental institutions, when committed by persons employed in, or supervising such institutions are similarly punishable.

Homosexual acts committed with persons under eighteen draw a maximum sentence of four years in jail. If the persons involved are of approximately the same age and development, the court may acquit both.

Indecent behavior against any person of the same sex is an offense when the offender violates the other person's decency or gives public offense; the maximum penalty is four years imprisonment.

The law does not distinguish between buggery and other homosexual offenses.

France

A person who commits a homosexual act with a partner under twenty-one is liable to imprisonment up to a maximum of three years and a fine of 50,000 francs.

Where the victim is under fifteen, the maximum prison term is ten years. Where violence has been used or where the offender is a parent or is otherwise in a position of authority, sentence can be coupled with hard labor. Where the offender is a parent of the victim, these higher penalties may also be levied if the victim is under twenty-one, unless he has been emancipated by marriage.

Offenses against public decency are punishable by imprisonment up to a maximum of two years and a fine of 12,000 francs.

The law does not distinguish between buggery and other homosexual acts.

Germany—Federal Republic

Unnatural sex acts (intercourse) between males are punishable, but homosexual acts between females are not unless they constitute some other offense such as indecent assault.

Where the offense is committed with a boy under fourteen or, if the offender is over twenty-one, with a partner under twenty-one, the maximum penalty is a prison term of ten years.

The same maximum penalty applies where the act is accompanied by violence or threats of violence or where the offender exploits a defendant. Male prostitution or soliciting for the purpose of such prostitution is similarly punishable. In other cases, the maximum penalty is five years imprisonment.

The law does not distinguish between buggery and other homosexual acts.

Greece

Unnatural sexual intercourse between males which involve abuse of a relationship of dependence arising from services of any kind, or the seduction of a person under seventeen, or financial gain, is punishable by a maximum sentence of five years imprisonment.

"Unnatural sexual intercourse" extends to all forms of indecency and is not confined to buggery.

Italy

No laws punish homosexual behavior as such.

For acts of sexual intercourse accompanied by violence, the maximum penalty is ten years imprisonment. Similar acts involving abuse of authority are punishable with imprisonment up to five years if no violence is used. These provisions govern heterosexual as well as homosexual intercourse. If the act does not involve physical violence, sentence may be reduced by one third.

Anyone committing an indecent act with or in the presence of a child under sixteen is punishable by a maximum prison term of three years. Prosecution is only by the victim or parent or guardian.

Public indecency is similarly punishable.

Netherlands

An act of indecency with a child under sixteen draws a prison term of six years. Similar provision covers sexual acts in which the offender abuses the temporary defenselessness of his victim, whatever his age. A person who, by violence or threats of violence, induces another to submit to an indecent act draws a maximum sentence of eight years imprisonment irrespective of age of the offender or the victim; this applies both to homosexual and heterosexual offenses.

The law also provides punishment of persons over twenty-one who indulge in homosexual acts with minors between the ages of sixteen and twenty-one. Maximum penalty is four years imprisonment.

The law does not distinguish between buggery and other homosexual acts.

There are special provisions for punishment of indecent acts by parents, guardians, or other persons in authority.

Acts of indecency committed in public places are punishable by a maximum sentence of two years in prison.

In practice, homosexual acts between consenting partners, both over twenty-one or both between sixteen and twenty-one, are not punishable unless public decency is affronted or under other aggravating circumstances.

Norway

Indecent intercourse between males is punishable by a maximum prison term of a year but is prosecuted only if deemed necessary to the public interest.

Special laws apply to sexual abuse of children, irrespective of the sex of the offender or victim; they therefore cover homosexual practices with children. These laws distinguish between "indecent intercourse" which comprises coition and other sexual acts and "indecent acts" which do not amount to indecent intercourse.

The maximum penalty for "indecent intercourse" with a child under fourteen is a prison term of fifteen years. If bodily harm results, it may be life. If the child is between fourteen and sixteen, the maximum penalty is fifteen years. Sixteen is the ordinary age limit but, if the youth is under authority or care of the offender, the age limit is eighteen, and the maximum penalty, if the victim is over sixteen, is one year.

The maximum penalty for an "indecent act" with a child under sixteen is three years imprisonment.

Public indecency is punishable by imprisonment up to three months.

Spain

Homosexual acts are not punishable unless they amount to indecent assault or cause public scandal or offend the public order.

Indecent assault incurs a maximum penalty of six years imprisonment.

Offenses "causing public scandal" incur a maximum penalty of six months imprisonment and a fine of 5,000 pesetas (about 400 dollars).

Offenses against "public order" incur a maximum penalty of thirty days in prison and fine of 1,000 pesetas (about 80 dollars).

Laws relating to rogues and vagabonds provide for "measure of security" against criminals whom the courts have declared to be dangerous and antisocial. Persons who habitually indulge in homosexual behavior may become subject to imprisonment under these provisions.

Sweden

A person committing a homosexual act with a child under fifteen is liable to a maximum penalty of four years imprisonment.

The law also prohibits:

1. Homosexual acts with persons under eighteen, if the offender had reached that age himself at the time of the offense.

2. Homosexual acts with persons under twenty-one, if the offender is eighteen or over and commits the act by abusing the other person's inexperience or dependence on him.

3. Homosexual acts with insane or mentally defective persons.

4. Homosexual acts with inmates of prisons, hospitals, almshouses, orphanages, or similar institutions, if the offender is on the staff.

5. Homosexual acts committed with any person if the offender has committed the act by grave abuse of the other person's dependence on him.

Maximum punishment in each of the above cases is two

years penal servitude. The penalty may be increased to six years if the offender is a parent or guardian or other person in authority.

Public indecency is punishable by a maximum penalty of two years imprisonment.

The effect of the foregoing is that homosexual acts between consenting parties over eighteen years of age are not punishable unless they affront public decency or where there are other aggravating circumstances.

chapter five

EXHIBITIONISM

GENERAL DISCUSSION

The sexual deviation called "exhibitionism" is the deliberate "indecent exposure" in public places of one's genitals in the presence of another person, usually of the opposite sex. It is one of the most common sex offenses.

Havelock Ellis describes it as "an impulse to expose a part of the body, especially the genital region, for a sexual reason either conscious or unconscious."

Since primitive peoples regard nudity as a natural state, exhibitionism of the body is common among them, but it survives in modern civilization as a neurosis. One finds manifestations of the exhibitionistic impulse in most children of prepubertal age. Among adult groups, today, various expressions of exhibitionism occur in nudist camps.

Regarding nudist colonies, some psychoanalysts feel that they serve as an outlet for people with exhibitionistic inclinations. However, nudists will deny that they are ever erotically stimulated by the sight of other nude bodies. They claim they successfully sublimate their sexual libido and that what they enjoy are the health advantages derived from exposing the body to the rays of the sun.

A recent issue of *Sexology* (March 1959) carried this item under the heading "Nudity and Decency":

"Nudist colonies seldom find a jurist who upholds them, but a recent case in Battle Creek, Michigan, brought a champion in the person of State Supreme Court Justice, John D. Voelker Judge Voelker is the author of the best seller "Anatomy of a Murder" which he wrote under the pen name of Robert Traver.

"The Judge wrote the majority opinion in a decision which held that five nudists, arrested in a police raid on a nudist camp in 1956, were not guilty of indecent exposure. As an example of the difficulty of deciding when exposure is indecent, the Judge gave the hypothetical case of a goose-stepping drum major whose skintight trousers ripped and exposed his nude person to 50,000 cheering fans. 'Would the police arrest the drum major in such a case?' the Judge asked.

"According to the Judge the 'one big indecency' in the case was the state police raid, 'descending upon these unsuspecting souls like storm troopers; herding them before clicking cameras like plucked chickens.' If nudism is illegal, he added, 'art galleries and museums would have to turn to the cultivation of fig leaves.' "

The prevalence of this impulse and of the complementary impulse of "voyeurism" (peeping) has led to the toleration of bubble and fan dances and strip tease in burlesque shows and night clubs. This toleration extends to summer resorts with their displays of seminudity. In the privacy of their homes, people often give vent to the impulse, as in the natural exhibitionism that occurs between husband and wife in the bedroom. Women who pose in the nude express unconscious (if not conscious) exhibitionism, as do women who wear low-cut gowns which partially expose their breasts or who wear Bikini bathing suits.

Perhaps, because such outlets are available to women, cases where women are brought to court for exhibitionism are very rare. Exhibitionism is almost exclusively a masculine sexual offense.

Whatever the attitude toward this sexual anomaly, it represents a sociopsychological challenge that can be met only by a continued scientific investigation of its psychopathology.

To give the reader some idea of the mental anguish the exhibitionist suffers, we cite this letter sent to Professor Em. Airi of New Delhi:*

"I am an unfortunate creature who implores your help. In everyday life, I am a normal man who does his work (that of a bank clerk) in an irreproachable manner. For two or three months all goes well, but then I am suddenly attacked by a kind of anxiety which impels me to spend hours on end, walking about the streets. I know that is far from being a good sign. Once when I felt an attack coming on, I took refuge in a mental hospital, thinking in that way to escape the inevitable. Alas, at nine o'clock in the evening, the impulse was too strong for me. I was quite lucid, but that man who clambered up the railings and jumped down on the outside was not myself. I was impelled by an invisible force which I could not resist. Out of breath, I ran as far as the suburbs. There, in a deserted street, I saw in the distance a young girl approaching. I hid myself, and I know the rest from the police report. As soon as I found myself near her, I opened my trousers, uncovered my genital parts, and began to masturbate. I remember vaguely that her wide-open eyes and her terrified look excited me to such an extent that I immediately had an ejaculation. At once I regained possession of myself, and I tried to run away but fell into the hands of the police.

"I beg of you to tell me if I am mad, if I ought to be shut up in a lunatic asylum, since I cannot be responsible for

---

* *Anthropological Studies in Sex Abnormalities of All Races and All Ages*, by Prof. Em. Airi, Capital Book Co., New Delhi, India, 1951.

my actions. I beg of you, also, to explain to the judges that I am not vicious, as they say, but an unfortunate creature who is suffering and who has been severely punished by nature."

PSYCHODYNAMIC MOTIVATIONS

Many unconscious factors are involved in exhibitionism. Many people consider the exhibitionist "oversexed," uneducated, and of low moral standards. On the contrary, many exhibitionists are cultivated and inclined to be moralistic. Among those arrested for this offense, distinguished persons not infrequently appear. They act out an irresistible compulsion.

Treatment usually discloses a pronounced sadistic component corroborating Bloch, Freud and Merzbach's conclusion that "exhibitionism is a weakened form of sadism." The sadistic intent is to embarrass the victim, and the act is usually accompanied, as in other aggressive acts, by feelings of guilt and remorse.

Furthermore, exhibitionism represents a regression to psychosexual infantilism. It is the symptom-consequence of an underlying psychosexual neurosis. Some men expose themselves before pubescent girls. According to Stekel: "During an attack, the exhibitionist is a child again and judges the world according to infantile standards. In the attacks, he usually resorts to children because then he, too, is a child."

Narcissism is found in every case of exhibitionism. The exhibitionist likes to attract public attention. He is usually in a dream-like state at the time, the impulse taking on a compulsive character which overcomes the conscious censorship of the intellect.

In men the urge to exhibit oneself before a woman often represents a substitute for sexual satisfaction or for repressed incestuous cravings. Latent homosexuality is also evidenced in the desire to prove his "masculinity" by exhibiting his penis to women.

Finally, inviting the risk of arrest implies a masochistic need to be punished.

CASE HISTORIES

Case 1. A nineteen-year-old boy was referred for treatment for exhibitionism. He exhibited himself for the first time at the age of fourteen. In the past five years, he exhibited himself before persons of the opposite sex in public parks, street cars, and busses, approximately a dozen times, incurring three arrests. He was released the third time on condition that his family place him under psychiatric treatment.

The family history showed hereditary and environmental taints. Both parents were highly neurotic. The father, a religious teacher, once attempted suicide because of an acute conflict between religion and sex. The patient's parents frequently exposed themselves before their children. The mother, for instance, thought nothing of taking a shower while her son (the patient) was there brushing his teeth. A maternal uncle had been in a mental hospital, while another who was a teacher, was discharged for exposing himself before his pupils.

In his exhibitionistic episodes, the patient usually selected girls in their early teens; on other occasions, his victims were middle-aged women (sister and mother substitutes). His penis was always in a state of erection during exposure.

While he was aware of the consequences if apprehended by the police, he found the impulse irresistible. A feeling of regret usually followed each exposure.

The exhibitionistic episodes followed this course: first would come a feeling of restlessness; after this would come fantasies about reactions to the exposure; then the actual exposure would take place. When it occurred, the patient would be in a stuporous state, and usually, he kept a fixed stare on his victim. The staring seemed to be associated with the reactions to nudity. He developed a "looking impulse" (voyeurism) before he developed a "being seen" complex. Actually, exhibitionism is the complementary form of voyeurism. Having experienced thrills in looking at his father and mother in the nude, he fantasied that girls would get thrills looking at his penis. To "be seen" thus became his urge, and it gave vent to incestuous fantasies directed toward his mother and sister. His desire, in late adolescence, to expose himself was an urge to re-experience what he had experienced in childhood. "The impulse to exhibit is an erotic imperative of the past." (Stekel)

Another interpretation is that the antisocial act is an expression of ambivalence toward the hostile father whom the son regarded as a "religious hypocrite." The patient attempted to overcompensate for his feelings of inferiority by developing an unconscious penis-narcissism. In exposing his penis before women, who were mother and sister substitutes, he was competing with his father, showing them that he had a better penis than his father or his brother.

His exhibitionistic acts generally followed periods of abstinence from masturbation. He disclosed that he masturbated while looking into a mirror. We see how the libido became fixed on the "eye" level.

There was evidence of a psychosexual attachment to his mother disguised in the patient's fantasies of the opposite sex. A forty-year-old woman before whom he exposed himself, was chosen because she resembled his mother. The younger girls were sister-surrogates. As Dr. Karpman points out: "Obliged to repress his incestuous cravings, the child's surging sexuality is led into aberrant avenues of expressions with exhibitionism as one of its adaptations."

On completion of his psychiatric treatment, the patient was advised to leave home and begin life again in a new environment. The parents hear from their son who is now employed in a city several hundred miles away. Judging from his letters, he is making a good social and economic adjustment with no indication of sexual difficulties. The exhibitionism has stopped.

Case 2. The patient was a married man with three daughters, two by his first wife and one by his second. After his arrest he underwent treatment for about thirty sessions extending over eight months. His attendance was irregular, and this was only one of the ways in which he manifested resistance to treatment. This limited its effectiveness and two years later, he was rearrested on the same charge. Treatment was then resumed under another psychiatrist.

At the treatment sessions, he revealed his childhood situation. The household was dominated by a hysterical, possessive mother who, herself, appeared to have had voyeuristic tendencies and to have stimulated her son's exhibitionism. His father was withdrawn and cold.

At fifteen he performed bestiality with a cow and a mare and repeated such acts several times during the next few years. His sexual fantasies were aberrant and exotic and included harem scenes, Lesbian love-making, bestiality, etc.

He had premarital relations with his first wife and again with the second who was a friend of the first.

In his exhibitionism, which consisted of exposing his erect penis, he was satisfied only if the woman was stimulated. The impulse was sudden and irresistible, and during the act he was in a stuporous or dream state. His dreams indicated exhibitionistic urges, narcissism, incestuous desires involving his daughters, coprophilia (associating the sexual act with defecation), and masked homosexuality. He was sexually precocious as a child, but this was accompanied by symptoms of acute anxiety (castration fear). Onset of exhibitionism occurred at five when he pretended he was a cow to be milked.

Legal Aspects

Every state in the union has some statutory prohibition against exhibitionism which may be found catalogued under Indecent Exposure, Exposure of Person, Lewdness, Lascivious Behavior, Public Indecency, Obscene Exposure, and analagous terms. Generally speaking, the behavior covered by these terms is an intentional exposure of the naked body, or private part thereof, in a public place. At common law, the indecent exposure of a person in a public place, willfully and intentionally, in the presence of others, was a misdemeanor. It is so regarded today in all our states, whatever legislative definition or classification given to it, and the penalties range from small fines to prison terms.

Back in 1663, the common-law condemnation for exposing the body was demonstrated by the punishment imposed on the court favorite, Sir Charles Sedley, when he stripped in mixed company and publicly displayed himself in the nude. Sir Charles was heavily fined, and spent a week in jail and was then released on his own bond, on condition of good behavior for one year. In 1733, a woman was freed after having been apprehended cavorting around unclothed to the waist. It was finally decided that her display was neither immodest nor immoral and, therefore, not unlawful. In Tennessee, in 1842, the owner of a slave who allowed his female charge to be seen in public places in a naked state was convicted on the ground of "lewdness," illustrating the common-law concept of the offense as exposure in a public place or where the public could have seen it. This is further illustrated by two old cases, the first in Missouri in 1922, where a male exposed his private parts before a married woman. The court held this not to be an act of indecency punishable by common law because the exposure was seen by one person only and performed in a place to which only one person had access. In the second case, the act was held to be an act of indecency because it might have been seen by casual observers.

In the following two recent cases the same line of reasoning obtains. A recent Virginia decision (by jury) convicted a defendant for "willfully, lewdly, and indecently" exposing "his person to a young girl, in a manner to shock the public sense of decency and morality." The witness testified that the defendant deliberately parked his car in an alley so as to block her access to a sidewalk and, while still in his car, exposed himself and "played with himself" in her plain view. The jury, following instructions on the law, decided that this was an indecent exposure in a public place, in such a manner as might be seen by the casual observer, as regulated by common law. In 1957, in a case involving a man exposing himself to two girls, a Maryland court ruled that an indecent exposure in a public place had occurred and was a common-law offense if the act were seen or likely to be seen by casual observers, even if only one person actually witnessed the act.

The state laws dealing with this offense differ in language and in scope. Some statutes specify that the act complained of must have been committed in a public place; others carry provisions covering the performance of such acts in the presence of children; others are more general and comprehensive. Courts vary in their interpretation of the law. In a Texas case, the defendant who had exhibited himself on a public road was indicted pursuant to a statute specifying that indecent exposure must be in public. The court found the indictment faulty, declaring that there is a difference between a public road and "in public." It could be possible, the court held, for the place of the act to be private. In a Georgia case, the court, following a statute which provided that the act must be notorious and public, dismissed an indictment against a defendant who exposed himself while plowing in a field 175 yards from a house where the state's female witness said she saw him. The court ruled that this act was neither public nor notorious because it was done in a field and not on a public road and, further, because it was witnessed by only one person. But in another Georgia case, the defendant was convicted of a notorious act of public indecency when he took pictures of his wife's private parts at the side of a public street and viewable by other persons.

In a more recent case, a defendant, seated in his parked car on a road bordering a river on one side and a golf course on the other side, was convicted under an indecent exposure statute on the testimony of two young girls and a grown woman who saw him exposed in the car. In another recent case, the court convicted a defendant who exposed his person and performed an indecent act before a single witness who could see it from a woman's dormitory window. On the other hand a Court of Appeals reversed a conviction based on a statute penalizing any notorious act of public indecency which tends to debauch the morals of the community. The court argued that, since only one witness testified to having seen the exposure (although more than one actually did see it), it was not such an act of notoriety or public indecency as to come within the statutory meaning of the offense.

Another case affecting a nudist camp illustrates the construction that may be put on an indecent exposure statute which defines the offense as any open or indecent exposure by a defendant of his or her person or of the person of another. The defendant in this case was the owner and operator of a nudist camp which was located in a rather secluded spot, about a mile and a half from the highway and surrounded by second-growth scrub oaks. When the police arrived at the camp site, they found several naked persons, including the defendant and his wife, six other married couples, three single men, and four children. The court ruled against the contention of the defendant that he had the right to enjoy the freedom of his own lands. The court agreed that it is the intention of the constitution to protect the individual in the peaceful enjoyment and occupation of the house in which he lives and the place in which he earns his livelihood and the things connected thereto, and to prevent an unlawful disturbance of his privacy and person; but the court went on to say, citing Hester vs. U. S., 265 U. S. 57, 44 S. C. 445, the constitution does not guarantee the privacy of open lands.

A few states, such as New York, Ohio, and Kentucky, have specific legislation regulating nudist camps, but it should not be inferred that the lack of a specific law allows nudist camps to operate unregulated in other jurisdictions. Nudists can be convicted under laws covering lewd behavior, other indecent-exposure statutes, or laws covering public nuisances.

There are many variations of exhibitionism or indecent exposure, and they are commonplace in the police files all over the country. Kinsey points out that exhibitionistic acts are the most frequent types of aberrant sexual behavior. The cases that enforcement officials are most familiar with involve men who frequent public toilets to expose themselves, men who expose themselves in public parks or in front of open windows or in their automobiles, and drunks, defecating or urinating in alleys or in public places. Convictions are readily obtained and jail sentences are generally imposed. Other common cases involve schoolteachers and camp counselors (no attempt is made here to condemn either as a group). As illustration, there is the case of a male teacher who invited "selected" students to stay after school and then exposed himself before them, individually and in various degrees; and another of a female teacher who requested two young boys to visit her apartment after school where they found her in a state of near undress. She requested that they come in and help her "wash" her undies.

Karpman made a study of 200 cases admitted to St. Elizabeth's Hospital, a majority of whom had been referred from prisons where they were serving sentences. One patient admitted that he had exposed himself about 300 times, and yet he was sent to prison for "rehabilitation;" another from this group, who had exposed himself only to an adult police officer, was sentenced to six months in jail; and still another had been incarcerated for exposing himself in front of the milkman. At least ten more of this group had from one to eleven previous convictions. This supported Karpman's contention that jail for these offenders has no effect; the men are sick persons who need medical help.

How, then, should the authorites deal with the exhibitionist? The community must be protected from them because exposure before children and certain adults constitutes a social menace. In certain cases, when the act has been offensive to the community or to a segment of it or, when it was done in flagrant violation of common decency or, if it is shown that actual harm was done, detention of some kind may well become a matter of necessity; but it must be recognized that jailing neither rehabilitates nor deters the offenders. Where detention becomes necessary, it should be recognized that the most effective remedy is evaluation of the offender by a psychiatrist and the treatment prescribed. This should be made available to each such prisoner.

Again, where no actual harm was done by the exhibitionist and no social danger followed from his act or, where the offense is an isolated episode, the defendant should be shown special consideration since rehabilitation of the offender could result without physical detention in an institution, and this would benefit both him and the public. With on-the-spot psychiatric help and intelligent understanding by the courts, many unfortunate people would not repeat their exhibitionistic acts and would be cured of their illness. Prison confinement usually delays the time when the next act can occur. A sympathetic legal approach along with proper medical treatment would go a long way in curing the illness.

SOME REPRESENTATIVE STATUTES REGARDING INDECENT EXPOSURE

Alabama — Code of Alabama (1940) — 1955 *Ed. Title* 14, *Sec.* 326, *Chap.* 51A

INDECENT EXPOSURE

It is unlawful for any person to expose or exhibit, or to procure another to expose his sexual organs or private parts in any public place or on the premises of another, or so near thereto so as to be seen from such private premises, in a vulgar and indecent manner.

Any person who violates the provisions of this section may, on conviction, be imprisoned in the county jail, or sent to hard labor for the county for not more than twelve months, or fined not more than $500.00, or both.

Alaska — Compiled Laws Annotated (1949) *Title* 65 — 9-6

INDECENT EXPOSURE AND EXHIBITIONISM

That if any person shall willfully and lewdly expose his person or the private parts thereof in any public place where there is present other persons to be offended or annoyed thereby, or shall take part in any model exhibition, or make any other exhibition of himself to public view, or to the view of any number of persons such as is offensive to decency, or is adapted to excite vicious or lewd thoughts or acts, such person, upon conviction thereof, shall be punished by imprisonment in the county jail not less than three months nor more than one year, or by fine of not less than $50.00 nor more than $500.00.

Arkansas — Statutes, Title 41-2701

INDECENT EXPOSURE

Every person who shall appear in public places naked or partly so, with the intent of making a public exhibition of his nudity, or who shall make any obscene exhibition of his person shall be deemed guilty of a misdemeanor.

Title 41-1127. Every person convicted on the above — fined in any sum not less than $50.00.

Title 41-1128. It shall be unlawful for any person with lascivious intent to knowingly and intentionally expose his or her private parts or genital organs to any person, male or female, under the age of sixteen years.

Title 41-1129. Penalty for above — confinement in penitentiary for not less than six months nor more than three years.

California — West's Annotated California Codes — Title 9
Sec. 311

1. Every person who willfully or lewdly either exposes his person, or the private parts thereof, in any public place, or in any place where there are present other persons to be offended or annoyed thereby; or

2. Procures, counsels, or assists any person so to expose himself or to take part in any model exhibition, or to make any other exhibition of himself to public view, or the view of any number of persons, such as is offensive to decency, or is adapted to excite vicious or lewd thoughts or acts....

Conviction under 2 above is a felony and punishable by imprisonment in state prison for not less than one year.

Conviction under 1 above, upon a first conviction after a previous conviction under sec. 288: any person who shall willfully or lewdly commit any lewd or lascivious act including any of the acts constituting crimes provided for in part one (1) of this code, or with the body, or any part or member thereof, of a child under the age of fourteen years, with the intent of arousing, appealing to, or gratifying the lust or passions or sexual desires of such person or of such child, shall be guilty of a felony and shall be imprisoned in the state penitentiary for a term of from one year to life.

Florida — Statutes (1957) *Chap.* 800

800.02. Unnatural or Lascivious Act. Whoever commits any unnatural or lascivious act with another person shall be punished by fine not exceeding $500.00 or by imprisonment not exceeding six months.

800.03. Exposure of sexual organs. It is unlawful for any person to expose or exhibit his sexual organs in any public place or on the private premises of another, or so near thereto as to be seen from such private premises, in a vulgar and indecent manner, or so to expose or exhibit his person in such place, or to go naked in such place; provided, however, that this section shall not prohibit the exposure of such organs or the person in any place provided or set apart for that purpose. Any person convicted of a violation hereof shall be punished by a fine of not more than $100.00, or by imprisonment in the county jail for a period of not more than sixty days.

Georgia — Code of Georgia Annotated (1953)

Lewdness and Public Indecency. Any person who shall be guilty of open lewdness or any notorious act of public indecency tending to debauch the morals shall be guilty of a misdemeanor.

Missouri — Vernon's Annotated Missouri Statutes

Title 38 — 563.150. Every person, married or unmarried who shall be guilty of open, gross lewdness or lascivious behavior, or of any open and notorious act of public indecency, grossly scandalous, shall upon conviction, be adjudged guilty of a misdemeanor.

Title 38 — 563.160. Any person who in the presence of a minor shall publicly expose his or her person to such minor in an obscene and indecent manner...punishment in penitentiary not exceeding five years, or in county jail not exceeding one year and a fine of $500.00, or both.

New Jersey — New Jersey Statutes Annotated

Title 2A:115-1. Any person who commits open lewdness or a notorious act of public indecency, grossly scandalous and tending to debauch the morals and manners of the people, or in private commits an act of lewdness or carnal indecency with another, grossly scandalous and tending to debauch the morals and manners of the people, is guilty of a misdemeanor.

New York — McKinneys's Consolidated Laws of New York, Annotated

Penal Law 1140. Exposure of Person. A person who willfully and lewdly exposes his person, or the private parts thereof, in any public place where others are present, or procures another to so expose himself, is guilty of a misdemeanor.

South Carolina — Code of Laws of South Carolina (1952)

Title 16-412. Any person who shall be guilty of willful and malicious indecent exposure of his person on any street or highway or in any place of resort shall be guilty of a felony and, on conviction, shall be punished by a fine or imprisonment or both in the discretion of the court.

Kansas — General Statutes of Kansas Annotated (1949)

Art. 9, Sec. 21-908. Every person who shall be guilty of adultery, and every man and woman (one or both of whom are married and not to each other) who shall lewdly and lasciviously abide and cohabit with each other, and every person married or unmarried who shall be guilty of open, gross lewdness, or lascivious behavior, or any open and notorious act of public indecency, grossly scandalous, shall on conviction, be adjudged guilty of a misdemeanor and punished by imprisonment in a county jail not exceeding six months, or by a fine not exceeding $500.00, or both.

Michigan — Michigan Statutes Annotated (1954)

Title 28 — Sec. 28.567 (1). Any person who shall knowingly make any open or indecent exposure of his or her person or of the person of another shall be guilty of a misdemeanor, punishable by imprisonment in the county jail for not more than one year, or a fine of not more than $500.00, or if such person was at the time of the said offense a sexually delinquent person, the offense may be punishable by imprisonment in the state prison for an indeterminate term, the minimum of which shall be one day and the maximum of which shall be life.

Ohio — Page Revised Code (Annotated)

Title 29 — Sec. 2905.30. Indecent Exposure or Obscene Language.

No person eighteen years of age or over shall willfully make an indecent exposure of his person in a public place where there are other persons to be offended or annoyed thereby, or utter obscene or licentious language in the presence of or hearing of a female.

Whoever violates this section shall be fined not more than $200.00 or imprisoned not more than six months, or both.

chapter six

RAPE AND LUST MURDER (NECROSADISM)

Rape has many definitions. The one given in the law dictionary is: "The unlawful carnal knowledge of a woman by a man forcibly and against her will." One could argue ad infinitum as to just what constitutes "force" or what is meant by "against her will." Bribing a woman with expensive gifts, plying her with cocktails to the point where she "feels her drinks," and situations where the woman teases a man and leads him on, are all factors which enter into this complex problem of sexual seduction. And there are those who believe that a normal woman, in reasonably good health, is incapable of being raped unless she is rendered unconscious or is tied down hand and foot.

For most people, the word "rape" connotes an act by a "sex fiend" who lurks in doorways and alleys waiting to pounce upon the first passing female. Dragging her to an isolated spot, he tears off her clothing, beats her into insensibility or a state of shock, and perpetrates against her an act of unwanted sexual intercourse.

This sometimes occurs but in many of the so-called rape cases, no actual unwillingness on the part of the female was present nor was there any force.

Nevertheless, rape is a serious psycho-legal problem if for no other reason that it is a capital crime in many states.

According to F.B.I. statistics published in 1955, reports from police in 2,543 cities showed that, in the category of rape alone, offenses averaged no fewer than 31 daily. The incidence or rape that year was almost 6% higher than in the previous year. Rape cases have increased by 110% in the past twelve years. The number of rapists under twenty has doubled.

Numerous factors are involved in the problems of rape. In many cases, investigation discloses that the alleged rape never occurred. In some cases, court records show that women complainants lied, making the charge to revenge themselves for being jilted. In other cases, the alleged victim was proved to have encouraged the intimacy. Having regretted the act for one reason or another, and having had guilt feelings, she sought to exonerate herself from responsibility by alleging forcible seduction.

Most women, including those who have had previous sexual relations, would be inclined to show some resistance to the advances of a strange man. A woman may not want the man to feel she submits easily; or she may pretend that she has never experienced intercourse before; others, fearing bodily harm, may submit at once.

Many women are masochistic by nature and prefer to feel that they have been forced into sexual relations, the violence making the act seem more erotic for them. They will even resist with the hope of provoking the man into using force.

Thousands of sexual seductions take place every day although only a few of them, for various reasons, come to the attention of the authorities. It may be said that women have been raped since the beginning of time, if we use the term in its broadest sense, namely, the sexual seduction or carnal knowledge of a woman not fully consenting.

Each case then must be considered on its own merits and care must be taken to guard against penalizing an innocent man for a crime he did not actually commit.

LEGAL ASPECTS

The laws dealing with rape contain many inconsistencies. What proof is necessary to establish an act of rape? There is disagreement as to the value and use of psychiatric evaluation of the person accused of rape; and there is certainly a lack of cooperation between the medical and the legal professions which is a detriment to true justice.

The rapist who commits the crime, commonly called statutory rape, should be differentiated from the one who uses force and violence. Let us, for a moment, consider the following: A recent survey in a large metropolitan area showed that out of 76 men charged with rape, only nine were finally convicted of rape by force. Another study showed that 20% of all charges against supposed rapists were dismissed because of insufficient evidence or the defendants were acquitted. Although 62% were convicted, most of the convictions were based on statutory rape, an act which involves relations with a girl under the legal age of consent.

The problem of rape becomes even more complicated when one takes into account that there have been female rapists, women who have raped men.

In an article, "Women Who Rape Men," Dr. Edward Dengrove reports: "Last year in Grand Haven, Michigan, a twenty-nine-year-old schoolteacher, mother of four preschool children, received a suspended two-year sentence for seducing one of her pupils, a boy of fifteen. She was charged with 'gross indecency,' although the New York Post quoted Prosecutor James Bussard as saying, 'The charge would have been rape if the sexes had been reversed' and reported that he spent a week searching law books for a proper complaint to file against the woman. Charges were not filed against the boy because the Post quoted Bussard, 'We figured it wasn't the boy's fault.'"

Dr. Dengrove states: "While rape is generally identified with violent assault by men upon women, many instances are known where the woman is the rapist and the man is the victim." He adds, "Usually such women are mentally disturbed."

A newspaper carried the story of a twenty-one-year-old man who had been raped by three girls in a car at point of knife. The women were arrested and held in $1,000 bail each, charged with lewd and obscene conduct and with being disorderly persons.

It is not, however, our purpose to point out the defects of adhering to a single and rigid definition of "rape." The intent is to show by discussion and actual case histories that rape is a psycho-legal phenomena and must so be treated. Too often the emphasis is placed on rape as a *crime per se,* and no consideration is given to the fact that the rapist is a mentally sick person. This is due to the lack of information on the part of otherwise well-meaning public officials; the expediency of satisfying the demands of a distraught community during rape scares; the lack of proper psychiatric evaluation and treatment of the sex offender; the lack of foresight and understanding by some lawmakers and judges; and the lack of closer cooperation and intelligent interworking ideas between the medical and legal professions.

It is true that jurists sometimes have difficulty because of terminological confusion. Often, psychiatrists are ridiculed by lawyers. Neurotics and psychopaths often experience and admit sexual pleasure from acts of cruelty.

Attenuated forms of sadism are manifest in everyday behavior. A child will often bite its mother's breast. We often laugh when someone slips on a banana peel or hits his head against a low ceiling beam. Children often act cruelly toward animals. Sadistic impulses are released in time of war, and both sides report the atrocities of the enemy. Sadism, therefore, is far more prevalent in the world than we like to admit. It is intimately connected with our sexual libido, as Freud and others demonstrated. Juvenile delinquents have been known to torture their victims in all kinds of ways, including acid-throwing and scarring their faces with a knife. The public fails to realize that these acts of cruelty have a *sexual root*. A better general understanding of the sexual instinct in all its manifestations will bring us closer to a true scientific understanding of crime and its motivations.

Sexual sadism occurs in both sexes. History provides many notorious examples. Society itself is guilty of sadism. Otherwise, why does the public refuse to abolish capital punishment? It seeks vicarious satisfaction in having a murderer murdered by the state. (The "lex talionis" principle of an eye for an eye.) We permit comic books to be illustrated with scenes of violence only because they have a profitable sale among children. People enjoy watching two men beat each other in a boxing ring. One hears among the spectators such exclamations as "Kill him!" "Finish him off!"

However, we are chiefly concerned here with the more pathological type of sadism. Many sexual sadists kill their victims out of fear of being identified should they be apprehended by the police. They wish to "destroy the evidence." A rapist or child-molester may become panicky and commit murder after realizing the seriousness of his act.

In some instances, the homicidal urge manifests itself in the form of an irresistible impulse. The sexual sadist does not know right from wrong at the time of his deed; he may have been unable to adhere to the right or failed to appreciate the emotional significance of his wrongfulness. Hence, he may not be legally and medically responsible for his crime.

The lust-murderer, married or single, usually harbors an overpowering feeling of hatred or vindictiveness toward women. He seldom experiences remorse after the killing.

Sexual sadism is a symptom of sexual inadequacy of some

kind. Sadists are incapable of establishing a normal, love relationship with their parents.

Joseph F. Fishman, author of an article "The Sex Criminal" *Sexology,* April, 1952) reports the case of a man who attacked and murdered a seven-year-old girl. He admitted that he was impotent with mature women and could gratify his sex urges only with little girls.

Dr. Louis London cites a case of a prisoner he had examined who murdered his child and had attempted to murder his wife. Dr. London detected certain sexual undertones in the crime. The prisoner had removed all his toenails and observed that he had been doing this since he was nineteen years old out of fear of ingrown nails. This implied a castration complex. Patients suffering from castration complexes have gouged out their eyes or inflicted other mutilations on themselves. Since a child may represent a genital symbol to a disturbed mind, the murder of the child, in this instance, could be attributed to the prisoner's castration complex.

Men with compulsive killing impulses also may suffer from an organic brain disease; or they may be schizophrenic, feeble-minded, epileptic, or psychopathically amoral.

THE PERSONALITY OF THE RAPIST

Psychiatrists are only too well aware that the rapist who forces intercourse on a strange woman is mentally ill and in need of psychiatric help. It would be well if more lawyers and judges recognized this fact also and acted accordingly. The rapist compulsion may be difficult to understand, in part at least, because our society assumes mutual fellowship and kindness and, especially so, in the sexual relationship. Therefore, the rapist who acts wholly with the intent to violate and injure seems incomprehensible to the average person.

But this in itself indicates that rapists are mentally sick. Dr. Benjamin Karpman, author of *The Sexual Offender and His*

Offenses writes: "All cases of rape that have come under the writer's care have proven to be profoundly abnormal. Why should a man violate a woman, then abuse her physically, inflicting all sorts of physical injury, occasionally even killing her? Above all, why should any normal man wish to secure a sexual outlet through the use of force when society provides more than fair opportunities for release of sexual tension through marriage, clandestine relations, and prostitution?" We might add that the impulse persists even when the release of sexual tension is readily available. Fifty percent of rapists are married.

Rape is a sexual deviation, the symptom of a disturbed or abnormal mind, and the offense should be evaluated by the law as such. A rapist may be alcoholic, epileptic, insane, feeble-minded, a severe neurotic, a psychopath, a sociopath, or a sex sadist.

Many rapists harbor a hatred and resentment of women with whom they feel inadequate, often having impotence reactions with them. As Dr. Charles Mitchell, clinical psychologist, observed: "By inflicting the greatest of indignities and outrages on a woman, he (the rapist) thus, to his own twisted and illogical satisfaction, asserts his dominance over woman and flaunts his manhood to the world at large."

Close study of rapists would disclose deep-seated, emotional conflicts stemming from frustrations in childhood and adolescence.

CASE ILLUSTRATIONS

Case 1. Dr. Caprio had occasion to examine a prisoner, aged 23, who was sentenced to death for the rape of a 3½ year-old girl. Before the sentence, the defense attorney pleaded for mercy on the grounds that the defendant, a previous sex offender, was unable to control his sexual impulses because of a brain disease. The death sentence precipitated a legal battle over the concept of legal insanity in court trials. The defense attorney challenged the so-called "right and wrong" test for legal insanity. He noted that at the trial, testimony for the prosecution contended that the child's injuries were such as to prevent her, when adult, from bearing children. However, the examining physician testified to the contrary.

Three other psychiatrists, in addition to Dr. Caprio, testified that the rape was attributable to the defendant's mental disease, *Encephalitis Lethargica,* and a neurologist further testified that the prisoner was still suffering from it. Despite this medical testimony that the defendant was not responsible for the rape to which he had been led by an uncontrollable impulse, judges imposed the death sentence. Further psychiatric study of the defendant was made and brought to the attention of the Governor of the state, who prevented the execution of this seriously sick man.

Case 2. In another case in which Dr. Caprio served as psychiatric consultant, he examined two men who were in prison awaiting trial for raping an adolescent girl. One denied having sexual relations with the girl. The other, who admitted the rape, was discovered to have been a patient in a mental institution, to have suffered several head injuries, and to have made two suicidal attempts. Both prisoners were examined by four other psychiatrists. All agreed that the defendants were mentally ill and should not be held legally responsible for their acts. The prosecutor, a man with political ambitions and responsive to public pressure, however uninformed, made light of the medical testimony and succeeded in obtaining a death sentence.

The mother of one of the doomed men requested that a personal plea be made by telephone to the Governor. This was done one hour before the scheduled execution. The Governor did not see fit to exercise his power of executive clemency. Both defendants were sent to death in the gas chamber.

Case 3. In another case, Dr. Caprio was asked to examine a young fellow who was detained in jail on a charge of "assault with intent to rape." Examination disclosed that the boy was not a 'sex-psychopath,' that he was not dangerous, and that his difficulty with the law was the result of sex ignorance. He had been out with his girl friend one evening, and a quarrel ensued. While driving home, he brooded over the altercation and suffered an attack of anxiety and depression. Noticing a middle-aged woman walking along the road, he suddenly stopped his car and went over to embrace her. In her terror, the woman fell to the ground screaming. The boy was apprehended by the police and charged with attacking the woman with intent to rape. When questioned about the details, he stated:

"After I had left my girl friend, I kept thinking of our quarrel. My mind was foggy. All I could think of was that I wanted to talk with some woman to tell her about my quarrel with my girl. I didn't mean to harm the woman and the thought of raping her never entered my mind."

The boy didn't seem to be the type to try to lie his way out of a difficulty such as this. He was a regular churchgoer, worked steadily and to the satisfaction of his employers, and had never been in trouble before. He became seriously depressed while in jail, feeling that he was being held for something he did not do. His girl friend visited him at the prison because she felt convinced of his innocence.

This young man knew very little about sex and had to be given an elementary course on the subject. It was recommended that he be placed on probation and be allowed to avail himself of psychiatric treatment. His attorney succeeded in getting him released on bond, and he proved trustworthy. He was responding favorably to treatment when the trial came up. Unfortunately, Dr. Caprio was then out of the city, and no psychiatric testimony was offered on behalf of this defendant. Five years imprisonment was imposed on this boy who needed treatment and re-education rather than jail, where he will be deprived of the psychiatric treatment he so badly needs.

Case 4. In the following case, Dr. Caprio and another psychiatrist examined a man charged with raping his two daughters. He was facing the death penalty. State psychiatrists submitted a report to the court that the prisoner was sane, that he knew right from wrong, and was therefore responsible for his acts. We however, found him clearly insane and recommended that he be committed to a mental institution. The judge accepted our conclusion and disregarded the report of the state psychiatrists.

When we questioned the man he would repeat:

"I love my children and could not help myself. I did what I did because of my love for them." If he were released, he said, he would on the very day of his release repeat his acts, his need to do so being uncontrollable. He remained preoccupied with sexual thoughts of his daughters.

Case 5. The following case involves a veteran, whom we will call Fred Jackson, who had served overseas where he had been "blown out" of his shoes thirty feet by a bomb explosion. He had received a citation for bravery. Upon his return to civilian life, he married and took a position on the local police force. Since his discharge from military service, Fred had suffered periodic headaches, the result of a brain concussion suffered in the explosion. Since he had experienced no visible injuries, he felt no need to complain about the headaches to the medical authorities. However, after a period of excellent service and a quiet married life, he took a few drinks one night with a companion and got into the difficulty for which he was incarcerated. There was no previous record of his drinking.

On this particular night, he masked the lower part of his face, walked to the front door of a private home, rang the bell, and when the man of the house answered, he placed his gun against him, saying "this is a stickup!" But he took no money, jewelry, or other valuables. He ordered the husband and his wife to disrobe, marched them into their bedroom, locked the husband in a closet, and proceeded to carry out what was described as acts of "sexual perversion" with the wife.

The husband shouted that he would suffocate unless released. Fred released the man who then was forced to witness more of the perverse acts. At one point he asked the husband to participate in a triangular sexual act. During this act, the husband wrestled with Fred for his gun, while the wife escaped to her next-door neighbor. The neighbor got a gun, returned to the bedroom, and shot Fred in the leg.

In the hospital where he was taken, Fred exclaimed, during a rambling and somewhat incoherent conversation that "someone shot me in my own home." When he came to from the anesthetic administered in the treatment of his wound, he had no recollection of what had happened.

Dr. Caprio and another psychiatrist diagnosed the above case as psychosis, acute pathological intoxication associated with sexual psychopathology, and an amnesia for the events of the outbreak. Their report concluded with a second diagnosis of post-concussion syndrome manifested by cephalagia, intolerance to small quantities of alcohol and states of intermittent amnesia evidenced by periods of extreme forgetfulness since his discharge from military service.

The psychiatrists for the State claimed that Fred was of sound mind at the time of his crime and therefore responsible for his acts.

Fred had been charged with *intent to rape* and rob, although the prosecution conceded that he had touched no valuables and that he had *not performed sexual intercourse with the wife*. Despite this evidence and the psychiatric testimony in his defense, he was sentenced to twelve years imprisonment. The prosecuting attorney intimated that the jury must not be swayed by the defense lawyer's account of his client's patriotic services to his country. Can you imagine what a sick veteran must feel when, after risking his life for those serving on the jury, no consideration is given to his citation for bravery and his recorded injuries?

Fred was a war casualty, a sick man whose place was in a veteran's hospital, not jail. How could his actions, clearly the result of a "sudden" blackout, be considered those of a man of sound mind?

THE INEFFICACY OF THE DEATH PENALTY

In sixteen states, the penalty for rape may be death or life imprisonment. During a nineteen-year period in this country, 316 men were executed for rape, an average of seventeen a year. Due to the intense public prejudice against rapists, the death sentence often is imposed despite plain evidence that the men were suffering from a mental illness.

The rules by which mentally sick defendants are bound in courts are confusing. In a recent decision, a leading federal judge stated: "The rule laid down by the court is general, indefinite, and puzzling to practical application." This judge admitted it to be "inhumane" to imprison insane criminals but he added that it would also be dangerous to turn them free. Much of the confusion stems from the so-called Durham Rule, which was discussed in detail in a previous chapter.

Because of the great prejudice associated with rape, a jury is generally inclined to favor the prosecution. We, the authors, have no intention of exonerating the rapist or excusing his acts. But, if society is to deal with such acts in an enlightened way, it must review its feelings about the entire concept of rape.

Before the admission of Alaska and Hawaii into the union, the crime rate, on the basis of known capital offenses per 100,000 people in the 42 states which impose capital punishment, was 7.04. In the other six states, where a person may commit murder or rape with the knowledge that his life cannot be taken from him, the crime rate, of which would elsewhere be capital offenses per 100,000 inhabitants, was 1.838. In other words, the rate in those states which impose capital punishment is more than three times as great as in the states that do not. It would seem clear, from these figures alone, that *the death penalty does not deter capital crimes* but may actually stimulate them!

Such statistics indicate that a realignment of thinking is in order by those who adhere to the ancient theory of "An eye for an eye—a tooth for a tooth." Vengeance is a poor substitute for intelligent thinking, and evaluation of both the offense and the offender are in the best interests of the community.

In a recent article entitled "Are We Executing Sick People?" in the June, 1959, issue of *Coronet*, Terry Morris describes the case of Roche who confessed to the rape murder of a fourteen-year-old school girl. The author wrote: "The facts of the case were not in dispute; the issue was whether Roche was insane at the time he committed the crime."

The defense psychiatrist testified that Roche was a schizophrenic. The psychiatrists for the prosecution conceded that he was a "severe schizoid personality" but without psychosis and, therefore, legally sane. After less than two hours deliberation, the jury returned the verdict of guilty. His appeal failing, Roche was electrocuted.

"Yet, in the opinion of the battery of top criminal lawyers, who defended Roche without pay, a madman had been executed, and the McNaughten rule had claimed still another victim."

Terry Morris ends his article by asking, "Are we executing sick people? Perhaps some soul-searching is in order."

The public shows little mercy for a sex killer or "thrill killer" even though he may be psychotic or a low-grade moron.

Dangerous sex offenders who are psychotic should be institutionalized. The execution of the insane sex deviate is a crime in itself.

RECOMMENDATIONS

1. The law should provide safeguards againt innocent men being charged with rape. They may be accused, out of spite, by a disgruntled woman or for other invalid reasons.

2. The trend should be, as it is in New York, to treat statutory rape cases (sexual intercourse with girls under the legal age of consent) as misdemeanors and not as felonies.

3. Laws should be changed to be more consistent among the various states and different jurisdictions.

4. The law should place more responsibility on the complainant. A higher degree of resistance should be required, consideration should be given as to whether there was actual penetration, and greater care should be given to discern if there was an actual rape or a mere case of sexual intercourse followed by vengeful afterthought by the complainant.

5. The above should also include complainants who were drinking companions or prostitutes, and situations where relations between the male and the complaining woman had lasted over a long period of time.

6. The age of statutory rape should be lowered.

7. The death penalty should be done away with altogether.

There should be established a standard by which a defendant can be accurately evaluated and a determination made as to his legal sanity or lack of it. Such a determination should be made only after careful psychiatric study by at least three impartial psychiatrists, not one, as is often the case today.

The authorities, entrusted with administering the law, should be required to have sufficient knowledge to understand the psychology of the criminal mind and what the psychiatrist is trying to establish. The doctors should confer with the lawyer, each expressing his views so that a concerted effort is made to arrive at a decision which protects the public and yet one which deals fairly with the mental capacity of the defendant.

There should be facilities set up for the treatment of mentally sick sex offenders with the view of their re-entering society as useful individuals, instead of merely putting them away for a period of time. As Dr. Emanuel Hammer, psychoanalyst expressed it: "Treating these people as outcasts has gotten us nowhere. It must be realized that they are sick. Their personalities warped, as much the victim of their illness as those they abuse. Their actions are compulsory. Psychotherapy, not punishment, may free them from their subconsciously motivated actions."

Prison hospitals should be built for the treatment of sex offenders. Only in this way can we avoid the error of executing sex offenders who are not responsible at the time of committing their offense.

chapter seven

PEDOPHILIA

GENERAL REMARKS

Pedophilia is a deviation of the sexual impulse characterized by the compulsive urge to accost or assault children sexually. The word is of Greek derivation and means "love of boys." It is a common sexual offense. In some cases, the offender merely fondles a child; in other cases, he persuades the child to commit a sexual act; in extreme cases, the pedophiliac inflicts bodily harm.

If a man accosts a male child, it is spoken of as "homosexual pedophilia." If the child belongs to the opposite sex, it is referred to as "heterosexual pedophilia." Some offenders approach children of either sex.

While most pedophiliacs are men, there are also women offenders.

CAUSATIVE FACTORS

The man who suffers from a morbid sexual interest in children is likely to be sexually inadequate. Unable to achieve satisfactory heterosexual relationships due to psychic impotence, he accosts children instead of women.

He does not seek gratification with a paid prostitute because of fear of humiliation were he to experience sexual failure.

204

All pedophiliacs suffer from sexual immaturity—an arrested development of the sexual libido.

In an article entitled "Pedophilia" *(Sexology,* January, 1955), Helen Kitchen Branson, a consulting psychologist states: "Based on forty-nine complete histories and three-year treatment procedures for child molesters, ranging in age from 22 to 79, there is some evidence that those men who are victims of this dangerous and unfortunate compulsion have never advanced from or may have regressed to an infantile stage of development when sexual stimulation and gratification were largely matters of viewing and manipulation of the genitals."

These sex offenders sometimes attempt penetration of some kind, but they are often satisfied merely with fondling the sexual organs of the child or having the child fondle them.

Very often, pedophilia is found among old men who are beginning to manifest symptoms of mental deterioration or presenility. Occasionally, a grandfather is accused of fondling the sexual organs of his grandchild.

The pedophiliac usually identifies himself with the child. The eroticism is derived from the knowledge that the sexually innocent child is being stimulated. For the adult, this represents a psychological return to the sex life of his own childhood. Pedophiliacs also feel less inferior sexually in their intimacies with children.

Case Histories

Case 1. A man in his late thirties was apprehended performing cunnilingus on his eleven-year-old-daughter (incestuous pedophilia). He confessed that he had been indulging in this sexual practice with his daughter for the past year and had warned her never to divulge what he referred to as their "secret." His wife's first impulse was to turn him over to the police. She decided, however, that he must be mentally ill and consulted her physician who, in turn, recommended psychiatric consultation.

On the husband's refusal to undergo psychiatric treatment, the wife left him, taking the daughter with her.

Case 2. In this particular case, a young married man had been charged with molesting children sexually. Testimony was given in court that he could be cured of his sexual affliction. The judge decided to give him an opportunity to avail himself of psychiatric treatment to which he responded favorably.

After having decided to divorce him, his wife changed her mind. For the sake of their two children, she agreed to give him another chance since he showed a sincere willingness to be helped.

During treatment, he submitted a detailed written story of his sexual experiences.

His parents were divorced when he was seven years of age. At this time, he experienced his first sexual awakening which he describes as follows:

"During a noon hour when the teacher left the school unattended, an eighth-grade boy took a girl of the same grade in the woodshed which has no door, so that everybody saw what they did. The boy pulled the girl's drawers down around her knees and had intercourse with her standing up. I felt no sexual thrill—only curiosity. There were about twelve kids, boys and girls, watching, and the boy kept telling us to go away, then warned not to tell the teacher. That same week, another boy and I pulled this same girl's dress up when she entered the schoolyard. I don't know why we did it. I think it was to look at her drawers. She yelled at us and chased us. Later this girl and I were playing at her house on a Saturday, and she asked me if I wanted to go with her, together with two eighth-grade boys, into the woods. They said I would have a lot of fun. I said, 'All right,' so we rode into the woods in back of her house on bicycles. When we got there, she stretched out on the ground and pulled her drawers down, and one of the boys put something on, which then looked to me like a leather thumb. I guess it was a rubber. These boys were brothers. They both had intercourse with her. One was the same who had had intercourse with her in the school woodshed. That same day they again took me into the woods where the girl again lay down on the ground and had intercourse with the boys. Then she told me I could peep between her legs and feel her there. I did this and then said I wanted to do the other thing. She said I wasn't old enough but took my penis out and fooled with it. I had no sensation but she let me lie on top of her, and I remember that I had no sensation. Then it was time to go home, and they said something awful would happen to me if I told anyone."

The above incident appears to have been the foundation for his voyeuristic tendencies. Since voyeurism and exhibitionism are interrelated, he also developed the impulse in adult life to expose himself before children. The seeds of his sexual neurosis involving children were all planted during his childhood.

Case 3. This third case involved an eighty-year-old man charged with contributing to the delinquency of a minor, a girl of fourteen. A successful business man, he had retired about fifteen years before and was living with his wife in a modest apartment. He informed us that his wife who had been brought up in a convent had been frigid ever since he married her. He had never enjoyed sexual intercourse because it upset her. As a result, he had had extramarital relations throughout his married life.

Several years ago, he met a girl of eighteen and persuaded her to visit him at an apartment he had rented for such occasions. Since he was impotent, he made sexual use of her a half-dozen times by fondling her sexual parts. For this, he paid her five or ten dollars, depending on the mood he was in.

One day she brought another girl who, she claimed, was

fourteen. The patient believed she was much younger, perhaps ten or eleven, and that the older girl lied about her age. The older girl left after asking him to give her friend the price of a pair of shoes, in return for which she would be nice to him. He fondled the small girl a few minutes, exposed himself and then gave her two dollars, which disappointed her, since she had been led to expect more. She complained to the older girl and the two of them told their parents. He was arrested and placed on bond. Psychiatric advice was sought as to whether he was dangerous and could be classified as a "sex psychopath" requiring institutionalization.

He was found to be suffering from pedophilia with exhibitionistic tendencies, and it was recommended that he be placed on probation and given an opportunity for psychotherapy. He proved quite conscientious and responded favorably to treatment.

There is no doubt that his sexual frustration with his wife contributed to his seeking outlets for his sexual urges outside of marriage. He had often entertained fantasies involving children but had never carried them out until he met the girl who introduced him to her younger friend. He developed acute anxiety symptoms and harbored suicidal thoughts as a result of his fear of being sent to prison. There was no point in sending a man of his age to an institution. It was improbable that he would benefit from hospitalization as such. Since he was not regarded as dangerous, the court granted him the chance to be rehabilitated. He gave up the other apartment and is successfully sublimating his sexual urges.

PSYCHO-LEGAL MANAGEMENT

Pedophiliacs guilty of criminal sex offenses very often require institutionalization. Their sexual aberration sometimes leads to murder.

Children brought into court to testify, are traumatized by

having to relate their sexual experiences in public. It would be wise to spare them the ordeal of the witness stand. Terrifying childhood sexual experiences often cause sexual maladjustment in later years.

Parents of such victim-children should be referred to psychiatrists for counseling. Sometimes the child requires psychotherapy from a psychiatrist who specializes in the treatment of children.

While pedophilia, like other sexual deviations, is curable, some pedophiliacs do not respond to treatment and repeat their offense.

In the series of cases studied by Helen Branson, she reports: "Where treatment before release extended for six months, and treatment after release for two years or longer, four showed an abatement of symptoms (three of these have been out for five years or longer in the general community; one has ended treatment of thirteen months, but it is yet too soon to predict with certainty that his improvement will be permanent). Two of the prisoners showed improvement in general personal adjustment and a lesser frequency of symptoms; but were convicted on the same or similar charge with a plea of guilty within five years after release. One man did not improve either during the six months of treatment before release or during the few months of treatment after release. He was again convicted and committed to a state mental hospital. It would seem hopeful, therefore, that treatment before release might lessen the tendency of these individuals to repeat the crime. Further research and experimentation, however, is needed."

In literature published to combat sex crimes and sex delinquency, strong emotional language should be avoided. Language can be effective without phrases that betray society's hatred of the sex deviates who are sick and need psychiatric treatment. Referring to a child-molester as a "vicious" and "degenerate criminal" accomplishes nothing. Warning literature disseminated among parents by law-enforcement officials, advising them to educate their children about accepting gifts from or taking automobile rides with strangers, is a wise preventive measure. However, it would be wiser still to avoid inflaming the emotions of parents by using such expressions as "the foul ravaging of the sex fiend" . . . the child-molester is "devoid of all semblance of moral decency as he seeks to glut his evil desires" . . . "the scarred souls and devastated lives of little children will be the fearsome price of failure to curb him in his vile deeds."

In reading a book we heartily recommend, entitled *Man's Right to Be Human* by George Christian Anderson, it was surprising to learn that clergymen are beginning to become psychiatry-minded to the extent of helping sex offenders receive the psychiatric treatment they need. The book contains an interesting example of how a pedophiliac or child-molester had been helped through the intervention of Mr. Anderson:

"When Joe came to see me that day in July, I knew he was in trouble—real trouble. Twice before he had been picked up by the police in cities away from home, but now he had repeated his offense in his own tiny village. Molesting little girls was a grave crime.

" 'I'm out on bail' were the first words he said to me as he climbed the porch steps of the Rectory. 'I'm in a daze, I swear I didn't do it.' It was quite obvious to me that Joe was sick, very sick. 'What made you do it?' I asked. He slumped into a porch chair and was silent. Then slowly he began, 'I don't know. I just felt an urge to touch them, and I couldn't stop myself. These feelings come on me almost every day.' Never before had I seen a person so despondent, so frightened, so alone. 'You really couldn't help yourself, Joe,' I reassured him. 'I'm going to get you help. Try not to worry. Everything will come out all right.'

"It was evident that Joe was suffering from a serious neurosis. As soon as Joe was gone, I picked up the phone and called a psychiatrist I knew and explained the situation. He agreed to see Joe the next day. I then spoke to the magistrate in whose court Joe had put up bail and explained that Joe was undoubtedly emotionally ill. He agreed to defer the case, pending the psychiatric examination. I then went to see Joe's sister with whom Joe lived, and interpreted to her how emotional illness beclouds our moral judgments and that Joe was more sick than a sinner. 'I can't face the disgrace,' she cried. 'What will they think of me when I go to church!' I was afraid to answer, for I knew that some of the parishioners would display something less than Christian forgiveness toward both her and Joe. Nevertheless, I was able to make her see that Joe was not as immoral as he was sick and that he needed love and understanding, and medical care, too, more than ever.

"Fortunately, the judge placed Joe in the care of the psychiatrist, who, by that time, had diagnosed Joe's condition and found that he had experienced only a minor regression. With good psychotherapy and with the kind of support one can get from a clergyman, Joe was restored to good mental health in less than a year. His immoral acts, or to put it in psychiatric terms—his deviation from moral values—had dramatically made Joe aware of his need of a different kind of life, which then became strengthened by psychiatry and religion."

In an October, 1959 decision, the United States Court of Appeals for the District of Columbia ruled that the uncorroborated testimony of an eleven-year-old girl was not sufficient to sustain a conviction of an indecent liberty with the same child. (Wilson vs. U.S.—U.S. App. D.C. Oct. 1, 1959)

The defendant was charged with assaulting the child in the bedroom of his home and was sentenced to serve a prison term of one to four years. At the trial, the sole testimony against the defendant was that of the minor girl, although the defendant's wife, a possible prosecution witness, refused to testify claiming privilege because of the husband-wife relationship.

The Court of Appeals, in reversing the decision, stated:

"Appellant was guilty if anyone was, for he, alone, was with the child at the time of the alleged offense. But there was no evidence of any sort, except the testimony of the child herself, that anyone took indecent liberties with her. In the conventional phrase, there was no corroboration of the corpus delicti.

"We now hold that the corpus delicti in a case such as this may not be established by the child's uncorroborated testimony on the witness stand. The adequacy of particular kinds and amounts of corroboration must be left for decision in particular cases as they arise."

The Court commented about a previous sex case involving homosexual solicitation (Kelly vs. U.S., 90 U.S. App. D.C. 125-194 F. 2nd 150) in which the complaining witness was a policeman. A conviction in that case was also overturned for lack of corroborative evidence.

"The complaining witness in the Kelly case was a policeman. A woman's uncorroborated tale of a sex offense is not more reliable than a man's. A young child's is far less reliable."

The Court, then, in a most interesting observation, quoted from a book written by two psychiatrists in 1952, *Psychiatry and the Law,* by Guttmacher and Weihofen. Relied on by the Court was the following excerpt:

"It is well recognized that children are more highly suggestible than adults. Sexual activity, with the aura of mystery that adults create about it, confuses and fascinates them. Moreover, they have, of course, no real understanding of the serious consequences of the charges they make. As a consequence most courts show an admirable reluctance to accept the unsubstantiated testimony of children in sexual crimes."

Also quoted in the decision is Wigmore, who says:

"No judge should ever let a sex offense charge go to the jury unless the female complainant's social history and mental make-up have been examined and testified to by a qualified physician" (3 Wigmore, Evidence Sec. 924 a 3rd Ed. 1940). The Court went further and cited from a 1937-38 report of the American Bar Association's Committee on the Improvement of the Law of Evidence, which states in part:

"Today it is unanimously held by experienced psychiatrists that the complainant woman in a sex offense should always be examined by competent experts to ascertain whether she suffers from some mental or moral delusion or tendency, frequently found especially in young girls, causing distortion of the imagination in sex cases."

In commenting on the above, the Court said:

"We have not adopted that view and do not adopt it now. But its existence has some tendency to confirm the traditional skepticism of courts toward the present sort of accusation."

The management of the pedophiliac becomes confusing and uncertain when it is noted that, although most states have statutes specifically directed against molesters of children, there are confusing dissimilarities in the provisions and in their enforcement. Here are some of the terms used in indictments for sexual offenses against children: contributing to the delinquency of a minor; lewd acts with children; indecencies with children; impairing the morals of a minor. Some states have enacted specific laws dealing with teachers having sexual relations with children, while other states rely on their catchall statutes, such as "lewd vagrancy" or "breach of the peace" to envelop the offender. Further difficulty may be encountered because many states, in addition to statutes of this kind, have made provision in their regular rape, sodomy, and other "serious" sex statutes for heavier penalties when children are involved.

The following are recommendations for the better management of this problem.

1. Determination of appropriate statutes with which defendant shall be charged.

2. Publicity and sensationalism should be avoided in cases involving children.

3. It should be borne in mind that children, both boys and girls, often fail to report pedophilic acts to their parents or to the authorities until long after a pattern of such practice has been established. Even then, some of these acts are not reported until the offender directs his attentions away from the one child and toward another. In other instances, the act is brought to light by the child only as a means of vengeance or malice.

Caution should be used not to convict a man on the uncorroborated testimony of the child alone. Consideration should be given to the question of whether the child was old enough to understand the nature of his or her act and, therefore, became an accomplice rather than the victim.

4. Authorities should inquire as to whether any harm, physical or mental, has come to the victim; how necessary it is to submit the child to the ordeal of court proceedings and the resulting publicity.

5. There is a need for more study of the so-called "Sex-Psychopath Law" which many states now have on their statute books and which are being used more and more as catchall for sex offenders against children. Up to now these laws have failed to deter or rehabilitate offenders, and a new approach is necessary.

6. Care must be taken in administering the sex-psychopath laws, that a person in need of treatment and not imprisonment is handled properly, and to guard against indiscriminate "putting away" of sex offenders who, for the most part, can benefit by psychiatric treatment.

7. Sex laws should be devised so that the offender is charged with an offense realistically related to the act committed.

8. There should be a separation and different treatment for those offenses involving young children and those involving teenagers, who better understand what they are doing. The law presumes the latter incapable of comprehending the nature of the act and holds them legally incapable of consenting to certain acts, but experience indicates that their degree of responsibility and their motives require investigation.

9. Individual psychiatric attention should be given to each sexual offender against children so that the lawyers and judges are apprised whether or not the man is merely neurotic—as in many cases—or a sexual psychopath and chargeable under stricter laws or legally insane and not responsible for his acts.

10. Special attention must be given in the field of geriatrics (ailments of old age) for those whose problems stem from senile or presenile conditions.

11. In sentencing child-molesters, judges should encourage rehabilitation and treatment rather than mere imprisonment.

12. As a crime-prevention measure, literature giving helpful information on these matters should be available.

In Montgomery County, Maryland, 80,000 leaflets were distributed by Police Superintendent James S. McAuliffe, advising children how to protect themselves against strangers who accost them. The pamphlets advised youngsters to report to the police: "Any adult stranger who tries to join in your play —asks you to go with him—tries to talk to you—wants you to go in the woods with him to find an animal or for any reason —shows you filthy pictures or makes filthy remarks to you— wants you to leave the group you are playing with—tries to have you disobey any of the rules in this pamphlet."

According to Colonel McAuliffe: "Ninety-five percent of such molesters prove to be just a nuisance, but the other five percent are dangerous characters."

Many parents are reluctant to report sex offenders to the police for fear the child will be psychologically traumatized by the investigation and questioning. They also fear the publicity involved.

McAuliffe assures us that the police exercise discretion in these matters. "We would do nothing to upset or embarrass any youngster; if necessary, we get policewomen to do the questioning or the parents to question him and then report to us." As for the publicity in court, he adds: "There is no difficulty in providing a private hearing if the witnesses desire it."

chapter eight

OTHER TYPES OF ABERRANT
SEXUAL BEHAVIOR

FETISHISM

Fetishism is a psychosexual aberration or complex in which the sex impulse or libido becomes attached to or fixated on some inanimate object (fetish) that constitutes a sexual symbol of the love object.

The term was coined by Binet who introduced the concept of this particular sexual deviation to science. It is derived from the Portuguese word "fetico" meaning charmed, a term originally stemming from the Latin "facere," to make. It conveys the idea of something artificially made. Eulemberg proposed the use of the phrase "sexual symbolism" but it was never permanently adopted. Havelock Ellis preferred the term "erotic symbolism."

The fetishist may be erotically attracted to a woman's shoe, stocking, glove, handkerchief, corset, undergarment, ornament, hair, or other article associated with her sex. Thus we have shoe fetishists, hair fetishists, fur fetishists, silk fetishists, leather fetishists, hair fetishists, etc. Fetishism may involve hair-snipping and stealing women's clothing. Such thefts provide erotic gratification to the fetishists who may even commit burglary or assault to secure the desired object. Because of this, fetishism has a forensic (courtroom) importance. Fetishists are very often aggressive and antisocial.

217

Fetishism occurs almost exclusively in men. Psychoanalysts classify this peculiar sexual phenomenon as a highly symbolical form of psychic masturbation. Fetishists are often spoken of as "symbolists."

Fetishism is a form of sexual regression, a retreat from adult sexuality to what Stekel refers to as psychosexual infantilism. Many fetishists harbor the delusion of being impotent with women, even though they never make an attempt at coitus. Their aberration assumes the nature of an obsession. It is compulsive in nature and is associated with sadomasochistic features.

Fetishism is akin to exhibitionism insofar as it is motivated by a compulsive impulse which the offender cannot control only because of his lack of understanding of the psychodynamic factors involved.

A twenty-six-year-old married man, arrested for stealing ladies' panties from clotheslines, was referred for psychiatric examination. He disclosed that, during his early adolescence, at the period of sexual awakening, he became fascinated by panties which his sister had carelessly left about in her bedroom. He became sexually stimulated whenever he entertained fantasies of what women looked like clad in panties. He finally began acquiring ladies' panties by stealing them from clotheslines. The stolen panties played a role in his masturbatory activities.

The court gave him an opportunity for psychiatric treatment which led to his rehabilitation.

Years ago, when school girls wore their hair in pigtails, some found to their surprise, after getting off a trolley or bus, that one of their pigtails had been clipped off. The offender or "braid cutter" undoubtedly was a hair fetishist.

The matter was taken up by the press, and people wondered what would make anybody go around clipping girls' hair. Very likely the hair clipper used the lock of hair as a masturbation stimulus. The cutting of the hair represents what psycho-analysts call "symbolic castration."

In many cases of fetishism, there exists an unconscious incest wish. The incestuous striving is applied to some symbol or representative of the person toward whom the wish is directed. In a case of hair fetishism reported in *Sexual Deviations,* a book which was coauthored by Dr. Caprio, the patient's mother and sister had black hair which became his chosen fetish. The patient's incestuous attachment to his mother and to his sister could not be attained in reality, so he chose a symbol of them, their hair, and used it in his autoerotic fantasies. His primordial attachment was to his mother. This incestuous fixation was the hidden root of the sexual impulse, as was shown by his recollections of how beautiful he thought his mother's hair was when he was a child. According to Stekel, fetishism always has its origin in childhood, since it is rare for the child to seek the genital symbol before puberty. In this particular case, the patient became aware through his analysis that, when he was twelve years old, the hair of his sister had a sexually stimulating effect.

Thus we see that the object may frequently be associated with an incestuous fantasy and represent the hair, the glove, the shoe, or undergarment of the mother or sister. Stekel tells us that "because of this obsession with the object for which he has so strong a sexual attraction, the fetishist very often becomes a collector of these objects or of representations of them." He refers to such a collection as the "harem cult," inferring that each additional object represents, in fantasy, a substitute symbol for another woman (a mother or sister surrogate).

Dr. John Oliven writes that the fetishist's "need is usually for possession; he is an inexhaustible collector of 'his kind of fetish;' and he may keep books punctiliously about the date and the origin of his acquisitions. Periodically, he looks, at, fondles, manipulates, smells, or kisses his objects, and this may suffice to gratify him. Some have spontaneous ejaculations during this activity; others 'use' the objects to produce masturbatory orgasm."

The object thus becomes for the fetish lover an emotional short circuit leading to erotic stimulation and satisfaction.

Fetishism is closely related to psychic impotence. For most fetishists, the contact with the fetish or object is a *conditio sine qua non* for the satisfactory performance of the coital act.

Franz Alexander sums up this phenomenon psychoanalytically: "It has always a phallic connotation and denies the absence of the penis in the woman." This theory is also shared by Fenichel and other psychoanalysts who explain fetishism as a refusal to acknowledge that a woman has a vagina. Stekel adds that it always develops into a depreciation of the female, regardless of the causes. According to Freudian symbolism, the shoe, foot, hand, or any other elongated object represents the penis. Fur is a symbolic substitute for pubic hair.

Karpman expresses the opinion that there is no fetishism in women because "the feminine experience of world and love is more bound to a concrete, personal level," adding that "males have active, visual imagery, while masturbating; women do not."

Fetishism is often confused with partialism. In partialism, the individual is erotically attracted to a certain part of a woman's body. The sexual fixation may involve such parts as the breasts, buttocks, thighs, legs, ankles, feet, or hands. Some observers regard partialism as a type of body fetishism.

It is not uncommon for the compulsive fetishist to indulge in other types of sexual aberrations such as exihibitionism, homosexuality, voyeurism, transvestism, and coprolalia. They may coexist in various combinations in the same individual.

One patient, described earlier in these pages, combined fetishism with voyeurism and coprolalia. He would cut out pictures of women from magazines and would masturbate while looking at them. He would also call up strange women on the telephone and use obscene language, masturbating while he was talking. He also used stolen women's clothes as accessories to masturbation. He peeped into windows where he could see women undressing and masturbated as he watched them.

Dr. Caprio was asked to give a psychological evaluation of an unusual hobby—collecting images of hands. The collector had secured hands wrought in marble, wood, ivory, stone, metal, crystal, and ceramics, in sizes from miniatures to over-size. His collection included plaques, paintings, drawings, and sketches of hands.

In speculating about the psychology of hand fetishism, we take into consideration the many possible associations connected with hands. One may have been impressed, as a child, by the hands of his mother, sister, teacher, or friend. If the impression was strong enough, it may develop into a fixation or obsession in adult life of which a seemingly innocent "hobby" may be the expression.

If the hands are associated with some past sexual experience, psychoanalysts would say that the hands become *genitalized*. In such a case the individual would be a "hand fetishist" who would find anything connected with hands erotic.

If the hand fetishism involves the hands of both sexes, we might conclude that the person's erotic attraction to hands is bisexual.

The urge to collect certain objects is not, in itself, abnormal nor does every collector's item have to have a sexual meaning. There are stamp collectors, women who collect teacups or spoons, men who collect first editions, and others who collect valuable paintings. Their motivations are not necessarily erotic.

Nevertheless one can speculate on what would make a collector go to considerable trouble and expense to hunt and acquire particular objects to add to his hoard. For one thing, a collector is somewhat of a narcissist. It tickles his vanity to own something most other people don't have. He gets a vicarious thrill seeking something "new" or "different." His hobby may be an outlet for some inner frustration. He may harbor a certain amount of exhibitionism (nonsexual) insofar as his collection attracts the attention of his friends.

These and other psychological factors may all enter into the phenomenon of hobby collections. In other words, there is a *normal* type of fetishism, that exists among normal persons.

By the same token, one must also realize that there are kinds of fetishism and types of fetishists that come under a different category. If an individual who boasts of an extensive collection of pictures of nude women is sexually inadequate, the psychiatrist is justified in assuming him to be suffering from a sexual neurosis. The same applies to pornography.

The man who collects guns may be normal or he may be neurotic. He may collect guns because he is an enthusiastic sportsman. But he may collect guns for quite another reason. According to Freudian psychoanalysts, a gun is a phallic symbol. Hence it would follow that a gun-collecting bachelor who displayed little interest in women and marriage might be compensating, in his collection of guns, for inadequate potency.

Psychoanalytic interpretations and speculations regarding anything are justified if one avoids sweeping generalizations and makes allowances for exceptions where the theory does not apply. Thus, we might say that, while every collector is not necessarily a fetishist, the compulsive fetishist is often a collector.

Binet was one of the first to conclude that fetishism is caused by some association of an object with sexual awakening. His conclusion was: "In the life of every fetishist there may be assumed to have been some event which determined the association of lustful feeling with the single impression."

Fetishism has its roots in childhood. It can be traced to some "accidental" experience during childhood or adolescence when the individual became sexually aroused by contact with some object belonging to or associated with his mother, sister, or some other woman. It operates somewhat like a conditioned reflex.

It develops as a result of psychosexual immaturity, a fixation of the libido at an early stage of development. Most patients can recall associations in childhood of an early sexual arousal focused on a particular object (their mother's or sister's shoes, glove, or undergarment).

Every case of fetishism must be studied and treated on the basis of the individual circumstances.

Since fetishism is a neurosis, it can be eliminated by proper treatment. Uncovering the initiating experience that channeled the libido into this course does not, by itself, effect a cure. If the condition has persisted a long time, it may require intensive psychotherapy and re-education.

Voyeurism

Voyeurism is a sexual deviation characterized by a compulsion to peep at persons undressing or engaging in sexual relations. The term is derived from the French "to see." Voyeurs are commonly called "Peeping Toms." Like exhibitionists, they are rarely dangerous. As a rule, they masturbate to excess.

We have already referred to the case of a young married man, the father of a child, who was arrested for peeping into ladies' toilets, through holes he had bored into the walls of public lavatories on the pretense that he was a plumber. In the course of his treatment, the reader will recall, his voyeurism was traced back to his childhood when he had peeped through the keyhole of the bathroom while his sister took a bath. This premature sex stimulation developed into a fixation in his later years. He was fortunate enough to be spared a prison sentence and to be allowed to undergo psychiatric treatment. To this he responded successfully, and society had the advantage of a man restored to normality instead of a convict.

TRANSVESTISM (Cross-Dressing)

In transvestism the deviate derives erotic gratification by wearing the clothing of the opposite sex. Certain male transvestites use make-up; others satisfy their urges by wearing a piece of feminine apparel. The transvestite has a psychic identification with the opposite sex. The female transvestite may imagine that she possesses a penis. It is difficult to detect a female transvestite, since many normal women wear slacks or dress in masculinely tailored clothes.

Dr. Benjamin Karpman in his book *The Sexual Offender and His Offenses* mentions the case of Dr. Mary Walker who received special permission from Congress to dress in male clothes. She rationalized that it was more appropriate to her profession to be dressed in male attire.

Persons classified as transvestites find the urge to dress in clothes of the opposite sex more or less compulsive. Many are married but seldom achieve complete heterosexual satisfaction from coitus. According to Dr. Karpman, transvestism is a manifestation of a strong unconscious homosexual drive which "dares not seek overt expression."

In one case, a patient who had been arrested for "indecent exposure" was referred to me for psychiatric evaluation. He had entered a candy store when no other customers were present. After making his purchase, he lifted his shirt to show the girl who waited on him that he was wearing a lady's corset and proceeded to tell her that he found it exciting to "show himself off." She became frightened, summoned the police, and he was taken into custody. He admitted that this urge for cross-dressing was compulsive and that he had been wearing corsets for many years. I learned that, as an adolescent, he had enjoyed watching his mother put on a corset, and he had apparently developed an identification with his mother. He was devoutly religious, prayed that he would not repeat his exhibitionistic acts, and managed to keep his transvestism a secret. His latent homosexual component was quite pronounced and was related to his libidinal fixation on his mother.

In another case, a mannish Lesbian found it erotic to wear men's shorts. On her job, no one suspected her cross-dressing tendencies. When she went to the ladies room, sometimes accompanied by a friend, she took precautions not to have her friend see that she was wearing what she described as her "jockey shorts." At home she would view herself before a mirror and place objects in front of her pretending she had a penis.

Transvestites, as a rule, are harmless insofar as they have no desire to assault anyone. At most, like the exhibitionists, they offend by the desire to attract attention.

Transvestism is a symptomatic expression of sexual maladjustment and, as such, is amenable to psychotherapy. Transvestities who are given understanding and insight into the nature of their disorder voluntarily abandon their cross-dressing activities. The psychotherapist treats the personality-neurosis rather than the symptom.

We strongly feel that there should be a world-wide agreement among surgeons not to perform a castration operation. Amputation of a transvestite's penis, because he wants to look and feel like a woman anatomically, should be outlawed by the International Congress of Surgeons. Such operations are illegal in the United States. They should be made illegal in other countries as well.

Suppose mannish Lesbians could have their breasts removed because they wanted to look more like a man. What kind of society would we ultimately have? Since what transvestites suffer from is a neurosis, they should be influenced to cure it rather than be aided in the neurotic drive to perpetuate their problem.

In some countries, a male transvestite may marry another

man. If such marriages were generally made legal, we could expect all sorts of complications as a result of women marrying women and men marrying men. We cannot appreciate the logic of a court in any country sanctioning such unions.

Some psychiatrists consider transvestism a sexual deviation separate from homosexuality. We consider all transvestites to be basically homosexuals, latent if not overt. A latent homosexual component constitutes the root-cause of transvestism.

FROTTAGE

In frottage (the term is derived from the French word rub) the deviate has a compulsive desire to rub himself against some part of the body of another person, generally of the opposite sex.

Some frotteurs achieve erotic gratification by rubbing or pressing against the buttocks of a woman in a crowded subway, bus, or street car. Frottage, therefore, is regarded as a mild form of assault. Frotteurs usually pretend that the rubbing was accidental.

This deviation differs from partialism (a fixation of the sexual impulse or libido on a certain part of a woman's body, such as the buttocks, breasts, and thighs).

A patient preferred to masturbate, rubbing his penis against his wife's buttocks rather than engage in the act of coitus. He related how, at the age of fourteen, he experienced an ejaculation while playfully wrestling with his sister. Following this episode, he made frequent attempts to excite himself sexually by rubbing against his sister's buttocks.

COPROLALIA

The word coprolalia is derived from "copro" meaning dirty and "lalia" meaning language or other forms of communication. The term is used for deviates who derive sexual stimulation from the use of obscene language during love-making.

Under coprolalia comes the practice of obscene writing on lavatory walls. The person who scribbles obscenities in public toilets or on walls gets vicarious sexual gratification from the knowledge that his messages will be read by others. Such a person is usually preoccupied with sexual fantasies of every description. To psychiatrists, coprolalia represents psychic or mental masturbation and is associated with sexual immaturity. Children often obtain pleasure by chalking four-letter words on sidewalks and are stimulated by the thought that this embarrasses children of the opposite sex.

Coprolalia is not uncommon among adults or married couples. Some husbands incite their wives to use obscene expressions during love play as a means of adding to their sexual excitement. When this becomes an absolute requirement on the part of the husband, a psychiatrist is justified in suspecting that he suffers from psychic impotence.

I treated a female patient, aged twenty-eight, who consulted me because of feeling nervous, tired, and depressed. She also slept poorly and was disturbed by a variety of neurotic fears.

In the course of the treatment, she disclosed that she was receiving letters containing obscene language from a man whom she had hoped to marry. The writer stated that he was unable to marry for a long time because he had to look after his mother. It was obvious, on examining these missives, that this man was sexually sick, tied to his mother's apron strings, and suffering from a severe case of coprolalia. In some of his letters, he referred to her as a "darling w——e" (the common name for a prostitute).

Such a person with a mother complex harbors two opposite attitudes toward the same woman. He both idolizes and degrades women, depending on his mood. This ambivalence (love-hate feelings for the same person) is interrelated psychoanalytically with the madonna-prostitute complex. The suffererer's ambivalence toward his mother is projected onto other women. In his subconscious mind, he wishes to defile his mother and embarrass her. This same psychology holds true for exhibitionists who sexually expose themselves before women.

We have had cases where men were arrested for selecting names of women in a telephone book, calling them up, and making obscene propositions to them over the phone. One such man called the wife of a minister and, on another occasion, a nun.

Coprolalia, like other miscellaneous sexual deviations, stems from sex ignorance, early faulty attitudes toward sex, or some experience in childhood that conditioned the person to this perverse type of sexual excitement. Coprolalia is curable, provided, of course, the individual actually wants guidance and enlightenment.

MIXOSCOPIA

The term, mixoscopia, is used by psychiatrists for sexual excitement derived from witnessing others in the sexual act.

Several years ago, a woman came to my office in a state of hysteria. She had gone through "a horrible experience" she said, and had never been the same since. This was her story.

One night, she was aroused by a noise at her bedroom window, which she had left open. She awakened her husband and as she did, heard a man's voice saying, "Don't move. Stay where you are or I'll kill you both." He then commanded them to remove their nightclothes and engage in sexual relations. He kept a flashlight focused on them. The husband was too frightened to perform adequately, but he was ordered to lie on his wife and pretend that he was consummating the act. The intruder did not rob them. He left, apparently sexually satisfied by watching them. The couple called the police, but the man was never apprehended. They moved to another community, but the experience had so traumatized the wife that she was left with severe and continuous anxiety symptoms.

Psychoanalysts have discovered that Peeping Toms get that way from having witnessed the sexual act during childhood or adolescence. Young boys who have witnessed their parents having intercourse, either by chance or by spying on them, are prone to develop this sexual deviation in later years. Peeping Toms get greater sexual thrills looking into bedroom windows rather than in actual sexual relations with a woman. We say that their sexual libido or impulse is fixated at the eye level and has never developed beyond this stage. The fact that they risk getting caught by the police adds to their sexual excitement. One might say that these voyeurs prefer to rape women psychologically rather than physically. The act of looking is to them the equivalent of coitus. It is usually accompanied by masturbation.

PYGMALIONISM

The word "Pygmalionism" is derived from Greek mythology. Pygmalion, a kind of Cyprus, was a sculptor. According to legend, he fell in love with an ivory statue of a girl that he had carved. He prayed to Aphrodite to animate the ivory statue. His prayer was answered, and he married the maid who had once been a statue.

In their practice, psychiatrists not infrequently have patients who have fallen in love with creations of their own, and react toward these objects as though they were alive. But Pygmalionism, as a psychiatric term, refers to unrealistic love that prefers an idealized image to the actual person. Men who idealize or idolize women in general are prone to this complex. The patient has a compulsion to place a certain woman on a pedestal. When he falls in love, it is with an ideal image, not a woman.

A twenty-seven-year-old man consulted me because of his inability to get along with people. He was an extreme introvert, shy and withdrawn, and subject to excessive daydreaming. After many sessions, he revealed that he was in love with "Diana," who turned out to be a female manikin he had purchased. When his landlady discovered the manikin in the closet of his room, he explained that he was a fashion designer and needed it for his work. He took Diana to bed with him and made love to her. He bought her clothes and talked to her as if she were a living person. But this behavior created anxiety states that caused him such mental distress that he felt he was losing his mind. In relating how this complex had developed, he described his sister as a very beautiful girl, a ballet dancer. As a boy he masturbated excessively, accompanying the act with fantasies of making love to his sister. He frequented an art museum where he stared at a statue of Aphrodite which, he claimed, reminded him of his sister. The undergarments he purchased for his manikin were similar to those he recalled as worn by his sister.

His deviation was explained on the basis of his sister fixation. On gaining insight into the cause of his complex, he was able to give up his injurious sexual play-acting.

Pygmalionism is a sexual oddity that rarely manifests itself in such an overt expression as described above. It usually exists in the disguised form of worshipping a woman, placing her on a pedestal, and keeping the love relationship platonic. The patient treats her as if she were a goddess instead of a human being. Psychiatrists have found that such men quite often suffer from impotence reactions. Pygmalionists rationalize their impotence with the belief that their love is equivalent to the pure love and respect accorded their own mother or sister. Complications arise when the wife of such a man begins to suffer from her inevitable sexual frustration.

KLEPTOMANIA

Although the term kleptomania refers specifically to a compulsive urge to steal, psychiatrists have discovered that it has sexual implications. Like pyromania (the compulsion to set fires) the act of stealing objects, that may or may not have a value to the person, is sexually motivated.

In one case, a young woman patient told me that when she was in her teens she was addicted to stealing gloves in department stores. Just as the dipsomaniac experiences a craving or "madness" (mania) for alcohol, she had an uncontrollable impulse to steal ladies' gloves even though they might not be her size. It was not need that prompted her. Her parents were well off and gave her any money she needed. It was also unimportant to her what she did with the gloves after she had stolen them. Some she gave away; others she kept.

It developed that she began stealing at a time when she was in love with a boy who demanded that she have sexual relations with him. He was attractive to her physically and she, too, desired sexual relations, but fear and guilt feelings made her withhold complete gratification though she permitted heavy petting. Her mother discouraged their relationship, warning her daughter that the boy was only interested in seducing her and that unless she broke off with him she might find herself an unmarried mother. It was then that the patient stole her first pair of gloves. The evidence indicated that the risk of being arrested by the police and the actual act of taking the gloves without payment represented a disguised wish for sexual intimacy with her boy friend. She was committing an act prohibited by her mother and her own conscience. It was a symbolic, sadistic revenge against her mother for interfering and, at the same time, her way of expressing, via the language of the unconscious, her desire for the prohibited intimacy.

Kleptomania is regarded by most psychoanalysts as the compromise consequence of an unconscious struggle between a sexual craving and moral censorship. It is a psychological disorder, rather than a crime. Very often the object stolen gives the psychoanalyst a clue to the type of sex sickness the offender is suffering from. A woman who will steal elongated objects, such as a screwdriver, may unconsciously express her desire for the male sexual organ. The man who steals ladies' handkerchiefs is probably a fetishist, deriving sexual gratification in his fantasies of the opposite sex.

In another case referred to me, the patient was the wife of a wellknown professional man. She had been arrested for shoplifting, stealing miscellaneous objects of little value or use to her. It was disclosed, during her analysis, that she was frigid. She blamed her inability to achieve sexual satisfaction on her husband. She got a thrill out of stealing instead. Her emotional reaction during the actual theft can be construed as an orgasm equivalent. The fact that her husband was an attorney and that she could cause him acute embarrassment by breaking the law, was evidence that she wished to punish her husband for leaving her sexually unsatisfied.

Police officials are now aware of the sexual root of such offenses as kleptomania and pyromania and in many instances refer offenders to psychiatrists for treatment.

SADOMASOCHISM

In all of us, there are sadomasochistic impulses which, if not controlled, can pass into the area of sexual deviation.

Many husbands have related that their wives, during the moment of climax, bit them, sometimes painfully. This so-called "love bite" is far more common than is imagined. It causes both partners added excitement. In most cases the "biter" manages to control the intensity of the bite. The love bite may be a residue of the cannibalistic impulse.

All of us, at one time or another, have heard mothers exclaim to a child or infant, "I love you so much, I could eat you up." Psychoanalysts explain this as representing part of the oral stage of development that all human beings go through. It is related to the breast-sucking stage during infancy.

It is not uncommon for an infant to bite the mother's nipple or to bite the mother's nose. Unconsciously, it is a wish to devour the love object (oral intake). Biting is an expression of a sadistic desire to inflict pain on the love partner.

One patient revealed to me that his wife bit him on the lip, causing it to become swollen, after he had rejected her proposal that they make love at a time when he found it inconvenient. He could not understand what motivated her to bite him. She told him she had been gratified by the act and had no regrets.

I have interviewed two Lesbians who admitted biting each other, and other acts of violence during their intimate relations.

In extreme cases, the biting results in the drawing of blood. The act of sucking blood following biting is known as vampirism.

In most cases, the manifestations described are mild and harmless. When they altogether escape the person's control, however, they must be regarded as sexual deviations requiring psychiatric treatment.

SALIROMANIA

One of the strangest of sexual deviations is called saliromania. The saliromaniac achieves erotic satisfaction or sexual excitement by deliberately destroying or *soiling* a woman's dress or underclothes or damaging or besmirching nude statues or paintings. The woman (often the wife) may be wearing the dress at the time, or is in a negligee when the act takes place.

The police keep on the lookout for boys or men who will smear a female statue in a public park with mud or paint. When the offender is apprehended, he is unable to offer a plausible explanation for what he describes as an "uncontrollable" impulse. This phenomenon is almost akin to the sadistic satisfaction some persons derive from poisoning dogs. They are both compulsive behavior of a sadistic nature.

Saliromania is derived from the French word "salir" meaning soiling and the Greek word "mania" meaning a mad craving.

While examining books on a public library shelf, a patient of Dr. Caprio noticed a strange man hurriedly zipping his trousers. He disappeared behind the other shelves. Suspecting that he was an exhibitionist, she reported the incident to the head librarian who noticed that the back of the woman's dress was wet and spotted. After retiring to the ladies' room, she discovered the wet stains to be semen. She concluded that the man had masturbated while she was leaning over the book shelf and had ejaculated over the back of her dress. She had been referred to Dr. Caprio by her physician who diagnosed her as suffering from an anxiety neurosis. She claimed this recent traumatic experience had contributed to her aversion to men and sex.

A sex offender of this kind, who exposes himself in a public place is basically an exhibitionist, but in this case, the man also suffered from saliromania. As you may surmise, this particular sexual aberration is sadistically motivated. The offender is driven by a desire to humiliate, degrade, or show in this peculiar fashion his contempt for the opposite sex. As a rule, this type of deviate, like the exhibitionist, does not inflict any bodily harm. He merely achieves an erotic thrill by embarrassing his victim and expressing his hatred or dislike of women. Or he may achieve this same satisfaction in a vicarious way by defacing or soiling the statue of a nude or semi-nude woman.

Professor Bruno Callieri, a psychiatrist at the University of Rome, reported in a recent issue of *Sexology* several examples of this type of sexual deviation.

He informs us that, in a famous museum of criminology in Germany, there is a photograph of a female statue spattered with black ink. Bloch, the German sexologist, described a case of a twenty-two-year-old printer arrested for pouring sulphuric acid on at least thirteen young girls. In another case, a boy experienced sadistic satisfaction by pouring ink on the dresses of women he desired.

In another case of saliromania, a young man harbored strong ambivalent (love-hate) feelings for his wife. He would surprise her with gifts of beautiful lingerie, ask her to wear a particular article of underclothing, and would then enjoy tearing it off her body and ripping it into shreds. This gave him sexual satisfaction. His wife, whom I interviewed, informed me that he would then impotently attempt sexual intercourse, leaving her frustrated and unsatisfied.

Analysis revealed that, as a boy, this man had been ambivalent toward (loved and hated) his mother, who was strict and domineering. He recalls how, whenever his mother angered him, he would go out to the back yard, pull his mother's underthings out of the clothes basket, and urinate on them. Once his mother caught him and gave him a severe whipping. In a subsequent session, he told how he had once torn several of his mother's dresses. There was no question but that he was projecting on to his wife his early feelings of hostility toward his mother.

Deviations of this kind are often found among men who suffer from sexual immaturity. They are generally impotent, getting greater staisfaction from the act of saliromania than from intercourse.

Analysis of every case of saliromania usually reveals some

association in the person's past that accounts for his sexual neurosis. There may be some unpleasant experience involving a particular color or a special type of garment. When the "libido" (sex hunger) becomes fixated or attached, as it were, to the associated object, then the offender finds himself driven by a compulsive impulse to act out his sexual drive.

In one case, a youth had the habit of throwing soot on light colored evening dresses. He had done this at least twenty-five times before he was apprehended by the police and sentenced to six months in prison.

In another case, a middle-aged businessman who was inclined to drink to excess consulted me upon the advice of his physician. His wife had left him, not because of his excessive drinking but for another reason. He would gather her expensive evening gowns, scatter them on the floor of his bedroom, trample and spit on them, and then urinate over them, all the while addressing profanities to her. This he did only when he was intoxicated. When his wife told him about it the next morning, he would deny any knowledge of having done such a thing. He admitted that he was sexually impotent and harbored considerable hostility against his wife.

During childhood it is not uncommon for young boys to become excited at the prospect of soiling the clothes of some person in the neighborhood who is singled out as a "sissy" or is disliked for one reason or another; and later coprophilic developments are likely to be fixations of such childhood activities. In a malicious childhood sport called "church on fire" a boy is told to stand in a corner with his eyes closed and yell, "Fire, fire." The other boys, as firemen, then urinate on him, and the victim usually runs home to his mother crying. To throw mud on a girl in a new dress is a similar, common boyhood aggression. Such actions in childhood are the source of saliromania in adult life. Psychoanalysts deem it a form of psychosexual infantilism insofar as it represents a manifestation of sexual immaturity and a kind of "psychic masturbation" by which sexual excitement is derived from the humiliation of a member of the opposite sex.

Various unconscious factors are associated with this sexual anomaly. A boy who is repeatedly told by his mother to keep himself clean, to treat all girls with the utmost respect, and, in general, never do anything that isn't "nice," may rebel and find it erotic to do the very opposite. In many cases of exhibitionism, a man exposes himself "indecently" in order to insult or offend a woman who unconsciously represents the nagging mother image. This rebellion or protest at the unconscious, if not conscious level, against everything "clean" and "nice" accounts for the desire (in a sex deviate suffering from saliromania) to degrade or soil a woman. When a man calls a woman dirty names, this is also a disguised form of saliromania. While it is separately categorized as "coprolalia," it can be regarded as akin to saliromania.

Dr. Magnus Hirschfeld describes a case of an army officer who could get sexual satisfaction only by having a prostitute daub herself in a tub of dirty oil.

Saliromania, as a form of sexual sadism, is apt to occur among persons subjected to overstrict parental discipline, or who have been rejected by their mothers or jilted during courtship.

Here, in Washington, D.C., statues of female nudes in public parks are occasionally defiled. One such statue suddenly acquired a brassière and ladies' underpants. While that was not exactly an act of besmirching, it was an act of derision causing spectators to laugh instead of admire the nude feminine form.

In more violent types of saliromania, a man may throw acid into the face of the woman who rejects him. You may recall reading about a movie actress who was threatened by her ex-lover that he would *disfigure* her beauty by scarring her face if she continued to ignore him. He was killed before his threat was carried out.

In certain husbands suffering from premature ejaculation,

analysis reveals that the spilling of the semen upon the woman's body before penetration was unconsciously motivated by a sadistic desire not only to leave the wife sexually ungratified but to "soil" her. In one case the wife was a dominating, agressive woman and the husband felt "castrated." He expressed his resentment by ejaculating prematurely over her thighs. Such cases can be classified as saliromania or its equivalent.

A case of exhibitionism which was reported and published by Dr. Caprio in a psychiatric journal, involved a young man whose sexual development during adolescence was traumatized by his mother's nudity. His mother used the bathroom without closing the door; when taking a shower, she would parade in front of him in the nude while combing her hair, never suspecting that this was dangerous. In later years, her son was arrested for exposing himself before women in a public bus. In subsequent psychiatric interviews, he disclosed that he had used his mother's underclothes to masturbate with, afterwards tearing them. After intensive psychotherapy, he was able to make a normal adjustment to the opposite sex.

Today, psychiatrists are convincing many judges that sex deviates are sick individuals in need of psychotherapy. Sending them to prison does not cure them. The interest of society is better served by having such offenders *rehabilitated* by adequate treatment rather than sentencing them to jail. Fortunately, the public is now becoming aware of the realities in these phenomena. And sex deviates after reading about the cause of their sexual neuroses, seek psychiatric treatment voluntarily.

It is gratifying that knowledge pertaining to the causes of sex sickness is being made more accessible to the reading public. It is only in this manner (realistic sex education) that we can foster healthier sexual relations.

chapter nine

INCEST

Discussion

Incest involves sexual relations or intimacies between members of the immediate family; mother and son, father and daughter, brother and sister.

The term originates from the Latin "incestum" or unchaste. "Incestum" refers to the "cestus" or "girdle" of Venus. In marriage this girdle was loosened by the husband as an omen of felicity. For any male in the family other than the husband to loosen the girdle constituted a violation of the cestus, or incest.

Psychodynamics

In a study of 203 incest cases, Dr. S. Kirson Weinberg, observes that overcrowding in homes raises the incidence of this crime. He also found that father-daughter incest occurred more frequently where the father dominated the household; mother-son incest where the mother dominated; and sibling (brother-sister incest) where parental domination was weak. Dr. Weinberg observes that generally the aggressive participants in incest are sex deviants inclined to drunkenness; they are impulsive, high-strung, nervous, irritable, lonely, and moody. Some are psychotic. In many instances the incestuous relationship includes various "perverse" practices such as fellatio, cunnilingus, and sadomasochistic acts.

The incest behavier is either motivated by overpossessive "love" or sexual lust. In his conclusions, Weinberg emphasizes the fact that the revlusion to incest is social rather than biological. As one might expect, incestuous relations generally produce sexual rivalries and disrupt family cohesions, and they have a direct traumatic influence on the personality stability of the persons involved. Because of these complications, which in turn bring about a loss of good social attitudes ("societal cohesion," to use Dr. Weinberg's term), incest has bad social effects which account for the almost universal taboos against it.

The problem of incest is interrelated with homosexuality. Unconscious incestuous urges are at the root of many heterosexual difficulties such as impotence and frigidity. It has been suggested by some psychoanalysts of the Freudian school that many sexual deviations stem from incestuous conflicts and fixations.

Dr. Benjamin Karpman thus explains this interrelationship: "The patient confronted with an incestuous fixation on the one hand and the incest barrier on the other, finds it necessary to effect a compromise that enables him to avoid or circumvent direct incestuous activities but, nevertheless, permits him to indulge his incestuous desires indirectly and perhaps symbolically. Thus, a man who has a fixation on his mother is terrified not only at the idea of having sexual relations with her but even at the idea of having them with any other woman, because every woman is actually or potentially a mother and, therefore, brings to his mind a picture of his own mother. Since libido must find an outlet, he resorts to the expedient of indulging in sex relations that will completely exclude the vaginal orifice. Consequently, he may indulge in fellatio, cunnilingus, or paederasty, which to him appear to completely remove the chosen activity from any implication of incest (we are of course discussing an unconscious mental process)."

Many male patients indulge in dreams and fantasies of sexual acts other than coitus with their mother or sisters. Thus, even in the unconscious, there is dream-censorship that bars incestuous coitus. In such fantasies, deviations become a safeguard against impregnating the mother or sister. This would tend to support Dr. Karpman's hypothesis. Stekel presented numerous cases of homosexuals who resorted to paraphilic (deviant) sexual practices in unconscious flight from incest.

CASE HISTORIES

One of the authors had the opportunity, together with another psychiatrist, of interviewing and examining a man who had had incestuous relations with his two daughters. He was facing the death penalty on a charge of rape and incest. The psychiatrist for the state found that the prisoner was sane and could distinguish right from wrong and that he was therefore responsible for his acts. We examined the prisoner and came to a contrary conclusion. We found him psychotic and advised that he be committeed to a mental institution. The judge accepted our opinion, disregarding the report of the state psychiatrist, and the prisoner was committed to a mental hospital.

The prisoner's wife, whom we interviewed, furnished the following information about her husband:

"My husband demanded intercourse every two or three days. After intercourse, he sometimes masturbated. He often wanted and tried sexual intercourse a half-dozen times. He used his mouth on my sex parts, but never asked me to put my mouth on his organ. He was extremely jealous. When he was in the Army, he thought that I cheated on him and made the threat that, if he ever caught me, he would kill me.

He once brought home some 'dirty' pictures and wanted to carry out some of the acts shown in the pictures. I never knew that he touched my daughters sexually. I did not know that before marriage he once tried to get fresh with his sister. He complained of frequent headaches. While in prison, after he had been arrested, he told me that he heard voices. He was very jealous of my daughers and forbade their going out on dates. He threatened the girls with bodily harm, telling them that he would kill them if they told on him. He often beat them and said that he got enjoyment out of doing it. He said that certain marks on his fingernails had disappeared since he was placed in jail. My younger daughter said he had intercourse with her two or three times a week. He would come home in the afternoon, when she returned from school, to have relations with her."

From the above, it appears that the patient suffered from satyriasis. He was constantly preoccupied with sexual fantasies, and never experienced full sexual satisfaction. He received sadistic gratification from beating his daughters. His hallucinatory experiences were of long standing, not the result of a confinement psychosis. It was our conclusion that he had been suffering from a schizophrenic type of psychosis and that his incestuous relations with his daughters were symptom-manifestations of his illness.

His sister, who we also interviewed, supplied us with the following information:

"I have an aunt who has been in a mental institution for many years. My brother tried twice to get fresh with me. I noticed that he would often stare into space. When he was nine years old, he pulled a knife on my mother.

"He came into my bedroom and was exposed. He had a stare on his face that frightened me. I told him to get out of my room, which he did. He never did well in school, claiming that he couldn't learn. He once ran away from home, and they had to broadcast over the radio that he was missing. He was afraid to go to church and was afraid of the priest. He was extremely jealous of me. When mother visited him in jail, he said, 'Mama, is it a sin to love my children?' He didn't think he did anything wrong and said to mother, 'Why are they doing this to me?' One time he thought someone was going to attack him, and he had a nightmare in his sleep. He told his daughters one time, 'I'll scar your legs so no one will look at them.' On another occasion, when I visited him in jail with his wife, I noticed that he had an erection while talking to us. He was never close to my father, who ruled with an iron hand. He could never take criticism. He threatened suicide in jail and asked his wife to bring him some iodine to kill himself with."

His suicidal threats are in keeping with his sadomasochism. His insight is extremely defective; he feels that he did nothing wrong and that his desire to have intercourse with his daughters was an expression of his great love for them. We found evidence of a pronounced Oedipus complex with a strong latent homosexual component.

The older daughter, Loraine, at first was reluctant to discuss the matter with us. She finally realized that we were trying to determine the nature of her father's mental illness, and she then told us the following:

"My father always carried a big pocket knife. I found out that he once pulled a knife on my sister. He was always beating my sister with his fists. She was covered with bruises. I was twelve years old when he raped me. However, the first time he bothered me was when I was ten, and he had come out of the army. When he raped me, I didn't scream. I was too afraid. He said, 'If you tell your mother on me, they will put me in jail.' He had relations with me about twice a month. Once a month he would put his mouth to my sex parts and wanted me to put my mouth on his organ. He would suck my breasts and bite them. One time I was afraid I was pregnant, and he began to hit me. Once, when he beat me, he made me bleed and licked the blood off my arm, bit my finger, and said, 'What would you do if the three of us got together?' My sister told me everything a week before he was arrested. She decided to tell the priest, and I felt relieved. I remember, also, that he would have intercourse three or four times in one afternoon, one time after another. Another time, he wanted our dog to have intercourse with me. He had rectal intercourse with me twice. He also wanted me to relieve him with my hand. He was never drunk when he had sex relations with me. He also said that he would kill me if anyone else would touch me. Then he would cry and promise not to touch me again."

When we questioned him, he reiterated that he loved his children and could not help himself and that he did what he did because of his love for them.

During our interviews with him, he wept and said that if he was released the next day he would repeat his incestuous relations, and that he could not trust himself, that his sex urges were uncontrollable. In fact, he admitted that, even though he realized that he was faced with the death penalty and had been told about the seriousness of his crime, he found himself compelled to masturbate while in prison and his masturbation was accompanied by sexual thoughts of his daughters.

Had the judge not been convinced that this man was suffering from a mental illness, had he accepted the opinion of the psychiatrist employed by the state, he would have subjected the state to heavy trial costs only to arrive at the same conclusion—that the man was insane and needed to be committed to a mental institution.

INCEST AND THE LAW

The legal aspects of the crime of incest are not generally as complicated as other sexual crimes, but the laws of various states differ both as to the concepts of the crime and the penalties imposed on convicted offenders.

Incest is the crime of sexual cohabitation between persons related within a degree wherein marriage is prohibited by law, and this, in turn, is based on Biblical prohibitions. Originally, incest cases fell under the jurisdiction of the ecclesiastical courts; there were no provisions covering it in common law. Our modern legal principles, consequently, expressed in statutory enactments were influenced by the ecclesiastical tradition.

Although it was practiced in ancient Egypt without restraint, and today there are African and Indonesian tribes which sanction the practice, incest is considered heinous in most cultures. In ancient Babylonia, incest was strictly forbidden, and death was the punishment for convicted offenders in England during the 17th century. Today, however, English law makes incest merely a misdemeanor.

Some statutory prohibition against incest exists in every state in the union, but the provisions have evolved from two separate concepts of the incestuous relationship. One focuses on the act of sexual intercourse between persons related within the degree where marriage is prohibited by law; the other focuses on the marriage, which entails penalties even where no intercourse has occurred.

As a result of this rather odd statutory development, there is no consistency among the states as to which of the two acts constitutes the incest. Some states have written their laws with the act of intercourse as the chargeable offense; others restrict the chargeable offenders to those related by blood; others include in-law relations among the offenders; and in others, incest is chargeable when there is marriage or sexual intercourse.

In eleven states, sexual intercourse is the basis for the crime, with no mention of marriage. The remaining states provide that either intercourse or marriage constitutes the crime, although three states provide separate penalties for each. It may be noted that the penalty for intercourse, in such cases, is greater than for mere marriage.

The penalties for incest range from one year and/or a fine of $500 in Virginia to a maximum prison sentence of fifty years in both California and New Mexico.

There is an occasional case reported of an incestuous relationship wherein the parties did not have knowledge of their relationship. Because of public policy, it is generally held that knowledge is not necessary to constitute the crime, although actual prosecution in such cases is rare and usually not resorted to.

chapter ten

PROSTITUTION

HISTORICAL BACKGROUND

The word "prostitution" comes from the Latin "prostituere" meaning "to lay out, expose," implying "to stand in a public place and offer one's wares, or offer one's body." A "prostituta" was a harlot. The term had specific reference to the "bartering of the female body." "Passim et sine dilectu" (indiscriminately and without pleasure) in the words of an early Roman law.

Ulpianus defined prostitution as follows: "A woman publicly plies the trade of prostitution, not only when she prostitutes herself in a house of ill fame, but also when she frequents the wineshops or other places, without proper regard for her honor. By this is to be understood the trade of those women who prostitute themselves to all comers and without choice. The term does not apply to married women who are guilty of adultery nor to girls who suffer themselves to be seduced. By it is meant prostituted women. She who publicly prostitutes herself, even without accepting money, is to be classed with those women who make an open trade of prostitution."

Prostitution has often been referred to as the "oldest profession." In the beginning, it was carried out in religious temples where women sacrificed their virginity to the Gods.

247

This period of so-called "sacred prostitution" was succeeded by "profane prostitution."

Solon, the Greek statesman who lived in Athens about 550 B. C., is considered the first public administrator to establish public, licensed brothels which in those days were called "Dicteria." From the taxes collected by the licensed brothels, Solon built a temple to the Goddess Aphrodite.

Today, commercialized prostitution exists in most parts of the world.

CALL-GIRL PROSTITUTION

Isadore Rubin, in an interesting article, "The Sordid Business" (*Sexology,* July, 1959) reviewed some of the facts about call-girl prostitution which had been previously revealed in a sensational radio broadcast (CBS) by Edward R. Murrow. In today's industrial society, he observes, prostitution takes a new form—the large scale use of high-priced call girls in big business, sales, and promotion.

To quote from the article: "A broker described how he had arranged for two girls to meet several purchasing agents. They were to let the man know that they were being treated to a paid professional performance. They were to play the part of show girls who were separated or divorced from their husbands and to flatter the men's egos by making them think they had really made a conquest.

"The result was a deal that netted the broker about $60,000."

We agree with Judge Anna Kross, Commissioner of Correction of New York, that police action per se is not the most effective approach to the problem of this kind of prostitution. Commissioner Kross points out that "prostitutes are not criminals and cannot be rehabilitated by an archaic, unsound, criminal procedure which robs the individual of her dignity as a human being."

Clinical studies prove that prostitutes are emotionally sick individuals and that their activities must be treated as manifestations of sickness. It is more intelligent to rehabilitate and re-educate the prostitute than to impose a fine which she can easily pay or a prison term which, experience shows, seldom has any good effect.

The Psychology of the Prostitute

In many instances, prostitution represents a form of pseudo heterosexuality resorted to in a flight from homosexual repressions. In short, many prostitutes are latent homosexuals indulging in sexual excesses with many men to convince themselves that they are heterosexual. In the course of their careers as prostitutes, a large percentage of them eventually feel no further need of the pseudoheterosexual defense and turn to Lesbian love.

While this hypothesis, namely, that prostitutes for the most part are latent Lesbians has been advanced by earlier investigators such as Lombroso, Moll, Carlier, Martineau, and others, there has never been any conclusive clinical data to substantiate it. Most of the literature on prostitution deals with the historical and sociological aspects of the subject; none deals specifically with the interrelationship between prostitution and female homosexuality.

Dr. Caprio had long felt that this subject required further investigation, particularly, with respect to the prevalence or nonprevalence of Lesbian practices among prostitutes. Some years ago, he conducted such an investigation in the major cities of the United States and Canada, interviewing professional prostitutes in brothels. In the spring of 1953, he returned from a tour around the world during which he interviewed prostitutes in the following cities: Havana, Cuba; Panama City, Panama; London, England; Paris, France; Vienna, Austria; Venice, Genoa, Naples, Rome, and Capri, Italy;

Honolulu, Hawaii; Tokyo, Japan; Manila, Philippine Islands; Singapore and Penang, Malay Peninsula; Hong Kong; Bombay, India; Cairo, Egypt. Wherever necessary, he engaged the services of a taxi driver who acted as an interpreter during the interviews with the prostitutes. However, his knowledge of French and Italian enabled him to conduct interviews without such assistance in a number of countries.

Lesbianism among prostitutes existed in all parts of the world. Wherever Dr. Caprio went, he found two or more prostitutes in each brothel who indulged in Lesbian activities during the intervals when they were not servicing men. These were carried out either for their own gratification or as paid performances. The audience consisted mostly of men but sometimes, couples were to be seen among the spectators.

The fact that prostitutes engage in Lesbian practices for their own gratification is not too surprising when one realizes that most prostitutes are frigid in their relations with men. (By frigid, we mean inability to experience a coital orgasm.) Forced to have sex relations with all kinds of men, whether or not they appeal to them, many prostitutes develop an aversion toward the opposite sex. Prostitutes who share this aversion and obtain no gratification from intercourse with their clients, sooner or later find that they are able to bring each other to a mutual sexual climax.

This is corroborated by Polly Adler, Madam of a famous brothel, whose memoirs received sensational publicity several years ago. Miss Adler observed: "Inevitably I had a few Lesbians, some of them troublemakers, some very peaceful souls. It's often been said that a prostitute becomes so tired of being mauled by men that she turns to a woman for tenderness. Maybe so, I have no figures on the incidence of female homosexuality, but it's my observation that it occurs in every walk of life."

The majority of prostitutes, who were interviewed in

brothels all over the world, frankly admitted that they were unable to achieve an orgasm with a male customer even in instances where he was physically attractive. But they simulated a passionate response so as not to disappoint the customer, knowing from experience that men deceived in this way were more apt to return.

Polly Adler further wrote: "Actually, of course, despite all the feigned transports of ecstasy (for purposes of increasing the tip) to ninety-nine out of a hundred girls, going to bed with a customer is a joyless, even distasteful, experience."

It is well known, of course, that some prostitutes have a "boy friend" usually one who is engaged in procuring customers. With these special lovers, the prostitutes are, in some cases, able to respond sexually. However, the majority of prostitutes interviewed told Dr. Caprio that they obtained their own sexual gratification either through solitary masturbation or through sexual intimacies with another prostitute.

The incidence of Lesbianism among prostitutes is especially high in countries where competition for business is keen and many must wait a long time between customers. This, it was reported, accounted for widespread Lesbianism among prostitutes in Tokyo and Bombay.

The prevalence of Lesbianism in brothels throughout the world has convinced us that prostitution, as a behavior deviation, largely appeals to women with a strong latent homosexual component. Through prostitution, these women eventually overcome their homosexual repressions.

We are further convinced, as we have already observed, that prostitutes, by and large, are victims of unresolved bisexual conflicts, that their flight into sexual intimacies with many men, rationalized by the profit motives, is symptomatic evidence of their fear of their own unconscious homosexual desires. As one might surmise, the majority of prostitutes come from homes disturbed by parental incompatibility. Having been deprived of a normal love relationship during childhood with their mother and father, their basic feeling of insecurity unconsciously impels them to seek out the affection of both sexes via intimacies with both men and women.

Since all prostitutes are frustrated, they attempt to find consolation for their feelings of insecurity and basic need for affection by seeking the love of some member of their own sex. They will either assume the role of the feminine-passive, love-starved daughter seeking the love of an older mother-surrogate, or they will take on the role of the Lesbian mother and seek out the love of some young girl who becomes their daughter-surrogate. In the latter case, the older woman is bestowing upon the younger girl the affection she was deprived of as a daughter.

Further evidence of the bisexual conflict in the prostitute can be found in the relationship between her and the special "lover" or the exceptional male client who falls in love and wishes to take her out of a life of prostitution. Such a relationship represents a need for father love. As observed by Dr. Wilhelm Stekel, Lesbianism often represents a flight from repressed incestuous desires.

In those instances where prostitutes do not engage in Lesbian activities, it is not because, unconsciously, they would not want to; the explanation lies in the fact that they have never been able to break through their homosexual repressions. They are unable to appreciate the fact that their pseudo-heterosexuality is in itself evidence of their strong homosexual component. Many prostitutes reported that, when they first entered into a life of prostitution, they never thought they would ever engage in homosexual activities. As the years went by, they became more and more aware of homosexual leanings which they previously did not wish to recognize, and ultimately they became active Lesbians.

There is still much more to be learned about the psychology

of the prostitute and, especially, its relationship to female homosexuality, if we are ever to handle the problem successfully.

PSYCHO-LEGAL CONSIDERATIONS

There are many who believe that prostitution, in one form or another, will always be with us, that it can never be completely abolished. That is why it has been referred to as a "necessary evil."

Formerly, girls of the "red-light districts" had very little education and their I.Q's were generally low. The modern prostitute often has an above-average education. Today, the "street walker" is being replaced by the "call girl."

Regulation by licensing, with compulsory periodic health examinations, has not proved successful. Regulation via "red-light districts" has many disadvantages. It promotes political corruption and intensifies the exploitation of the prostitute.

There are laws against prostitution in every state. Many convicted prostitutes are fined and sent to workhouses.

In an editorial in the June 8, 1957 issue of its *Journal,* the American Medical Association re-endorsed a resolution originally passed in 1942:

"First, that the control of venereal disease requires elimination of commercialized prostitution; second, that medical inspection of prostitutes is untrustworthy, inefficient, gives a false sense of security, and fails to prevent the spread of infection; third, that commercialized prostitution is unlawful and physicians who knowingly examine prostitutes for the purpose of providing them with medical certificates to be used in soliciting are participating in an illegal activity and are violating the principles of accepted professional ethics."

After a careful study of the pros and cons of prostitution, we are of the opinion that legalized prostitution has more disadvantages than advantages.

THE UNITED NATIONS COMMITTEE REPORT

In an article which appeared in *Ace* (October, 1959) entitled "Why U.N. Raps U.S. on Vice Girls," Loren B. Spangler is of the opinion that we Americans are the most advanced people on the face of the earth in every field but one—our attitude toward prostitution.

The United Nations issued a report recently under the title "The Supression of the Traffic in Persons and of the Exploitation of the Prostitution of Others" (Issued by the U.N. Economic and Social Council).

We agree with the author of this article that it would be wiser and more scientific to regard prostitution as a form of sex sickness rather than a crime. It would be much more effective, in the long run, to attack the causes of prostitution, treating the prostitute as a sick person in need of psychiatric treatment rather than as a criminal.

Having a policeman in plain clothes escort a girl to her place of business, watch her undress, give her money, and then arrest her is, according to the author of the article, a bad way of dealing with prostitution. We agree. Under such a system, there is likelihood of cases coming to court, charging entrapment. It also exposes detectives to bribery and other temptations.

"The practice used in certain countries of entrusting the detection of such offenses to a special police vice squad or to plain-clothes police officers cannot be commended.

"Many people doubt even the wisdom or justice of accepting in such cases the evidence presented by the police officer who has prepared the charge, and the courts before whom the cases are brought generally frown on such methods of police espionage and entrapment."

Max Lerner, columnist of the New York *Post,* concurs. He feels that city and state officials should "combine forces in pushing for the U.N. proposal; namely, that prostitution as a crime should be abolished from our statute books and think-ing." He adds: "Our police should find other and better things to do than to tap call-girls' wires and make raids on them, and we should turn our energies to some of the sources from which the prostitute (full-time and part-time) springs."

Both Mrs. Anna Kross, Commissioner of Correction of New York City, and Chief Magistrate John M. Murtah claim: "The traditional police approach to the problem of prostitution is futile and corrupting."

It is interesting to note that the report of the U.N. indicates that in Soviet Russia, "radical changes took place in the country which included the elimination of unemployment, the intensification of social services, the raising of the level of living, and the realization of the full equality of men and women. The U.S.S.R., has observed that these changes have eliminated the conditions giving rise to prostitution; namely material insecurity and the lack of legal safeguards for women."

The report contends: "Governments should enact legislation for the abolishment of any form of the regulation of prosti-tution, and particularly for the closing of licensed or tolerated houses."

The United Nations Committee further states: "The most effective way to eradicate a social scourge is to remove its cause. . . . Women become prostitutes through inclination, need or persuasion. But the final decision . . .is determined by their mentality and the circumstances of their environment.

"Prostitutes have generally slight mental or physical ab-normalities (instability, abnormal lack of emotion, excita-bility, pronounced nervousness) and a great number of them suffer from psychosexual immaturity. The number of prosti-tutes who are psychologically and emotionally normal appears to be very limited. On the other hand, the number who are actually 'feeble-minded' is relatively low.

"Most prostitutes," according to the report, "start their

calling at an early age and there is evidence in recent years of increasing prostitution among girls of fifteen or younger."

There exists a close interrelationship also between prostitution, alcoholism, and narcotic addiction. Approximately 50 percent of the prostitutes are drug addicts.

Statistics show that 69 percent of the male population of the United States has some experience with prostitutes. The U.N. Committee states: "The relationship between the prostitute and the customer is by no means the meeting of an abnormal and a normal individual, but both show deficient integration in the structure of their personalities and of their sexual behavior."

chapter eleven

SEX AND CENSORSHIP

Evidence of erotica occurs in virtually every civilization in history. Through the ages, "sexual love" has been depicted in works of art. In India, carvings in ancient temples depict varied sexual practices.

In the Berlin Museum, there is a vase described by Furtwangler: "A naked woman is in the act of binding her sandal on her left foot; she is bending forward, draws the red bands towards her with both hands, and, in order to be nearer her foot, has let herself down partly on her right knee, so that the space is admirably filled. A flat basin at her feet hints that she has just washed herself. On her right can be recognized the outline of a large phallus in the open space turned towards her."

In the Berlin Aquarium, there is a red-figured painting on an Attic Hydria (water vessel) of the fifth century B.C. It represents a naked girl with full breasts and still fuller buttocks, carrying a gigantic phallus in the form of a fish under the left arm.

A collector of erotic sculptures, including an original by Rodin, paintings, and drawings permitted us to view his unique collection, the most outstanding of its kind in the country. It contains evidence, in art representations, that homosexual practices existed in different races, cultures, and periods.

In a recently published book dealing with erotica, by Ralph Ginsberg*, Dr. Theodor Reik, prominent psychoanalyst, wrote in the introduction:

"If erotica exercises such a passionate spell and awakens such general interest can we still say 'ugly as sin.' It seems sin is very attractive to most, if not to all of us. If it were as repulsive and ugly as they say, why should so many and forceful prohibitions be necessary."

Another well-known analyst, Dr. Benjamin Karpman, writing in the *Journal* of the American Medical Association, notes:

"Contrary to popular misconception, people who read salacious literature are less likely to become sexual offenders than those who do not, for the reason that such reading often neutralizes what aberrant sexual interests they may have."

Alec Craig, in his brilliant review of antiobscenity law, predicts that society's attitude toward erotica will become more realistic:

"Our society allows any amount of sexual stimulation at all times by poster, newspaper, cinema, theatre, and women's dress in public; but it frowns on sexual satisfaction and aids thereto. In the society of the future (if indeed men are advancing to a better world), I believe that this emphasis will be reversed. Life will be less sex-obsessed but, at proper times and seasons, physical love will be restored to its ancient dignity, variety, and gaiety. Both modesty and the art of love will come into their own again. In that society, the erotic book, we may expect, will play a part."

According to Ralph Ginsberg, collections of erotica are to be found in the Library of the Vatican in Rome (25,000 volumes and 100,000 prints), the British Museum in London (20,000 volumes), the Institute for Sex Research at Indiana University, the Bibliotheque Nationale in Paris, the Library of

---

* *An Unhurried View of Erotica* by Ralph Ginsberg, Helmsman Press, New York, 1958.

Congress (5,000 erotic works), the New York Academy of Medicine, and the New York State Psychiatric Institute.

In the course of my travels through the Scandinavian countries, including Finland and Denmark, I was surprised to note the acceptance of nudity in works of art. There are no fig leaves on the many nude statues in the public squares and parks. The people evidently have a healthy attitude toward nudity. Most American tourists marvel at the frankness with which sight-seeing guides point out nude sculptures.

Perhaps we could learn from the Scandinavians. It is often censorship that intensifies the eroticism of a work of art. Paradoxically, a fig leaf incites greater curiosity and intensifies the very condition it is supposed to allay. Realism in art is wholesome learning, the healthy impression that nothing is really obscene in itself. The nude (male and female) forms are portrayed as something beautiful.

At newsstands in the Scandinavian countries, picture magazines of men and women in the nude are sold, and many of the pictures show the pubic hair. In the United States, the pubic hair in a picture is sufficient to have it condemned as obscene, and, in some cases, women's breasts may be shown only if the nipple is removed from the drawing or the photograph.

In Europe, erotic art seldom involves any problems. For one thing, no one gives it that much importance. The emphasis is placed on the beauty of the anatomical figure. To conclude that a picture of a nude woman is *art* if it shows no pubic hair, and is *obscene* if it does show hair, is rather ridiculous. We smile at the thought that a Mohammedan woman would feel less embarrassment by having the lower part of her body bared than her veiled face. But Europeans similarly smile at us for letting pubic hair become the deciding factor as to what constitutes obscenity. It is even more amusing when we consider that the portrayal of female buttocks is regarded as not obscene, while the front view of the female body *is* so regarded.

PORNOGRAPHY AND OBSCENITY

Pornography refers to "obscenity" in art and literature. The term is derived from the Greek word "porne" meaning prostitute and "graph" meaning writing. The term obscenity is derived from the Latin "obscenus" meaning ill-looking or filthy. It has come to imply that which is indecent, immoral, and corrupting.

Unfortunately, scientific books dealing with case studies of sexual pathology were originally condemned as "pornographic." In recent years, however, the courts decided that this contravened scientific freedom and common sense and allowed their publication. Thus, such works as Havelock Ellis' *Studies in the Psychology of Sex* are now available.

Pornography, as a sexual deviation, applies to those sexual deviates who, for the purpose of monetary gain, print and sell pictures of nude men and women indulging in sexual intercourse or other acts of sexual intimacy to purchasers who seek sexual excitement by such means. The same holds true for literature which similarly stimulates sexual urges and which contributes nothing to science. Such writings describe sexual intimacies in obscene or leering language.

Pornography attracts many persons because it gratifies the residue of the infantile, polymorphous, perverse sexuality in every human being. It gratifies morbid impulses for the forbidden; in others, pornographic literature stimulates the sexual fantasies and provokes masturbation.

The libido of persons who are morbidly interested in or collect pornographic art and literature is fixated at the paraphilic (sexually deviated) level.

A so-called normal person would not traffic in pornography. The person who risks going to jail for selling obscene material suffers from an unconscious sexual neurosis. He rationalizes that he is in the business or "racket" of pornography solely for monetary gain, but at the unconscious level, it represents an expression of his unresolved latent homosexual component. Like the prostitute who deludes herself into believing that she is in the "business" only for the money, the dealer in pornography is unaware of the fact that he is a victim of unconscious motivations. He is a sex deviate (scoptophiliac) who derives erotic satisfaction from looking at obscene pictures depicting various kinds of sexual practices. A certain curiosity in obscene material exists in many normal individuals. But the normal person would never become involved in selling such material. The pornographer, on the other hand, may be suffering from impotence, obtaining his sexual gratification at the psychic masturbation level via paraphilic fantasies.

A twenty-five-year-old man came to analysis because he was unable to ejaculate during coitus. His attractive young wife was deeply distressed by her husband's sexual disorder, since she wanted children.

In the course of his analytic sessions, the patient brought a collection of pornographic pictures which he had amassed over a period of five years. He used them in secret masturbation, and his wife did not know about them.

His mother ran a boarding house, and when the patient was a child, he peeped into the rooms to watch the boarders dress and undress. In addition, he was an only child, and there was a neurotic intensity in his attachment to his mother. One of the symptoms of the neurosis was his need to look at obscene pictures as a means of confirming his potency. His libido was fixated in his "harem" of nude women in the pictures (psychic infidelity). In actual coitus with his wife, the incest taboo blocked him from ejaculating.

In the course of treatment, he gained insight into his latent homosexuality, his Oedipus Complex, and other fixations; he was able to give up his collection of pornography and the masturbation to which it was an accessory; and after that he succeeded in ejaculating and impregnating his wife.

The dissemination of pornographic literature has increased

in recent years. A report of the U.S. Senate Subcommittee to Investigate Juvenile Delinquency revealed that the traffic in pornography has risen from $100,000,000 to $300,000,000 annually, that dealers in this business depend upon school children for their profits, and that such pornography has been directly connected with juvenile sex offenses. Commenting on this report, John Carleton in a magazine article, "Pornography: It's Flooding Our Schools," (*Pageant*, July, 1955) adds that in Buffalo, New York, a man was seized while distributing 500 rolls of pornographic "party" film; and, in one haul, Detroit police confiscated pornographic material with a retail value of more than a million dollars.

Thus pornography, as a business, exploits and traumatizes school children for monetary gain. The pictures circulated among them are often of a sadomasochistic nature, promoting these unwholesome trends among children. Indeed, pictures of semi-clad women in chains being whipped or tortured are permitted to be advertised in magazines sent through the mails. No one can possibly defend such traffic, and one can only approve the three bills dealing with this problem now pending in Congress. One has already received Senate approval. Such measures should be differentiated from measures continuing or setting up censorship of art and literature.

In the *Washington Star* (January 28, 1959), there appeared a news item captioned "Anti-Pornography Bill Strikes at Production." It referred to a bill sponsored by Senator Kefauver of Tennessee, with Senators Carroll of Colorado, and Langer of North Dakota, as cosponsors, to curb pornography in the District of Columbia. The measure was hailed by Deputy Police Chief Roy E. Blick as a weapon to protect the city from pornography peddlers. Under the terms of the bill, the police would be free to seize equipment turning out obscene literature. This provision would enable them to confiscate one machine known to be producing 15,000 copies of a lewd booklet per hour.

"Unscrupulous characters who corrupt the morals of our young people for profit have been meted out small punishment indeed in the District," Senator Kefauver said when introducing the bill. He said police officers had testified at hearings that the sentences against "purveyors of indecent materials" were generally from $100 fine or 60 days' imprisonment to $250 or 90 days. "In some instances," said Senator Kefauver, "such fines can be paid out of the profits garnered in a short time with little effort by the pornographer."

His bill was aimed at depriving such pornographers of their manufacturing or sales machinery. According to Chief Blick, this would help cripple distribution.

Holman Harvey, author of "Help Stamp Out This Vile Traffic,"* writes: "Obscene photographs and lewd movies for 'private showing' aimed at school children, circulate by the millions and constitute a dangerous threat to the morals of our youth. . . . Today and every day, a torrent of some 200,000 circulars, offering this obscenity for sale, will pour into our cities and towns—by mail, by express, and by thousands of peddlers on foot and in cars. The U.S. Post Office Department estimates that last year's organized traffic in pornography reached a peak value of *half a billion dollars.* . . . Three fourths of this immense output is skillfully aimed at and is reaching American school children from ages down to eleven and up through high-school age."

Some 50,000 parents wrote to the Post Office Department or to their senators and congressmen, urging that something be done about the matter.

There is a clear relationship between the dissemination of pornography and the incidence of crime. F.B.I. figures indicate that boys of eighteen and nineteen are committing more rapes today than males in any other age group. From a Massachusetts city comes the report that a teenager raped a sixteen-year-old girl. Search of his room revealed fifty pornographic

* Published in *Reader's Digest,* March, 1959.

pictures beneath his mattress. In Colorado, a student molesting two teen-age girls was found to have pornographic literature in the glove compartment of his car. And in a Pennsylvania city, the statement appeared: "Pornographic literature has stirred up male youths who then go out and commit 'gang rape.'"

Holman Harvey, in his concluding remarks, advises his readers: "Make sure your children receive a sound and sensible education in sex so that they can cope with any perversions that may be thrust upon them by the dirt peddlers."

Pornography has been referred to by newspaper reporters as a multimillion-dollar business. Its chief headquarters are in New York City and Los Angeles. The people in this business get a four percent return (cash-in-advance) from advertisements sent out to mailing lists. According to one report, more than fifty million circulars of this nature were mailed in 1958. Obscene films sell from $25 to $50. Obscene books sell from $3 to $25 each. Professional prostitutes are paid $50 for a performance in such films; "amateurs" receive $30.

Effective control requires the cooperation of the public. Said Chief Inspector Stephens of the Post Office Department recently: "We mean to present the cases as fast as we can get evidence. We need not just twenty or thirty circulars from a community but hundreds, if possible. Only in this way can we show, beyond doubt, that degrading and obscene mail penetrates many homes in a community. And only in this way can the law hope to be a real weapon against pornography."

The New York *Daily News*, in an article by Richard McGowan, reports that alert customs inspectors keep about fifty-thousand pieces of imported "smut" from reaching U.S. dealers and customers each year. Four special investigators serve the Port of New York under the direction of fifty-two-year-old Irving Fishman, whose official title is Deputy Collector of Customs. Every year approximately fifty thousand pieces of obscenity come into Fishman's office. Many negatives come from Sweden, Finland, Germany, and France.

Describing an incident where the smugglers attempted to fool the inspectors, Fishman said; "Recently we made a spot check on a shipment of cans of movie film. We ran some of it off. It went through the projector, foot after foot, and seemed to comprise nothing but Mickey Mouse cartoons. But some instinct made us keep the film running.

"It's a good thing we did. The middle section was about the filthiest stuff I've ever seen. It had been dressed up deliberately to try to fool us."

Efforts to keep out real smut can only be commended, but the effort to do so through the censorship of literature is both harmful and futile. Its futility was commented on by Henry Miller, author of *Tropic of Cancer*. In his experience, censorship defeats itself. We are inclined to agree. When a book is banned, attention is drawn to it, and its sales are stimulated.

In an article, "When Is a Book Obscene?" by Thomas B. Morgan (*Cosmopolitan*, August 1959), Henry Miller is quoted as follows: "As one accused of employing obscene language more freely and abundantly than any other living writer in the English language, it may be of interest to present my own views on the subject. Since the *Tropic of Cancer* first appeared in Paris, in 1934, I have received many hundreds of letters from readers all over the world; they are from men and women of all ages and all walks of life, and in the main are congratulatory messages. Many of those who denounce the book because of its gutter language professed admiration for it otherwise; very, very few ever remarked that it was a dull book or badly written. The book continues to sell steadily 'under the counter'—the only effect censorship has had upon its circulation is to drive it underground, thus limiting the sales but at the same time insuring for it the best of all publicity—word of mouth recommendation—it is a book which appeals especially to young people and which, from all that I gather directly and indirectly, not only does not ruin their lives, but increases their morale. The book is living proof that censorship defeats itself."

The paradox in censorship is that the censor is generally the book's best salesman. Often a publisher hopes that a book will be banned and its commercial success thereby assured. With the same motives, some authors set out to write a book that will be banned and then become a best seller.

An intelligent differentiation must be made between the kind of obscenity that has no relation to art or literature, which is published solely to make money through exploiting sexual urges, and that which is considered artistic and literary. To use such words as "dirty," "filthy," and "smut" of such work is wrong. In any case, the epithets merely stimulate interest in the censored work.

Today, we use the term "sexual deviations" in preference to "sexual perversions." We feel it would be more intelligent to avoid the connotation that there is a "dirty" or "filthy" side to sex.

Clergymen and other self-elected censors should not have the power to determine what is obscene and what is not obscene. If a committee is to be appointed, it should include an attorney, a psychiatrist, a sociologist, an educator, and perhaps other professional people capable of giving an objective opinion.

Merely negative censorious attitudes are being checked by our courts. A Spanish postage stamp featuring a nude (Goya's "The Naked Maja") became the center of a Post Office Department censorship dispute. United Artists, in their plans to release a film entitled "The Naked Maja," used in their publicity, reproductions of the masterpiece by Goya, one of the most treasured works of art in the Prado Museum in Spain. United Artists, protesting a Post Office ban, claimed: "There is nothing obscene about the great work of art" and pointed out that the Post Office Department has never before banned the used of reproductions of "The Naked Maja" in other publications, listing some thirty publications that have shown the pink-skinned nude without government interference, all the way back to 1923. Among these was a two-page, full-color spread of the painting in *Life*, in 1950 and a postage-stamp reproduction issued by the Spanish government and reprinted in stamp advertisements for many years.

The American Civil Liberties Union called on the Postmaster General to remove the ban contending it is a "restraint on freedom of expression guaranteed by the First Amendment."

Even more important was the case of the controversial novel, *Lady Chatterley's Lover* by D. H. Lawrence, which was declared not obscene in a federal court ruling. This will be commented upon in the legal aspects section of this chapter.

SEX CENSORSHIP IN MOTION PICTURES

The Motion Production Code was formulated and formally adopted by the Association of Motion Pictures Producers, Inc. (California) and the Motion Picture Association of America (New York) in March 1930. The Code as presented in part under the following headings contains all revisions and amendments through 1954.

General Principles

1. No picture shall be produced which will lower the moral standards of those who see it. Hence the sympathy of the audience shall never be thrown to the side of crime, wrongdoing, evil, or sin.

2. Correct standard of life, subject only to the requirements of drama and entertainment, shall be presented.

3. Law, natural or human, shall not be ridiculed, nor shall sympathy be created for its violation.

Sex

The sanctity of the institution of marriage and the home shall be upheld. Pictures shall not infer that low forms of sex relationship are the accepted or common thing.

1. Adultery and illicit sex, sometimes necessary plot material, must not be explicitly treated or justified, or presented attractively.

2. Scenes of Passion

a. These should not be introduced except where they are definitely essential to the plot.

b. Excessive and lustful kissing, lustful embraces, suggestive postures, and gestures are not to be shown.

c. In general, passion should be treated in such manner as not to stimulate the lower and baser emotions.

3. Seduction or Rape

a. These should never be more than suggested, and then only when essential for the plot. They must never be shown by explicit method.

b. They are never the proper subject for comedy.

4. Sex perversion or any inference of it is forbidden.

5. White slavery shall not be treated.

6. Abortion, sex hygiene, and venereal diseases are not proper subjects for theatrical motion pictures.

7. Scenes of actual childbirth, in fact or in silhouette, are never to be presented.

8. Children's sex organs are never to be exposed.

Vulgarity

The treatment of low, disgusting, unpleasant, though not necessarily evil subjects should be guided always by the dic-

tates of good taste and a proper regard for the sensibilities of
the audience.

Obscenity

Obscenity in word, gesture, reference, song, joke, or by
suggestion (even when likely to be understood only by part of
the audience) is forbidden.

Profanity

Pointed profanity and every other profane or vulgar expression, however used, are forbidden.

No approval by the Production Code Administration shall
be given to the use of words and phrases in motion pictures
including, but not limited to, the following:

Bronx cheer (the sound); chippie; God, Lord, Jesus Christ
(unless used reverently); cripes; fairy (in a vulgar sense);
finger (the); goose (in a vulgar sense); hot (applied to
women); in your hat; "Madam," relating to prostitution;
nuts (except when meaning crazy); pansy; razzberry (the
sound); s.o.b.; son-of-a; tart; toilet gags; whore.

It should also be noted that the words "hell" and "damn,"
if used without moderation, will be considered offensive by
many members of the audience. Their use, therefore, should
be governed by the discretion and the prudent advice of the
Code Administration.

Costumes

1. Complete nudity is never permitted. This includes nudity in fact or in silhouette or any licentious notice thereof by
other characters in the pictures.

2. Undressing scenes should be avoided and never used,
save where essential to the plot.

3. Indecent or undue exposure is forbidden.

4. Dancing costumes intended to permit undue exposure or indecent movement in the dance are forbidden.

Dances

1. Dances suggesting or representing sexual actions or indecent passion are forbidden.

2. Dances which emphasize indecent movements are to be regarded as obscene.

Locations

The treatment of bedrooms must be governed by good taste and delicacy.

Titles

The following titles shall not be used: titles which are salacious, indecent, obscene, profane, or vulgar.

In the preamble to the Code, the following appears:

MOTION PICTURES ARE VERY IMPORTANT AS ART

Though a new art, possibly a combination art, it has the same object as the other arts, the presentation of human thought, emotion, and experience, in terms of an appeal to the soul through the senses.

Here, as in entertainment, art enters intimately into the lives of human beings.

Art can be morally good, lifting men to higher levels. This has been done through good music, great painting, authentic fiction, poetry, drama. Art can be morally evil in its effects. This is the case clearly enough with unclean art, indecent books, suggestive drama. The effect on the lives of men and women is obvious. Note that it has often been argued that art in itself is unmoral, neither good nor bad. This is perhaps true of the thing which is music, painting, poetry, etc. But the thing is the product of some person's mind, and the intention of that mind was either good or bad morally when it produced the thing. Besides, the thing has its effect upon those who come into contact with it. In both these ways, that is, as a product of a mind and as the cause of definite effects, it has a deep moral significance and an unmistakable moral quality. Hence, the motion pictures, which are the most popular of modern arts for the masses, have their moral quality from the intention of the minds which produce them and from their effects on the moral lives and reactions of their audiences. This gives them a most important morality.

1. They produce the morality of the men who use the pictures as a medium for the expression of their ideas and ideals.

2. They affect the moral standards of those who, through the screen, take in these ideas and ideals.

In the case of the motion pictures, this effect may be particularly emphasized because no art has so quick and so widespread an appeal to the masses. It has become, in an incredibly short period, the art of the multitudes.

Under the heading of "Sex," the following appears:

Out of regard for the sanctity of marriage and the home, the triangle, that is, the love of a third party for one already married, needs careful handling. The treatment should not throw sympathy against marriage as an institution.

Scenes of passion must be treated with an honest acknowledgment of human nature and its normal reactions. Many scenes cannot be presented without arousing dangerous emotions on the part of the immature, the young, or the criminal classes.

Even within the limits of pure love, certain facts have been universally regarded by lawmakers as outside the limits of safe presentation.

In the case of impure love, the love which society has always regarded as wrong and which has been banned by divine law, the following are important:

1. Impure love must not be presented as attractive and beautiful.

2. It must not be the subject of comedy or farce or treated as material for laughter.

3. It must not be presented in such a way as to arouse passion or morbid curiosity on the part of the audience.

4. It must not be made to seem right and permissible.

5. In general, it must not be detailed in method and manner.

Recently the House of Delegates of the State of Maryland approved a compromise movie-censorship bill that would make it a crime for any one to show to persons under eighteen any movie that would be obscene for them.

LEGAL CONSIDERATIONS

The problem of the use of the mails to disseminate literature, books, articles, advertisements, scientific and medical matters, pictures and what have you which are considered pornographic or obscene in character and, therefore, nonmailable under law, has long been a concern of lawmakers. It remains today an intolerable, unsolvable, and bothersome dilemma. For it seems that no matter what the definitions and tests may be, as set down by the courts, these are constantly changing and being challenged. The result is an ever-changing structure of the relevant law and ever-shifting legal views on how best to cope with the problem.

There were common-law prohibitions against obscenity as far back as the 16th or 17th century when punishment was imposed for the exhibition of things then considered obscene. Our first federal law regulating obscenity and the publication and dissemination of obscene writings was put on the statute books in 1842. The problem persists.

In a magazine article published in August, 1957, J. Edgar Hoover stated that the traffic in illicit literature, commonly called pornographic, is a most lucrative business, probably reaching a dollar volume of about half a billion dollars a year. Law officers consider it a major cause of the rising rate of sex crimes in the country and Mr. Hoover, too considers it a major factor in sex violence all over the country. In crimes reported by police for cities with a population over 2,500, the number of persons involved in sex offenses rose from 38.5 per 100,000 in 1953, to 41.7 in 1954, 45.3 in 1955, and 47.5 in 1956.

While most states have statutes of some kind dealing with the dissemination of pornography and obscenity, the penalty on conviction is generally a light fine amounting to $50 or $100, which as observed earlier, does very little to discourage a peddler of this material from moving on to the next town and taking his chances, for the profits far outweigh the risks. Consequently, federal, rather than local regulation is, for the present, most important. However, although under federal law, it is a felony to use postal facilities for sending obscenity through the mails (or to transport the same by common carrier, i. e., trains or busses) there is no federal prohibition against the use of private vehicles for the same purpose. Smut peddlers, therefore, confine their activities locally where there are weak state or city laws.

In 1958, Public Law 85-796 amended parts of the then existing federal laws to make specific provision to stop up a gaping loophole. Hitherto, the pornographers could be arrested and tried only in the jurisdiction where the material was mailed. Consequently, dealers had sought out districts where the penalties were light or where prosecution was easy to evade. In the revised regulations, criminal responsibility is continued to the point of mail delivery so that wherever pornography is received, warrants of arrest can be issued against the purveyor.

One of the most important reasons for amending Title 18, Sec. 1461 and 1462, U.S. Code in 1958, stemmed from a court ruling in one case: United States vs. Ross, et al. (205 Fed. 2nd 619) which ruling promulgated the changes in the then existing federal statutes. Ross was indicted in Topeka, Kansas; Detroit, Michigan; and Los Angeles, California for mailing pictures of nude women in one state for delivery in another. The pictures were mailed in California for designation in Kansas and Michigan. The California courts acquitted Ross because the material was found not to be obscene there while, in Kansas, the indictment was dismissed because the courts ruled that, under existing law, a prosecution could only be maintained at the point of mailing inasmuch as the law then read: "Whoever knowingly *deposits for mailing* or delivery anything declared by this section to be nonmailable . . . ." Because of the dilemma caused by this case the changes made in 1958 were as follows:

Paragraph 8, Title 18, Sec. 1461, U.S. Code: Whoever knowingly *uses the mails for the mailing, carriage in the mails, or delivery* of anything declared by this section to be nonmailable, or knowingly causes to be delivered by mail according to the direction thereon, or at the place at which it is directed to be delivered by the person to whom it is addressed, or knowingly takes any such thing from the mails for the purpose of circulating or disposing thereof, or of aiding in the circulation or disposition thereof, shall be fined not more than $5,000, or imprisoned not more than 5 years, or both, for the first such offense, and shall be fined not more than $10,000, or imprisoned not more than 10 years, or both, for each such offense thereafter.

Similar changes were made in Sec. 1462.

Paragraph 1, Title 18, Sec. 1462, U.S. Code: Whoever brings into the United States, or any place subject to the jurisdiction thereof, or knowingly uses any express company or other common carrier, for carriage in interstate or foreign commerce—

Whoever knowingly takes from such express company or other common carrier any matter or thing the use of which for carriage is herein made unlawful—

Shall be fined not more than $5,000, or imprisoned not more than 5 years, or both, for the first offense and shall be fined not more than $10,000, or imprisoned not more than 10 years, or both, for each such offense thereafter.

That part of Title 18, Sec. 1461, defining what material is nonmailable has remained virtually unchanged through the years and is described as follows:

Every obscene, lewd, lascivious, indecent, filthy, or vile article, matter, thing, device, or substance; and

Every article or thing designed, adapted, or intended for preventing conception or producing abortion, or for any indecent or immoral use; and

Every article, instrument, substance, drug, medicine, or thing which is advertised or described in a manner calculated to lead another to use it for preventing conception or producing abortion, or for any indecent or immoral use; and

Every written or printed card, letter, circular, book, pamphlet, advertisement, or notice of any kind giving information, directly or indirectly, where, or how, or from whom, or by what means any of such mentioned matters, articles, or things may be obtained or made, or where or by whom any act or operation of any kind for the procuring or inducing of abortion will be done or performed, or how or by what means conception may be prevented or abortion produced, whether sealed or unsealed; and

Every paper, writing, advertisement, or representation that any article, instrument, substance, drug, medicine, or thing may, or can, be used or applied for preventing conception or producing abortion, or for any indecent or immoral purpose; and

Every description calculated to induce or incite a person to so use or apply any such article, instrument, substance, or drug, medicine or thing—is declared to be nonmailable matter and shall not be conveyed in the mails or delivered from any post office or by any letter carrier.

Title 18, Sec. 1462, states in part: Whoever brings into the U. S., or any place subject to the jurisdiction thereof, or knowingly uses any express company or other common carrier for carriage in interstate or foreign commerce—

a. Any obscene, lewd, lascivious, or filthy book, pamphlet, picture, motion-picture film, paper, letter, writing, print, or other matter of indecent character; or

b. Any obscene, lewd, lascivious, or filthy phonograph recording, electrical transcription, or other article or thing capable of producing sound; or

c. Any drug, medicine, article, or thing designed, adapted, or intended for preventing conception, or producing abortion, or for any indecent or immoral use; or any written or printed card, letter, circular, book, pamphlet, advertisement, or notice of any kind giving information, directly or indirectly, where, how, or of whom, or by what means any of such mentioned articles, matters, or things, may be obtained or made.

Title 18, Sec. 1463, deals with the mailing of indecent matters on wrappers or envelopes, and Sec. 1465 regulates the transportation, in interstate or foreign commerce, of obscene matters.

A case illustrative of how the change of law has affected the pornographer is the following:

From October 1958 through December 1958, about 15,000 solicitations were made by two Los Angeles men under the name of "Bill Prada," containing a come-on type letter with a nude picture of a woman. It is reported that in one five-week period they took in over $12,000.

Complaints were made to the Post Office Department from people in Massachusetts, Texas, Ohio, New York, New Jersey, California, Michigan, Pennsylvania, and other states. The two men were indicted in Minnesota on charges of 35 counts of mailing obscene matter in Minnesota, alone, and on charges of conspiracy to violate federal statutes against obscene mail.

Under the old law, they could have been prosecuted only at the point of origin, that being California, and conviction in that state would be difficult to obtain. However, under the revised law (Title 18, Sec. 1461, U.S. Code, as amended) prosecution was pressed in Minnesota, that is at the point where the material was received.

On October 8, 1959, Postmaster General Arthur E. Summerfield addressed The Women's Club of Cleveland, Ohio. The topic of his speech was "Obscenity In The Mails: How You Can Stop It."

Mr. Summerfield said, in part, the following: "This racket involves the use of the United States mails for the wholesale promotion and conduct of mail-order business and pornographic materials.

"I say it is huge advisedly. We can estimate at present that the sale of these materials through the mails is running at more than five hundred million dollars a year.

"The especially vicious aspect of this racket is the fact that these purveyors of filth are aiming their attention more and more at the nation's children—teen-age boys and girls, and even younger.

"They are dumping pornographic sewage into the hands of hundreds of thousands of our children through the family mailbox—most of it material that has not been ordered—material intended to solicit the sale of utterly obscene pictures, slides, films, and related trash.

"We have testified before the Congress that the purveyors of these vicious materials were aiming their racket more and more at our nation's children. We have pledged to Congress our intention to carry out an intense, continuing effort to stop the vast growth of this racket, and eventually to stamp it out entirely.

"Typical statements made before the Senate Committee on August 29, 1959, were those of Monsignor Thomas A. Donnellan, Chancellor of the New York Archdiocese, who presented the views of Francis Cardinal Spellman of New York that congressional action is necessary to protect the rights of parents to educate their children in an atmosphere reasonably free from defilement.

"Dr. Julius Mark, Senior Rabbi of Temple Emanu-El of New York, testified on that same date: 'Far more serious than the Communist menace, far more grave than the domestic problems we have noted, far more urgent than the need for discovering new wonder drugs and vaccines is the alarming increase of antisocial behavior among our youth.'

"Our inspection service estimates that as many as one million teen-age children will receive pornographic filth in the family mailbox this year, offering even still worse photographs, magazines, slides, and films for sale. This means that one out of every thirty-five children of school age in the nation will be exposed to the demoralizing effect of pornography.

"The sales volume of mail-order obscenity has doubled in the last five years and, unless vigorously checked, can double again over the next four years. This would mean that by 1963, we could be expecting one school child out of every eighteen to be the target of these purveyors of filth.

"Complaints received by the Post Office Department, mainly by indignant parents, totaled 50,000 in our fiscal year 1958. In the fiscal year 1959, they numbered more than 70,000.

"During the 1959 fiscal year, we carried out more than 14,000 separate investigations, of which some 10,000 were based on complaints sent to us by aroused parents. Arrests during the 1959 fiscal year rose to 315, the highest on record.

"Peddling pornographic poison to children is a heinous

crime. And that community which does not punish the criminal to the full extent of the law is failing in its duty—failing just as surely as if it were to allow sales to children of liquor or dope."

Mr. Summerfield pointed out that the Post Office Department, alone, cannot stamp out this vicious racket, that everyone must help. He added in conclusion:

"First, parents should save all materials received, including the envelopes and all enclosures.

"Second, parents should report the material immediately to their local postmaster and turn the material over to him, either in person or by mail.

"Finally, all citizens, whether or not their children have been touched with this filth, can help by backing up members of Congress and local officials in their growing effort to stamp out this evil."

Mr. Herbert B. Warburton, General Counsel, U. S. Post Office Department, wrote a recent article in *This Week Magazine* on the same subject. In the article entitled "You and the Law and Smut," Mr. Warburton said that the three biggest and most basic questions which the parent is confronted with in connection with pornography and its transmission through the mails are: How big is the racket? How bad is it? What can parents do?

He answers the first question by saying that this industry probably reaches a half-billion dollars yearly. In answer to the second question, Mr. Warburton states that about sixty percent of the material sent through the mails is not "actionable," about twenty percent goes further than any pretense of art and is lewd by most standards, and the remaining twenty percent is called "hard-core" pornography, i. e., actually hideous. The third question is answered by suggesting that all complaints be turned over to the postal authorities at once, who will then refer the matter to the Postal Inspection Service.

Mr. Warburton comments on a very important, and frustrating thing, that is the fact that the pornographer often uses first-class mail to transmit his wares, and even the Postmaster General cannot tamper with or open a piece of first-class mail. The offender, then, is clever and difficult to apprehend, although during 1958, there were forty-five percent more convictions than the year before. He concludes by saying: "The filth peddlers can be beaten if parents and the Post Office work together."

The courts have come to realize that the concepts of "obscenity and pornography" are elusive ones and defy any standardization of treatment or categorical consideration for many reasons. For example, material deemed obscene in one generation may not be considered so in the next generation; what is considered obscene in one locale may be proper in another locale. Despite this, however, the term "obscene" has generally been considered to be definite enough to allow court action upon which to base criminal prosecution under our federal laws.

The English case, decided in 1868 (Regina vs. Hicklin, L. R. 3 B. Q. 360, 371) laid the groundwork for much case law in America. That case set down the rule which seemed to base obscenity on whether the matter in question depraved and corrupted those whose minds are open to such immoral influences, that is, particularly susceptible persons such as children, the weak-minded, and the elderly. Under this concept, the test was restricted to a very narrow construction, and an entire literary work or book might be considered obscene because of an isolated passage. Two prime examples of this are Dreiser's *An American Tragedy,* held obscene because of selected portions in 1930 (Commonwealth vs. Fiede, 271 Mass. 318) and Edmund Wilson's *Memories of Hecate County* held obscene because of one chapter (1947—N. Y. vs. Doubleday & Co., 237 N. Y. 687).

This test, however, does not now pertain to modern American law. The total effect is no longer judged by an isolated excerpt upon particularly susceptible persons. It was probably first seriously criticized in an old case (1913) in New York by Judge Learned Hand, who stated that the rule was outdated and Mid-Victorian (U. S. vs. Kennerely, 209 Fed. 119). Later cases have followed the break from the old rule, an example of which is the case involving James Joyce's novel *Ulysses*. In 1933, a federal court ruled that the test of obscenity to be used regarding books and printed matter is its effect on a person with average sex instincts, and that such a work should not be declared obscene unless its tendency to arouse the sexual desires of the average reader outweighs its artistic, literary, or scientific merit. (U. S. vs. "One Book Called *Ulysses*"— 5 Fed. Supp. 182.) The same rule was used in a 1945 case involving a book on marriage and sex (Walker vs. Popenoe— 149 Fed. 2nd 511) and was followed in determining the distribution of such books as *God's Little Acre* and *Forever Amber*.

Another recent significant case was decided by the Supreme Court in 1957 (Roth vs. United States, 354 U. S. 476). Roth conducted a business in New York in which he used circulars and advertising matter to publish and sell books, photographs, and magazines. He was indicted and convicted, pursuant to Title 18, Sec. 1661, U. S. Code, for mailing obscene circulars and advertising an obscene book. The Supreme Court, in affirming the conviction on other grounds, nevertheless rejected the test of obscenity by the effect of isolated passages upon the most susceptible persons as being unconstitutionally restrictive of the freedoms of speech and press. The rule was stated as follows: "It is therefore vital that the standards for judging obscenity safeguard the protection of freedom of speech and press for material which does not treat sex in a manner appealing to prurient interest."

Mr. Justice Brennan, speaking for the Court said: "However, sex and obscenity are not synonymous. Obscene material is material which deals with sex in a manner appealing to prurient interest (i. e., material tending to excite lustful thoughts). The portrayal of sex, e. g., in art, literature, and scientific works, is not itself sufficient reason to deny material the constitutional protection of freedom of speech and press. Sex, a great and mysterious motive force in human life, has indisputably been a subject of absorbing interest to mankind through the ages; it is one of the vital problems of human interest and public concern."

The court, in making this new test for obscenity, quoted with approval the charge made by the trial judge to the jury, part of which is stated here:

"The test is not whether it would arouse sexual desires or sexual, impure thoughts in those comprising a particular segment of the community, the young, the immature, or the highly prudish or would leave another segment, the scientific or highly educated or the so-called worldly-wise and sophisticated, indifferent and unmoved . . . the test in each case is the effect of the book, picture, or publication considered as a whole, not upon any particular class, but upon all those it is likely to reach. In other words, you determine its impact upon the average person in the community. The books, pictures, and circulars must be judged as a whole, in their entire context, and you are not to consider detached or separate portions in reaching a conclusion. You judge the circulars, pictures, and publications which have been put into evidence by present-day standards of the community. . . ."

The case of Sunshine vs. Summerfield (D. C. D. C. 1955—249 Fed. 2nd 114) involved the publication and mailing of a nudist magazine. A federal court commented as follows: "Whether a magazine is obscene and nonmailable is to be determined by the test of the normal, reasonable person and such person's determination."

In this case, the court held that photographs taken of children in frontal view and which revealed diminutive and underdeveloped genitalia are not obscene, although it was indicated that photographs, taken at close range of the pubic area, are as a matter of law and fact obscene and, therefore, nonmailable. It was further stated that nudity is not "per se obscene," considering its general acceptance, in works of art, medical and scientific journals, books and magazines, literature, religious articles, and the like. Pictures which show the human form merely in the nude and which, beyond that, do not reveal the actual pubic area or male or female genitalia are not obscene or nonmailable.

Similar tests have been set down by federal courts in Ohio and California (Volanski vs. U. S.—CA Ohio, 1957, 246 Fed. 2nd 842; Bonica vs. Olesen—D. C. Calif., 1954, 126 Fed. Supp. 398).

An interesting and recent decision by the Judicial Officer of the Post Office Department points up the above view. The case is Greenleaf Publishing Co., H. E. Docket No. 4/202, decision dated November 10, 1958. This case concerned the magazine *Rogue for Men*. The department was seeking to refuse a second-class permit to this publication on the grounds of obscenity. After a departmental ruling denying the mailing privilege, the case was reviewed. In reaching the final decision, the Judicial Officer—whose decision is final insofar as the Post Office Department is concerned—observed that this magazine fell into a "borderline obscenity" category and stated: "I believe that the Supreme Court is looking with increasing disfavor on borderline obscenity cases. . . .

"Upon an independent review of the official record of this proceeding, including the evidence, the pleadings, and the transcript, I conclude that the magazines are not obscene. While they are replete with stories concerning sex and pictures of partially nude females, I do not believe they transcend current community standards as required by the Roth test. The toleration point in reading materials becomes more liberalized each year. While *Rogue for Men* certainly may understandably not be the type or reading matter a mother would want her ten-year-old to read, this is not the standard which is to be applied in determining these questions. Other more effective sanctions are available at the local level which can meet the problem of morality and the effects of bad reading habits on youth."

To similar effect is the case of The Filmsters, P. O. D. Docket 1/30, decision dated 10/17/58. This enterprise offered several motion pictures for sale through the mails, one of which depicted two females in bras and net panties, engaged in "wrestling" on the bed, with the final scenes concentrating on their posteriors. One of the females wore panties which obscured the pubic region but clearly revealed the anus. In his decision, the Judicial Officer wrote: "In my opinion, it is not obscene. The Supreme Court defined obscene material as 'material having a tendency to excite lustful thoughts.' While I cannot rule out the possibility that this film would have such an effect (sic) on some persons, I believe it would so appeal only to the deviate or the childlike mind and not the average member of our national community. It is the latter and not the former which provides the standard." (Butler vs. Mich., 352 U.S. 380.)

Another important case which cleared the way for the mailing of scientific materials is the following: United States of America, Libellant vs. 31 Photos, 4¾"x7" in szie, and various pictures, books, and other articles—Institute for Sex Research, Inc., at Indiana University, Claimant.

In the above case, the United States filed a libel suit under provision of Sec. 305 (a) of the Tariff Act of 1930, claiming that certain materials sent through the mails to the Kinsey Institute from abroad were obscene and immoral within the meaning of the act.

The United States District Court for the Southern District of New York, in its October 1957 decision, stated:

"The question presented is the meaning of 'obscene' in Sec. 305 (a) of the Tariff Act of 1930, and if the section prohibiting importation of 'obscene' material prohibits that which may be assumed to appeal to the prurient interest of the 'average person' . . . of the only person who will have access to the material, will study it for scientific research, and if as to them who have access to it, there is no reasonable probability that it will appeal to their prurient interest. . . .

"It is possible, instead of holding that the material is not obscene in the hands of the persons who have access to it, to speak of a conditional privilege in favor of scientists and scholars to import material which would be obscene in the hands of the average person . . . for it is the importer's scientific interest in the material which leads to the conditional privilege, and it is this same scientific interest which requires the holding that the appeal of the material to the scientist is not to his prurient interest and that, therefore, the material is not obscene to him. . . .

"There being no dispute in this case as to the fact that there is no reasonable probability that the libelled material will appeal to the prurient interest of those who will see it, it is proper that the motion of the libellant for an order that the libelled material be forfeited, confiscated, and destroyed, be denied; and that the motion of the claimant for summary judgment dismissing the libel and releasing the libelled material to it, be granted." (Edmund L. Palmieir, Judge.)

It is of interest to note that the American Law Institute, in 1957, tentatively adopted in its model penal code the following definition of obscenity: "A thing obscene is if, considered as a whole, its predominant appeal is to prurient interest, i. e., a shameful or morbid interest in nudity, sex, or excretion, and it goes substantially beyond customary limits of candor in description or representation of such matters."

Constant attacks have been made on the constitutionality of the federal laws governing obscenity and pornography as violations of the safeguards of free speech, free press, and the concepts of equal protection under the law (1st and 14th amendment). However, the courts have regularly confirmed the constitutionality of these laws. It seems to us that there are strong arguments against the case for arbitrary government control. These arguments should be resolved if we are to reach a clear and final determination of just what the law is and how it is applicable.

Perhaps some of these arguments would follow the thoughts set forth here:

It should be shown that, from the social standpoint, real harm is done by the publication and dissemination of the "obscene" material.

Studies should be undertaken to indicate what effect, if any, such publications actually have on the people in whose hands they fall and the resulting effect on their attitudes and conduct.

A determination must be made as to just what constitutes an immoral act or an act of indecency. Can you legislate against anything other than an actual overt criminal act? And are mere words, drawings, and suggestions, overt acts such as to constitute criminal behavior?

Special consideration should be given to those works which deal with scientific, medical, and legal problems involving sexual behavior.

Whose word is to be taken or in whose judgment can a writing be condemned as obscene and nonmailable? Definite and clear standards must be established.

Uniform legislation should be considered so that there is continuity of thought among the various states and harmony with the federal laws.

A historic court decision was rendered in July of 1959

which further illustrates the trend toward a lessening of governmental control over the printed word. The case involves the D. H. Lawrence novel, written some thirty years ago, entitled *Lady Chatterley's Lover.* The book was banned from distribution through the mails by the Postmaster General in June of 1959, after he had determined that it was an "obscene and filthy work."

Federal District Court Judge Frederick Bryan, of New York, issued a restraining order which prevented the government "from denying the mails to this book or to the circulars announcing its availability." He ruled that the Post Office Department had no right to act as censor and that he personally did not find the book objectionable. The decision of Judge Bryan, in part, stated:

"To exclude this book from the mails on grounds of obscenity would fashion a rule which could be applied to a substantial portion of the classics of our literature.

"I hold that, at this stage in the development of our society, this major English novel does not exceed the outer limits of the tolerance which the community as a whole gives to writing about sex and sex relations."

The story related in the book is that of an illicit relationship between an English woman or social position, married to a paralyzed husband, and the gamekeeper of their estate.

The U.S. Supreme Court, on December 14, 1959, rejected a Los Angeles law as being unconstitutional, which made mere possession of an obscene book by a bookdealer a crime. This may well be a landmark case.

The Superior Court of California had held that Eleazar Smith, the bookdealer, was subject to the local law even though he did not read the book in question or know it was obscene. The book involved was *Sweeter Than Life,* written by Mark Tyron, and is the story of a Lesbian who seeks revenge against men.

A majority of the Court held the ordinance invalid, because it did not require any proof that the dealer knew the book was obscene. The Court said that if a bookseller is held responsible for the contents of every book in his shop, he might not want to stock any books at all, and thus the public would be deprived of its right to purchase books that are not obscene in any sense. Justices Black and Douglas expressed their opinion that all laws against obscene writings are in violation of the First Amendment. Two other justices, Frankfurter and Harlan, said the conviction of Mr. Smith should be reversed because the trial judge did not permit expert testimony on whether or not the book was obscene, according to "contemporary community standards" (the test laid down by the court in the Roth case in 1957).

Mr. Justice Brennan, who wrote the majority opinion, stated that although the Court had upheld federal and state anti-obscenity laws in the past, the government has no right to restrict the sale of books that are not obscene: "If the bookseller is criminally liable without knowledge of the contents, he will tend to restrict the books he sells to those he has inspected; and thus the state will have imposed a restriction upon the distribution of constitutionally protected as well as obscene literature. . . . And the bookseller's burden would become the public's burden, for restricting him, the public's access to reading material would be restricted."

Back in 1930, the movie industry, sensing the need for some form of censorship, compiled the rather strict Motion Picture Production Code. Prior to that time, there were no industry restraints. Joseph I. Breen, who had widespread newspaper experience, was named administrator of the code. The main provisions of this code have been given earlier in this chapter.

The code remained in effect, as originally written, until 1956 when there were some changes which made the rules more lenient and abolished certain taboos. For instance, the subjects of narcotics, prostitution, abortion, and kidnaping were removed from the forbidden list; the subject of mixed marriages may now be handled within the discretion of the producer; and scenes of a baby being brought into the world may now be shown "with discretion, restraint, and within the careful limits of good taste."

In 1957, the New York Court of Appeals, in the case of a movie called *The Garden of Eden,* ruled that nudity per se is not indecent. And in 1959, the United States Supreme Court overruled a decision by the New York censor involving the picture *Lady Chatterley's Lover.* It held unconstitutional that part of the New York law prohibiting the showing of a motion picture which is "erotic or pornographic" or which "portrays acts of sexual immorality, perversion, or lewdness or which expressly or impliedly presents such acts as desirable or proper patterns of behavior." The Supreme Court declared that the above provisions are in violation of our constitutional guarantees of free speech. Mr. Justice Stewart wrote: "What New York has done is to prevent the exhibition of a motion picture because that pictures advocates an idea . . . that adultery under circumstances may be proper behavior. Yet the First Amendment's basic guarantee is of freedom to advocate ideas. The state, quite simply, has thus struck at the very heart of constitutionally protected liberties."

The decision actually means that reference to, or advocacy of a certain pattern of behavior, even though it may be frowned on by a majority of the community, cannot be banned. In other words, there can be no censorship of ideas. Implications and references to those things which some consider pornographic and obscene cannot be regulated. It remains, then, that only those things or acts that are obscene per se can thus be regulated. The commission of an immoral act itself can still, according to this viewpoint, be banned from a motion picture screen; however, the advocacy of the same act may not be subject to the same regulatory ban.

It seems that the Supreme Court has tried to express the thought that supression of ideas in this country is contrary to our constitutional rights and that such rights outweigh the personal or group interpretation of what is right or wrong, moral or immoral, good or bad.

chapter twelve

BIRTH CONTROL, STERILIZATION
AND ABORTION

BIRTH CONTROL ("PLANNED PARENTHOOD")

Contraception is legal in every state but two: Massachusetts and Connecticut.

Connecticut's 79-year-old law forbids the use of any drug or medical articles for preventing conception. It also makes it unlawful for doctors to give any advice at all on birth control. The constitutionality of this is being challenged. Dr. C. Lee Buxton, chairman of the obstetrics department of Yale Medical School, is one of the leading challengers.

It is unfortunate that laws against birth control remain on any statute books. We feel strongly that citizens have a legal right to family planning.

Methods of avoiding an unwanted pregnancy have been resorted to since the beginning of time. But the first birth control clinic was established in New York City in 1923. Its founder was Margaret Sanger.

Psychiatrists know that birth control plays an important role in sex enjoyment. Without it, many women are handicapped in their capacity for sexual satisfaction by a fear of pregnancy.

Part of the modern woman's sexual responsibility is to know how to use proper contraceptive methods after marriage so that fear of pregnancy does not inhibit her marital relations.

Information regarding birth control, or to use a more modern term, "planned parenthood," can be obtained by writing to: The Planned Parenthood Federation of America, 501 Madison Ave., New York 22, New York.

Dr. Alan F. Guttmacher, Director of the Department of Obstetrics and Gynecology, Mount Sinai Hospital, New York City, describes planned parenthood as "planning births so that every child is a wanted child, born to a mother and father who are prepared to take the responsibility of caring for him. It means spacing one's children so as to safeguard the health of both mother and child. It protects the parents and the child." He adds: "It protects the mother who is ill . . . the mother who is exhausted from bearing too many children until they can properly support them. Above all, it protects the child, so that he will not be considered a burden when he arrives."

The modern woman is entitled to have sex relations without fear of pregnancy. Men who refuse to use a contraceptive have no right to object to their wives wearing a diaphragm. Either method is far preferable to the withdrawal method in intercourse, still used by too many husbands. This is both frustrating for the woman and bad for the husband. By the intelligent use of approved contraceptive methods, it is possible to enjoy sex relations without the crippling fear of pregnancy.

In Sweden, through a special sales organization called Sexual Hygiene, the National League for Sexual Education, which enjoys government support, supplies contraceptives of high quality at the lowest price. In spite of the fact that the prices are considerably lower than those in the open market, this business makes a considerable profit, which is utilized to finance the other activities of the National League. The technical laboratory of the National League produces pessaries, of a construction that has been internationally recognized, jellies, and tablets (chemical contraceptives).

According to the United Nations' estimates, the world population will reach six or seven billion in the next forty years. At this writing, 5,400 children are born every hour, or 47 million annually. Since this increase outpaces the production of food and housing, this threatens a continually declining world standard of living.

Some churches are in favor of planned parenthood. For example, in 1946, the General Convention of the Protestant Episcopal Church stated: "We endorse the efforts being made to secure for licensed physicians, hospitals, and medical clinics, freedom to convey such information as is in accord with a more wholesome family life, wherein parenthood may be undertaken with due respect for the health of mothers and the welfare of their children."

In 1929 the Universalist Church at its General Convention issued the following statement:" Birth control is one of the most practicable means of race betterment. This Convention urges the immediate repeal of such federal and state laws and that physicians and socially minded persons establish in every center of population, clinics where those needing it may receive contraceptive advice under medical supervision."

At a meeting in England in 1958, the Bishops, comprising the Lambeth Conference of the Anglican Communion, issued this statement: "There are many lands today where population is increasing so fast that the survival of old and young is threatened. . . . In such countries population control has become a necessity. Abortion and infanticide are to be condemned, but methods of control, medically endorsed and morally acceptable, may help the people of these lands to plan family life that children may be born without a likelihood of starvation."

From a psycho-legal standpoint we are in favor of population control, and any ban on the use of contraceptives under medical advisement is, in our opinion, a violation of the "civil rights of the patient." Many physicians believe that contraception is a part of sound public health practice. As a matter of fact, an oral contraceptive pill is now being perfected and will soon be ready for distribution.

An article entitled "Planned Parenthood" published in *Candida* (Vol. I, No. 3) dealt with the problem in New York Hospitals: "In July a physician advised Dr. Morris A. Jacobs, City Hospital Commissioner, that he was going to provide a Protestant woman with a contraceptive device. The physician held that her health was of such a nature that the bearing of another child would be dangerous to her. The Health Commissioner forbade the physician to do it."

Dr. Jacobs was upheld in his decision by the Catholic authorities, and Catholic physicians of the city, generally, were in agreement with him. Opposed were the Protestant Council of Ministers and various Jewish groups, as well as some lay societies and medical organizations.

Rabbi Edward E. Klein of the Stephen Wise Synagogue, presented the issue in a direct challenge to the New York citizenry:" The recent action of New York's Commissioner of Hospitals has raised the issue of whether or not planned parenthood is morally and religiously acceptable. Basically, the stand of the commissioner is an infringement of civil rights— the civil rights of the patient, the civil rights of the Protestant and Jewish communities.

"A physician is entitled by the nature of his profession to pursue his work in accordance with the best legal and medical procedures. Protestant and Jewish patients are entitled to receive the best medical treatment even though some procedures may be contrary to the teachings of other faiths. To intrude theological dogma into medical practice in a city hospital, dangerously breaches the separation of Church and State.

"It goes without saying that persons whose religion opposes planned parenthood must have the right to refuse to resort to it. And a physician who does not believe in it must have the right to prescribe it. But in a pluralistic society such as ours, such views must not be imposed on those who differ.

"Not all religions believe that planned parenthood is contrary to the will of God. Many religionists hold that planning for parenthood—rather than violating the law of nature and of nature's God—applies our God-given intelligence and scientific knowledge, in which God also reveals Himself to healthy family living."

The birth control issue received world-wide publicity recently when President Eisenhower was asked whether the United States should, on request, give aid to foreign countries on birth control. The President concluded it was not our business to furnish such aid, an opinion which was shared by many.

An article entitled "World Birth Control Challenge" by Robert Coughlan, appeared in *Life* (November 23, 1959). It represented a survey of the whole field of scientific birth control research.

According to the article, it is estimated that the population of the United States, with a 1.6% annual increase, will double itself to 350 million in the next forty years. In India, if the present birth rate continues, there will be some 775 million Indians, twenty-five years from now and by the end of the century at least a billion. As for the mainland of China, the population is increasing there at the rate of more than a million a month; forty years from now, there will be a billion and a half Chinese.

It has been further estimated that by the year 2000, the world's population will reach seven billion. Every year the population increases by 44 million.

Julian Huxley, while head of UNESCO, summarized the situation as follows: "Everything points to one conclusion. While every effort must be made to increase food production, to facilitate distribution, to conserve all conservable resources, and to shame the 'have' nations into a fairer sharing of the good things in the world with the 'have nots,' this alone cannot prevent disaster. Birth control is also necessary on a world scale and as soon as possible."

World birth control is becoming a reality. It is inevitable. Its spread is evidence of the triumph of intelligence over ignorance and prejudice. Social and religious attitudes toward population control are bound to change. We predict, too, that the United States will play an important role, in the near future, in the population control of other countries.

In India, the government has recently appropriated over a million dollars to the Ministry of Health for a family-planning program. At the Third International Planned Parenthood Conference in Bombay, India, Sir Radhakrishnan expressed himself as follows: "Marriage is the union of man and woman, and it is completed by the arrival of children. Those who wish to avoid children for personal reasons or for reasons of comfort or for reasons of leading independent lives, are not encouraged to do so. All the same, if you subject women to frequent childbirth, you will be guilty of cruelty to human beings, you will be undermining their health, you will be making difficult, marriages which otherwise might have been successful. If, therefore, your intention is to safeguard the health and happiness of family life, you must determine the time of childbirth. I take it that to determine this is family planning.

"The question is sometimes raised whether it is not true that God sends children into this world and that we should not interfere with the will of God. I may tell you that, if God has given us any intelligence, He has given it to us to be used. Intelligence is a divine gift, which we must use. . . .

"Civilization is a progressive control of nature; while in the animal world it is the environment that selects who survives and who does not survive, man is given intelligence to adapt himself to the environment. The duty which the human individual has, is to find out what the social needs are and then make adaptations. Yet, we have had infanticide, we have had pestilence, we have had floods and earthquakes, and we have had all sorts of evil practices in this country. We have interfered with nature, we have controlled nature by reducing the death rate, combatting disease, prolonging life by preserving ourselves from floods and earthquakes. In all these matters, we are using human intelligence. But when it comes to limitation of population, it is said that we are interfering with nature. The fact of nature is excessive production, and we should use our intelligence to control excesses."

STERILIZATION LAWS

According to hospital reports, tubal ligation (a sterilization operation) is performed at the rate of between three and four percent of all deliveries, or about 180,000 every year. However, some authorities claim that this number is too low, that there are well over a half a million sterlizations every year considering that 200,000 vasectomies (sterilization of the male) also occur.

Twenty-eight states have laws permitting sterilization (permanent birth control) of mental defectives for eugenic reasons.

But legal problems sometimes arise in connection with the operation. Eugene Fleming, author of an article on sterilization in the July, 1959 issue of *Cosmopolitan,* informs us that "many doctors avoid vasectomy out of fear of a civil suit. If a physician were sued by a sterilized man's irate wife or, more likely, his second wife and the court ruled the vasectomy illegal, the physician's malpractice insurance would be useless. A few years ago, a civil suit for $30,000 was filed by a childless second wife against a physician who had vasectomized her husband during his first marriage. Like most cases of this kind, the suit was settled out of court."

Sterilization requires the signed consent of both husband and wife.

We feel that sterilizations are justified in many instances for socioeconomic reasons. The legal issues in the various states involving these operations should be clarified.

In Sweden, the Royal Medical Board, in accordance with a law passed in 1941, authorizes sterilizations for the following reasons:

1. If there is reason to assume that the subject would transmit to his or her offspring, hereditary mental diseases, imbecility, other serious disease, or a serious physical handicap (e. g., blindness, deaf-muteness) i. e., for eugenic reasons.

2. If because of mental derangement or an asocial way of life, the subject is found obviously unable to assume the legal and moral responsibility for the proper fostering of children, i. e., for social reasons.

3. If pregnancy would entail serious danger to a woman's life or health due to illness, physical defect, or weakness; i.e., for medical reasons.

The consent of the subject is required if he or she has the legal capacity, i.e., is able to understand the purport and the consequences of the legal act.

Persons lacking legal capacity may be sterilized without their consent, but physical coercion cannot be used in performing the operation.

Sterilization may be authorized by two doctors who must certify the illness or defect.

One of the aims is to reduce imbecility, and this has already been accomplished.

While we endorse this plan of sterilization, we do not endorse castration operations. It is our opinion that castration does not necessarily prevent sex crimes.

THE PROBLEM OF ABORTION

According to the new Kinsey group report *Pregnancy, Birth and Abortion*: "One out of every ten upper-class American women becomes pregnant some time in her life prior to, or outside of, marriage. Of these who become pregnant while unwed, the chances are that nine out of ten will have an abortion, unless a hasty marriage is arranged."

In an article entitled "The Activity of the Consultation Bureau for Sexual Hygiene and Abortion Cases in Stockholm," given to us by Mrs. Margareta Soderblom, Attaché, Royal Swedish Embassy, Washington, D. C., Dr. Verner Westberg writes:

"In 1912, Margaret Sanger, a young American nurse, was called twice within six months to the home of Jacob Sachs, a young chauffeur, living in the New York slums. Both times he had found his wife in great pain after attempted abortions. She was surrounded by three young children and died ten minutes after the young nurse had been called on that occasion. Margaret Sanger was moved by profound pity and asked herself what could be done to save unfortunate women from unhygienic abortions and to avoid the necessity for such abortions. The same feeling as those experienced by the young American nurse in 1912—feelings of pity and desire to do something for these unfortunate women—have been felt by many socially minded people in Sweden, especially during the thirties, when the number of criminal abortions in our country rose to about 20,000. In Sweden, this sympathy for women who had become pregnant against their will and who in their distress turned to illegal abortionists, became so widespread that a law was passed on the 17th of June, 1938, laying down conditions for the interruption of pregnancy. This law was altered in 1941 and 1942, and the regulations governing permissible abortions were made less stringent in 1946."

Swedish legislation allows possibilities for legal abortions. Women are warned that "the results of abortion performed by incompetent individuals may be fatal for life, health, and future fertility."

As part of its struggle against illegal and incompetent abortions, the National League opened in 1941, in Tureholm, a home for mothers. They live in a pleasant environment during the last months of pregnancy, feeling secure, and being spared the feeling of loneliness and forlorness which in many cases accentuates the need for abortion. They also are spared the criticism of people lacking in understanding. Also, after the delivery, mother and child can stay on for sometime in the home, while practical details are taken care of so that the mother does not have to be separated from her child. The financial support has largely come from gifts and drives. The first gifts to this home came from His Majesty, the King, and the late Prime Minister of Sweden, Mr. Per Albin Hansson. During the last few years, the municipal authorities of Stockholm have granted money for this work, supervised by the National League. Altogether over 400 mothers have stayed at the home, half the number both before and after the delivery.

New legislation concerning abortions was enacted in 1938. According to that legislation, pregnancy may be interrupted artificially in the following three cases:

1. When illness, physical debility, or weakness would endanger the life or health of the woman (medical or mixed social grounds).

2. When rape or other criminal acts caused the pregnancy (humanitarian grounds).

3. When it may be presumed that the woman or the father of the child, through inheritance, would transfer insanity or mental debility or, also, grave disease or other disabilities on the progeny (eugenic grounds).

Abortion for reasons other than disease or disability may not be performed after the twentieth week of pregnancy. The Medical Board has to authorize the abortion in the case of eugenic grounds and also when mental condition of the woman prevents her from giving a valid consent to this measure. In other cases, the doctor performing the abortion together with another doctor in an official capacity should, in a formal report, give the motives for the abortion.

The following represents how the problem of abortion is managed in various countries.

Sweden. In 1938 a law was passed allowing induced abortions for medical, humanitarian, and eugenic reasons.

From 1946 to 1951 inclusive, 28,447 approved abortions were performed. The fatality rate was about one per thousand. The combined operation of abortion and sterilization is performed in over twenty-five percent of legal abortions.

Norway. The new abortion laws are similar to those in Sweden.

Denmark. In 1939, a law was passed liberally interpreting therapeutic abortion which it permitted: 1) When the interruption of pregnancy is necessary to avert serious danger to the life or health of the woman; 2) When the pregnancy is due to rape or incest; 3) When there is intimate danger that the child, due to a hereditary disposition, will become a sufferer from insanity, mental deficiency, major mental disorders, or serious and incurable bodily disease. In Denmark, consideration is also given to psychiatric reasons. According to Gebhard, over 500 cases of authorized abortions revealed that over half of them fell under the psychiatric classification. Weight is also given to social circumstances, and abortion is permitted if there is no other available solution to the social problem.

Iceland. A law permitting abortion for medical and social reasons was enacted in 1934. In determining to what extent childbirth is likely to endanger the health of a pregnant woman, certain facts are taken into consideration, namely, how much time has elapsed between each child in the family and whether the woman's domestic conditions are difficult either on account of many children, poverty, or serious ill health of other members of the family.

Finland. A legal abortion is permitted according to a law

passed in 1950, for medical, humanitarian, and eugenic reasons. It is reported that over an eighteen-month period in the Woman's Clinic of Helsinki University, about one fifth of the legal abortions were done on psychiatric grounds and approximately the same proportion on eugenic indications.

Russia. In November 1955, Russia, for the second time, instituted a broad program of permissive legal abortion.

China. According to Gebhard, Communist China has recently legalized abortion but details are difficult to secure.

Latin-America. Oddly enough, while the Latin-American countries are predominantly Roman Catholic, some abortion laws are rather liberal. In Argentina, as far back as 1921, abortions for rape pregnancies and pregnancies conceived by insane females were legalized. It is reported, also, that the penalties for criminal abortion are mild.

Japan. In Japan, a legalized abortion program has been in operation for many years.

England. The penalties for abortion in England are exceedingly severe. However, there is evidence that the courts in England have adopted a more liberal attitude toward therapeutic abortion, particularly when psychiatric indications were present.

United States. The statutes in our country indicate that abortion is permissable only when performed by a licensed physician and is necessary to "preserve" or "save" the life of the mother. In some states, the statutory provisions refer to the "health" or "safety" of the woman. At a recent conference on abortion, sponsored by The Planned Parenthood Federation of America, thirty-eight participants represented specialized fields of knowledge, including obstetrics, psychiatry, and sociology. The conference made the following recommendations regarding abortion statutes in the United States:

"Authoritative bodies, such as The National Conference of Commissioners on Uniform State Laws, The American Law

Institute, and The Counsel of State Governments, should study the abortion laws in the various states and frame a model law that could perhaps jointly, be presented to the states for their consideration to replace existing statutes. These bodies, in their deliberations, must be mindful that the border zone between legal and illegal abortions is at present narrow and shifts frequently, depending on personnel and locale. Such commissions should recognize that, when current statutes are interpreted exactly as written, almost no therapeutic abortions performed today are legal, since the improvement of modern medicine, it rarely becomes necessary to perform an abortion to save life. They should also recognize the mounting approval of psychiatric, humanitarian, and eugenic indications for the legal termination of pregnancy; the propriety of such indications merits extensive study and appraisal, and the commissions should engage in such study in order to be able to give careful consideration to the advisability of so modifying abortion statutes as to give the physicians latitude to include these indications in their recommendations for therapeutic abortions."

RECOMMENDATIONS

Laws must continually be modified to fit the times. Unfortunately, while this is true, the world is constantly handicapped by resistance to change. We suffer from obsolete laws and ways of living. Many people cling to ancient prejudices and taboos. The more progressive must help the uninformed to give up thinking based on superstition and fear.

Take capital punishment for example. We still cling to the ancient law of an "eye for an eye." Tragically enough, we carry out the barbaric ritual of giving the person condemned to death a sumptuous meal including his favorite dessert, and the opportunity to receive religious consolation from a clergyman. Then we place a noose around his neck or gas him or have him shot by a firing squad, as they do in Utah, or shock him to death by electricity. People who advocate the death penalty are afraid that its elimination might remove deterrents to murder. But established data proves this fear to be unfounded. Capital punishment does not deter homicide.

In other respects, we have made considerable progress in eliminating obsolete laws and replacing them with more intelligent ones. We have taken a more liberal attitude toward other aspects of living.

When we made the drinking of alcoholic beverages illegal, we simply expanded and enriched the underworld. Finally, our lawmakers concluded that it was far healthier to allow people to buy good liquor in licensed stores and that this would eliminate bootleggers and reduce corruption. Those aims were accomplished. It may possibly be true that more people, today, drink than before, but then the majority of people who drink alcoholic beverages now handle alcohol more intelligently. In those who do not, it is not alcohol that causes the trouble but some emotional maladjustment which makes them use alcohol as a crutch or as an escape mechanism.

People fear to liberalize the abortion laws. They believe it will lead to greater promiscuity and immorality. This is a fallacy.

We would be better off to adopt the policy which progressive countries all over the world have adopted on abortion. Let's face it; those other countries are ahead of us in that respect. We predict that if the abortion laws were modified and if all forms of birth control were made legal for *medical, humanitarian,* as well as *eugenic,* reasons, similar to those already in existence in other countries, we would see a sharp decrease in the number of abortions. We would eliminate the existence of criminal abortionists in the same way that we eliminated bootleggers. We would have a lower mortality rate. Abortions would be performed by competent physicians only. We would

have a lower illegitimacy rate; and while it may sound para-
doxical, we also predict that the sex mores in general would
improve.

The liberalization of our obsolete abortion laws is inevitable.
The trend is already in this direction. However, there are still
too many illicit abortions performed, and the problem remains
a serious one that calls for closer attention by the legal and
medical professions and the public at large.

Many years ago, a resident surgeon at a hospital performed
a craniotomy (a form of abortion) as an emergency measure
to save the life of a mother, since there wasn't enough time to
prepare her for and perform a Caesarian. Her pulse was weak
and her blood pressure was falling rapidly. The surgeon made
this decision to save the life of the mother. He was asked to
resign from the staff, because the hospital did not permit
such an unauthorized operation on religious grounds. What
was the logic in penalizing a doctor who had acted to save
a human life?

At a conference on abortion, a physician made an impas-
sioned denunciation of abortion as *murder,* and he violently
opposed any recommendation for liberalizing the abortion
laws. It was quite obvious to the other participants that, while
he denied this, his views were based on his religious convictions and not on objective scientific knowledge or experience.
At the same meeting, a well-known woman obstetrician asserted that considerable hypocrisy existed among physicians
who oppose the liberalization of the abortion laws. She cited
the case of a desperate woman who consulted a physician
about the need to have her pregnancy terminated. The physician informed her that, because of his religion, he could not
consider the abortion himself but would send her to a physician
who would do it. The speaker could not approve of such
hypocrisy.

People behind planned parenthood and people behind the

movement for liberalizating abortion laws are as sincere as any other group in wanting to bring about a healthier and better society. No intelligent person or group seeks to foster immorality. On the contrary, it is for moral considerations that they advocate steps that would make abortions eventually unnecessary or, at least, reduce them to a minimum. They are trying to remedy a grave situation. They are in the same category as those who advocate compulsory sex education in our schools, a step which would also contribute toward fewer abortions, since many pregnancies out of wedlock are caused by sex ignorance.

chapter thirteen

PSYCHO-LEGAL MANAGEMENT

PREVENTION OF SEX SICKNESS

As long as a large proportion of the population remains uninformed or misinformed, the high incidence of sex sickness will continue.

The following are a few of the major benefits that would result if people availed themselves of the sex education they need, and each one made a sincere endeavor to bring about a better sexual adjustment in his life.

1. There would be definitely fewer sex crimes. Sex offenders are sexually ignorant.

2. There would be less sexual delinquency among teenagers.

3. The divorce rate would be reduced. Most divorces are caused by sex incompatibility.

4. The number of abortions performed each year because of unwanted pregnancies would be diminished. Selfishness and ignorance on the part of reckless males are responsible for the complications of illicit relationships.

5. There would be less susceptibility to homosexual relations.

5. There would be less susceptibility to homosexual relations.

If wives realized that they had a certain sexual responsibility in marriage and cooperated toward making their husbands and themselves happier sexually, there would be fewer sex

307

crimes and less sex sickness in general. A good wife gives and shares love, and is careful not to frustrate the sexual ego of her husband. Merely increasing the population by bringing babies into the world does not discharge her duty to society. It is the quality of the relationship between husband and wife that determines the security of the family, the community and the nation.

SEX SICKNESS OR SEX UNHAPPINESS CAN BE PREVENTED OR REMEDIED

The mature wife should not tolerate any serious sexual difficulty that could be corrected either through self-education, with her husband's cooperation, or, if need be, with the help of a psychiatrist. There are thousands of wives in our country who are afraid to seek help with their sexual problems only because their husbands forbid it, either because of their male vanity or because of the expense involved. Many of these same husbands think nothing of spending money freely for personal luxuries but balk at contributing financially to much-needed counselling.

Every mature woman has a right to demand an improvement in the sexual relationship with her husband. Many husbands should be given an ultimatum—they must either cooperate, particularly if they are at fault, or face the consequences of a separation.

The mature wife is one who recognizes the need to remedy any sexual difficulty that exists, makes an attempt to educate herself and her husband in ways of correcting the problem, applies this knowledge tactfully, and insists, when necessary, on seeking professional help. It is unintelligent for any couple to do nothing about a sexual problem that threatens the security of their marriage.

Parents need to be enlightened so that they can avoid situations in the home which favor the development of sexual conflicts in their children. They should take precautions against having their children overhear or witness sexual relations, and be made to realize that an exaggerated fear of sex, implanted in their children, may lead to psychosexual difficulties in adult life.

Regarding the prevention of homosexual patterns, Dr. Spurgeon English, Professor of Psychiatry, Temple University Medical School, presents the following rules to guide modern parents:

1. The child should have warmth from the mother. With the warmth the mother should combine affection so that the male, in particular, has memories of pleasant experiences with women and will want to re-establish ties of intimacy with women later in life.

2. He should have a sexual enlightenment free of taboos or disgust in relation to heterosexual union.

3. He should have the interest of a man during his growth, so that he identifies himself with masculine attitudes, particularly those pertaining to responsibility and home formation including a satisfaction in parenthood. The first and second rules apply also for the woman. Third, she should have from early life the warm interest of a man so that she feels a kinship with the life of a man. When we consider how many fathers ignore their daughters rather completely during their whole development, it is not surprising that there is so little ability for women to like men and to get along with them. In certain instances where warmth and understanding of men and pleasure in physical intimacy with them is lacking, a leaning toward emotional and physical satisfaction is the result. Hence parents who are concerned about a homosexual adjustment in their children should inquire into the family pattern which encourages a heterosexual adjustment.

Parents must learn to regulate their own emotions before their children. If parents are incompatible, quarrel, shout and bicker with each other, such an atmosphere indirectly harms their children sexually.

In everyday family intimacy there are also hazards to the child's normal sexual development.

Stekel's rule was: "In the presence of children, act as you would before adults."

If all parents would observe this rule, they would automatically eliminate such causes of childhood sex shocks as these:

1. Carelessness about privacy on the part of parents during intercourse.

2. Carelessness about nudity before children.

3. Carelessness in leaving for the children's eyes evidences of contraception, menstruation, pornographic pictures.

4. Parental indulgence in profanity or obscene language.

Parents should observe the following basic guides:

1. The child is sexually susceptible throughout his life; neither pamper nor tyrannize, but give him his fair share of love and discipline.

2. Observe decency and care in your own sexual behavior around your child even in his earliest years and behave as you would around adults.

3. If harmful influences inside or outside the home have already caused some sexual maladjustment in your child, do not let the problem fester. If you do not have enough sex education to deal with it yourself, take it to the family doctor or psychiatrist.

Parents should examine their own attitudes toward sex before passing them on to their children. The child can't be expected to adopt a normal attitude if the parents regard sex as something taboo or shameful. Unconsciously, a child will sense the parents' sexual disorder or disharmony.

The most important thing in any child's sex education is to teach him about love and what it implies. When you teach him by example and guidance that love is good, you are indirectly teaching that child the finer side of sex, because love and sex are so inextricably interrelated.

A normal love relationship between parents and child acts as a foundation for a good sexual adjustment for the child when it grows up. Love and common sense in gradually imparting information about the physical aspects of love to your child, in accordance with his years, are his best guarantee of a good sexual adjustment.

THERAPEUTIC CONSIDERATIONS

Modern treatment of sex offenders differs considerably from methods used years ago. Castration and even decapitation were once the penalties imposed on sex offenders. Castration was abandoned after it was discovered that sexual abnormalities are psychic in origin and not localized in the genital organs. It was for this reason that the opposition to castration was supported by scientists like Hirschfeld, Moll, Feré and others.

Glandular injections proved of no avail.

Religion, as a "therapeutic discipline," attempts to control the expression of abnormal instincts. However, religion has not always enabled the homosexual, the exhibitionist, the sadist, or transvestite, for example, to repress their antisocial cravings. To recommend an ascetic life to them may intensify their difficulty and result in a severe anxiety neurosis. They must be made to understand the psychological cause of their affliction.

Dr. Milton H. Gurvitz, a New York psychologist, reported the good results of intensive psychotherapy in the treatment of eighteen males convicted of exhibitionism. He observed that "therapy directed at this type of long-term rehabilitation and ego building rather than at specific symptoms resulted in sixteen of the eighteen sex offenders being free of sex offenses at the present time."

Since we are now convinced that homosexuality is an acquired or a psychogenic disorder and not a congenital condition due to biological or hereditary factors, the method of treatment must of necessity be a psychological one.

Scientific literature shows that many homosexuals, among them the "exclusive" or "compulsive" types, have been cured by psychoanalysis. Ernest Jones, the biographer of Freud, states that psychoanalysts obtain a large proportion of cures among inverts.

The late Dr. Emil Gutheil, editor of the *American Journal of Psychotherapy*, stated: "There have been cures; all experienced psychiatrists have them. These cures should be better known to give hope to these people." He deplores "the generally defeatist attitude of some psychiatrists regarding successful therapy, which has induced the homosexual to accept his role as something God-given."

He goes on: "In every single case a neurotic structure can be discovered. Therapy seeks to lower anxiety and to remove the unnecessary defenses against the opposite sex. In the treatment do not ask why the homosexual is so, but what stops him from being heterosexual. If you find out, you release the heterosexual element."

The policy of self-acceptance and resignation recommended by some therapists is unwise, since many inverts do not wish to accept the status of homosexual. Such advice gives the person a feeling of futility, as though homesexuality was inborm and psychotherapy would prove fruitless.

Modern psychoanalytic treatment concentrates on changing the basic character structure (the personality pattern). Treatment thus eliminates the mental block that bars the patient from a heterosexual adjustment.

This is in keeping with the views of Dr. Clara Thompson, author of *Changing Concepts of Homosexuality*, who states: "Psychoanalysis must deal primarily with the personality structure, realizing that the symptom is a secondary development from that."

In brief, homosexuality can be regarded as a personality problem, associated with feelings of sexual immaturity and insecurity.

As we might expect, many inverts do not wish to be changed. They prefer to think that their affliction is a congenital one, so that they can use this as an excuse for not assuming the responsibilities associated with marriage and family life.

Many desire to live a life of dissipation and are indifferent to the penalties exacted by society. They are unwilling to give up contact with homosexual circles.

Others, because of their struggle with this problem, seek help. Many are sincere and make a genuine effort to respond to treatment. A willingness to be cured is halfway to health. This particularly applies to homosexuals. The prognosis is therefore a favorable one wherever there exists the genuine wish to be helped.

Treatment consists in enabling the patient to develop insight into the personality problem which led to his homosexual pattern.

A young college graduate summarized a few of the insights he gained following psychotherapy:

1. "As a growing boy and until I graduated from college, I was unsure about my masculinity. Many of my traits and interests seemed feminine. I finally realized that the mixture of masculine and feminine feelings was wholly a psychological matter.

2. I came finally to see that my sex problem arose out of emotional insecurity. It was essentially a problem of emotional illness.

3. It was only after my feelings of guilt became an intolerable burden that I sought treatment.

4. I learned that I was, in effect, constantly trying to return to the habits of life established in childhood.

5. I was basically attempting to satisfy only myself, to

gratify myself erotically. On understanding this, I found that the need for this type of living fell away and became less insistent. I realized that, as a fully mature male, my real and lasting satisfaction were to come through being more genuinely responsible about my own life, so that I might marry and have a family life in which I would achieve the maximum feelings of confidence, security, and success.

6. It was not until I gained these insights about my problem that I came to understand myself, and thus achieved a clear aim in life. I have come to accept my past experiences, however unhappy and frustrating they were, as a part of a life which is now more ordered and wholesome."

In an article entitled "New Hope for Homosexuals," originally published in *Sexology* (1958), Albert Ellis had this to say regarding the treatment of twenty-eight male and twelve female homosexuals with intensive therapy:

"These patients were treated for their homosexual problems of neurosis rather than for their homosexual desire or activity in itself. They were judged to be distinctly or considerably improved when they began to lose their fears of the other sex, to receive gratification from sex relationships, to be effective partners in these relationships, and to lose their obsessive thoughts or compulsive actions about homosexuality.

"It was found that of the male patients, sixty-four percent were distinctly or considerably oriented toward heterosexuality after treatment, while thirty-six percent were still as strongly homosexual as before.

"Of the male patients (numbering twenty-three) who had some desire to achieve heterosexuality, almost eighty percent became distinctly or considerably more heterosexual. Every single one of thirteen males who had a strong desire to achieve heterosexuality became distinctly or considerably more heterosexual.

"Of the twelve female patients seen for intensive psychotherapy, all became distinctly or considerably oriented toward heterosexuality in the course of treatment, even though two of them had no desire to change when they first were seen.

"The findings of this study seem to show that when treated for their underlying problems and neuroses rather than for their homosexual behavior in itself, a high percentage of fixed male homosexuals—and a quite high percentage of those who are particularly eager to become heterosexual—can be helped to become heterosexually oriented.

"When Lesbians are similarly treated, results are even more promising."

Dr. Ellis gives the following example of a fixed homosexual he treated. It should convince the reader that homosexuality should be handled as a symptom of the underlying neurosis rather than as a clinical entity. When the neurotic blocks to heterosexual relationships are removed through insight therapy, the homosexual often finds that he no longer desires sexual contacts with his own sex.

"A case in point is that of a thirty-five-year-old male I recently saw who had been exclusively homosexual all his life. This patient came for therapy partly because he had psychosomatic complaints for which no physical origin could be found. He was born and raised in Brooklyn; had a shy, uneventful childhood; spent three unhappy years in the navy; always did well in school; and was reluctantly carrying on his father's business after the father had had a serious stroke.

"This fixed homosexual patient had a few dates with girls when he went to high school but was afraid to make any sexual overtures for fear of being rejected, and consequently had never kissed a girl. While in the navy, he was plied with liquor by two other sailors and induced to have his first homosexual experience at the age of nineteen.

"Since that time, he had engaged in homosexual acts every two or three weeks, always making his contacts at public urinals and never having any deep relationship with his partners. He occasionally dated girls, mainly to pretend to outsiders that he was heterosexual, but he was not attached to any of them and never made any advances or got seriously involved.

"This male homosexual was one of the first patients to be treated with a special approach which the writer had developed during the last several years. This approach, called 'rational psychotherapy' directly penetrates and attacks the basic irrational beliefs by which individuals continually reindoctrinate themselves and maintain their emotional disturbances.

"In the case of this homosexual patient, he was shown at the start of therapy that there would be no concentration of getting him to stop his homosexual desires or activities. The goal of therapy, he was told, would be to help him overcome his irrational blocks against heterosexuality.

"These blocks, it became quickly apparent, stemmed largely from his terrible fear of rejection. He was so convinced that he might be rejected if he made active sexual approaches to either women or men, and that this would be terrible, that he arranged his sex life so that no active approach of any kind was necessary—and he just put himself in a position where aggressive males could pick him up. Women, in our culture, would not normally be so aggressive as homosexual males; consequently, he adhered to homosexual participations.

"The patient's fear of rejection was traced to his being a rather chubby and unattractive boy and having his own mother continually remark that he would have trouble finding and winning an attractive girl.

"This fear was brought to light again and again in the course of the therapy; and it was not only revealed but was forcefully, consistently attacked by the therapist, who kept showing the patient that it is silly and self-defeating for anyone to care too much about what others think, since one is then regulating one's life by and for these others, rather than for oneself.

"While this individual's fear of rejection and his consequent restricted homosexual behavior were being questioned, he was encouraged to date girls so that he could in actual practice overcome his fears concerning them.

"He was warned that his first attempt at dating might be embarrassing, but that only by working through such situations, with the help of the therapist, was he likely to overcome his irrational fears of heterosexuality.

"The patient had two abortive dates with women but was able to learn from them; and finally had a successful sex contact. While he was seeing these women, the therapist went over with him in detail his behavior with them.

"He was given specific instructions in regard to how to make dates; what to expect from females; how to understand them and their problems; how to avoid being discouraged when he was rebuffed, etc. His mistakes and blunders were discussed in an objective, constructive manner; and he was shown how, instead of blaming himself for his mistakes, he could put them to good self-teaching uses.

"After he had seen the therapist for three months, the patient met a woman whom he thought was most desirable and was sure, at first, that he would not be able to attract. The therapist consistently encouraged him to keep dating her, even when things looked black in their relationship; and the patient did persist.

"As a result of the therapist's continually undermining his homosexual's irrational ideas leading to his feelings of inadequacy and fear of rejection, as well as his own proving to himself that he could provide sexual and emotional satisfaction to a female, his basic philosophy of his own worthlessness was rudely shaken.

"Although his homosexual tendencies were barely mentioned

after the first two sessions, and no specific attempt was made to get him to give up his practices, he completely and voluntarily stopped all homosexual behavior as soon as he began to get along with females.

"After several months of treatment, he changed from a hundred percent homosexual to virtually a hundred percent heterosexual. All his waking and sleeping fantasies became heterosexually oriented, and he was almost never interested in homosexual outlets again.

"This case confirms what the writers have pointed out on previous occasions: namely that the neurotic element in homosexuality is not the homosexual activity or desire itself, but the exclusiveness the fear, the fetishistic fixation, or the obsessive compulsiveness which so often accompanies homosexuality.

"The aim of psychotherapy, therefore, should be to remove these elements; to free the confirmed homosexual from his underlying fear of, or antagonism toward, heterosexual relations, and to enable him to have satisfying sex-love involvements with members of the other sex. When the therapist and patient work together toward this goal, hope for homosexuals can be effectively realized."

Homosexuals can be educated out of their sexual immaturity.

The first step is to accept the fact that homosexuality or any other kind of sexual complication is bound to interfere with the desired goal of marital love-happiness.

The second step is to accept the fact that homosexuality is a sexual neurosis, an emotional deviation. It is psychological in origin and can only be treated successfully by psychological or educational methods.

The third step is to probe into those influences that led to the development of the present deviated patterns. Understanding the problem makes self-discipline easier.

The fourth step is to avoid unhealthy or defensive rationalizations that tend to prevent the development of normal sex-love attitudes.

The fifth step is to cultivate the inspiring friendship of persons who are well adjusted in their love life. Sex health and love happiness are contagious.

The sixth step is to seek and find a better remedy for inner loneliness.

The seventh step is to convince oneself that love is an emotional attitude, that one is capable of thinking normally about sex, love, and maturity; that as one thinks, so shall it be. Attitude is all-important in understanding and correcting sex troubles.

The eighth step is to want to become a well-integrated, emotionally mature person—to live right, to think straight, to grow and improve in every way. This wanting must come from within. No one can give it. Successful self-discipline follows this inner determination to change.

There are inverts who make every attempt to convince the psychiatrist that they are incapable of developing a sexual interest in the opposite sex. Obsessed with the idea that they would prove impotent and sexually inadequate, they feel that even an attempt in this direction would prove a fiasco. That most homosexuals are impotent is a fallacy. It is true that many overt, effeminate inverts suffer from psychic impotence and are heterosexually inhibited because of their fear of not maintaining an erection during coitus, but this reaction is actually a pseudo impotence.

I have treated many male and female homosexuals, and after assuring them that their impotence and frigidity reactions were psychogenically motivated, have been told in a follow-up of their cases that they had been able to carry out coitus successfully.

The homosexual uses his fear of impotence as a rationalization for not attempting heterosexual relations. This same principle holds true for Lesbians who are frigid insofar as men are concerned.

Inverts must be made to realize that marriage per se is no cure for homosexuality. Helping the homosexual to develop his personality, teaching him how to sublimate successfully his sexual drive in socially acceptable channels, and helping him to establish a goal in life are psychotherapeutic steps that are necessary if the result is to be permanent.

It is difficult to achieve any kind of favorable response to psychotherapy if the patient prefers to associate or even live with other homosexuals, since he is generally influenced by his homesexual friends who usually succeed in getting him to break his good resolutions.

Many deviates drink to excess. Consequently, when an invert has a homosexual roommate, and he himself continues to drink to excess during treatment, the prognosis is usually very poor. His continuing with psychotherapy is motivated by a pseudo desire to be helped. Encouraging inverts to establish friendship with sexually well-adjusted persons brings them closer to a therapeutic goal.

The psychiatrist must also take the occupation of the invert into consideration. Occupational exposure to homosexual temptations makes the response to treatment more difficult. In the therapeutic management of sexual deviates, the patient must learn to exercise self-discipline if he is to make an adequate sexual adjustment. The psychiatrist should recommend a change in occupation when indicated.

A psychotherapeutic philosophy of life, based on principles of mental hygiene and intelligent living, is also necessary for a therapeutic success.

HYPNOTHERAPY FOR SEX OFFENDERS

Krafft-Ebing was the first to recommend hypnosis in the treatment of homosexuals. Another advocate was van Schrenck-

Notzing who subjected his patients to as many as 150 hypnotic sittings. He also recommended frequent visits to brothels. While some responded to this prescribed therapeutic program, others reverted to their previous homosexual practices. Hypnosis, then, appeared too superficial to effect a lasting cure.

For such reasons, Freud discarded hypnosis in the treatment of nervous and mental disorders and hypnosis fell into disfavor. Recently, however, new approaches to hypnosis in psychotherapy have rehabilitated this technique. Magazine articles have reported phenomenal benefits from hypnosis. *Life* (October, 1958) published a pictorial article describing some of its current uses. Hypnosis has been successful in painless childbirth (without anesthesia), in dentistry (the painless extraction of teeth), in the management of psychosomatic ailments (symptom removal by suggestion), in cases of stammering, and as a tool for uncovering key conflicts of traumatic experiences repressed or buried in the subconscious.

In my own experience, the results of hypnoanalysis and hypnotherapy in the therapeutic management of sex offenders who have been referred to me by the courts, have proved most encouraging. The reliving of the traumatic sexual events in one's past under hypnosis was more complete and obtained more quickly than through the free association method of psychoanalysis.

The patients were much more relaxed and had a feeling of well-being following their hypnotic sessions. They felt more inclined to tell everything under hypnosis than they would in a waking state on the couch under psychoanalysis.

While psychoanalysis and psychotherapy remain the preferred methods of treating sex offenders, there are certain drawbacks. Psychoanalysis requires a long period of time—lasting from one to three or more years—and is often beyond the patients' means. Most sex offenders cannot afford to be psychoanalyzed. Inexpensive, short-term hypnoanalysis and hypnotherapy have been found equally effective.

The types of sex offenders most amenable to hypnotherapy are Peeping Toms, exhibitionists, homosexuals, fetishists, and pedophiliacs.

An explanation is given to the sex offender of the how and why of hypnosis and what is expected of him in the way of cooperation in achieving the desired hypnotic trance. During hypnoanalysis, after the hypnotic or receptive mental state has been induced, he is instructed to go back into his childhood and relate the significant events of his past bearing on the development of his sexual patterns. During his sessions, he is encouraged to develop his own insight into the psychological factors responsible for his sex sickness. Toward the end of each session, he is given posthypnotic suggestions as to what to keep in mind in order to better understand and control his sexual impulses. The recommended minimum number of sessions is three per week, if this is at all possible. The duration of the treatment varies from three to six months.

CASE HISTORIES

Case 1. Harry, a teenager, charged with molesting an eight-year-old girl, told the judge that the girl had made the advances and that she had engaged in sex games with other boys. The girl's parents denied this, and Harry was unable to convince the court that he had not taken the initiative. Under hypnoanalysis, Harry admitted to certain sex practices with the girl but only after he had been encouraged by her. Harry came from a broken home and had had a very unhappy childhood. He was given a course of sex instruction and subjected to post-hypnotic suggestions which helped him to understand the relationship of his early feelings of insecurity with his particular sexual problem.

Case 2. Charles, a first-year college student, was arrested one night for loitering in a public park while intoxicated, and soliciting for immoral purposes. The man he approached was a vice squad police officer in civilian clothes. The court did not fine or sentence Charles but agreed to have him undergo psychiatric treatment. Under hypnosis, he recalled his first homosexual experience during early adolescence. He had been seduced by an older boy and had several further homosexual experiences. As he grew older, the urge for contacts with his own sex became compulsive in nature. His father, a prominent citizen in the community, had little contact with him; on the other hand, his mother was oversolicitous. After psychotherapy of nearly six months duration, Charles began—for the first time—to realize the nature of his problem and the cause of his actions. When last seen, he was well adjusted and happy and able to carry on a meaningful and trouble-free life in his community.

Case 3. Jim had been arrested for indecent exposure. He was in his late twenties and had exhibited himself many times before being apprehended by the police. He was given ten sessions of hypnoanalysis and hypnotherapy. The court dismissed the charge placed against him after a report was sent to the judge, indicating successful completion of his treatment. He was told to keep in touch with Dr. Caprio regarding the adjustment he was making on his own, and he promised to inform the doctor should he ever experience the urge to exhibit himself again. It has been over six months, and no discouraging news has been received from him.

Ninety-seven percent of the sexual offenders treated by this means of hypnoanalysis and hypnotherapy, using the rapid induction technique, claimed they had been rehabilitated to the extent that the impulse to repeat the offense completely disappeared.

The future of hypnosis as a specific and successful method of treating sexual deviates appears promising.

The prognosis is good if the offender exhibits a genuine willingness to be cured. Hypnosis must convince the sex offender, beyond a doubt, that he *can* be cured.

How Should the Police Handle Sex Cases?

The police, too often, adopt a callous, brutal attitude toward sex offenders. We interviewed a transvestite, a married man who related that, after he had been arrested for wearing female underwear, he was forced to parade before a group of detectives, behind closed doors, who roared with laughter to see him in a brassière and girdle. Such insensitive treatment aggravates the tragedy. This particular offender seriously contemplated suicide because of his humiliating experience.

There should be a modification of existing police practices. We refer particularly to plain-clothes men who are carried away by their enthusiasm to enforce the law. We believe the system of encouraging vice squad men to go out and bring in cases of homosexual offenses for the police records is a dangerous one, and we agree fully with Judge Ploscowe who stated: "There is a pernicious practice in many police departments which requires every member of a vice squad to produce a certain number of arrests if he wishes to stay on the squad."

We had occasion to examine a defendant whom we had to hospitalize because of his determination to commit suicide, following his arrest by a vice squad agent. While under the influence of alcohol and in the men's room of a Washington hotel, he misinterpreted the "friendliness" of a stranger who turned out to be a police officer. The district attorney's office approved of hospitalization rather than risk the defendant's committing suicide. He is presently receiving psychotherapeutic treatment.

The authors have encountered so-called "entrapment" cases where a police ambush is set to catch a suspect where circumstances surrounding the act and the arrest, especially in homosexual cases, raise questions. The testifying psychiatrist in such a case must, of course, be on his guard about his patient's statements to him. However, many cases are on record where sex squad officers frequent public places to start conversations with a suspect. The entrapped person is then charged with soliciting for an immoral purpose.

When such a case is heard in court, psychiatric testimony to the effect that the defendant is not homosexual is common, if, in fact, such is the case. It is then up to the judge or jury to decide the issue. We have dealt with cases of this type in which the charges were dismissed by the judge because of insufficient evidence. But there have been cases where the judge did not question the testimony of the arresting officer and found the defendant guilty.

There arises in these "entrapment" cases a serious question of constitutionality. The general practice among law enforcement officers is to use all kinds of decoys and other methods of enticing a person to commit a criminal act. For example, narcotic squad men sometimes pose as dope addicts to trap dope peddlers, and vice squad agents often hang around places frequented by prostitutes in the hope that one of the girls will proposition them. The courts have generally gone along with this kind of police activity. However, when the criminal act has been actually instigated by the police officer, the courts will dismiss the charge on the grounds of entrapment.

There was a recent case, involving one of our popular ballad singers, who was arrested and charged with a sexual offense, to wit, propositioning a police officer for an illicit purpose. At the trial, it was stated that the defendant had actually been importuned and encouraged to commit the act complained of by an undercover police agent. The jury, in freeing the accused, said that this was entrapment and that the arrest was, therefore, illegal. We advocate close scrutiny of all such cases.

We have to thank those jurists who keep in mind the general

rule in modern law which states: "Where police officers incited, induced, instigated, or lured the accused into committing an offense which he otherwise would not have committed and had no intention of committing, entrapment exists. And the defendant, though he has committed the offense, will not be convicted."

All sex offenders arrested by the police should be given a psychiatric examination. The police department and the courts should be guided by the recommendations of the psychiatrist.

Police officials should be given lectures on sex crimes and other aspects of sex by psychiatrists to foster a more intelligent understanding of sex offenses.

SEXUAL BEHAVIOR PROBLEMS IN THE MILITARY SERVICE

Considerable confusion exists in the military service concerning the meaning and implications of homosexuality. Consider the government ruling that any man accused of "suspicious" conduct of having so-called "homosexual tendencies" is a poor security risk. This is contrary to modern psychiatric opinion.

Dr. Benjamin Karpman, an authority on the subject, has this to say on homosexuals as security risks:

"The type which can be a security risk is rare. The silly, shallow homosexual is not interested in politics; the serious, intelligent homosexual, if interested in politics, is more likely to be conservative to compensate for his sexual unconventionality. The linking of communism with homosexuality is absurd."

While an overt homosexual who deliberately attracts attention may be considered unqualified for a responsible position, many homosexuals do not fall in this category and behave with discretion. Others who may exhibit effeminate tendencies indicative of homosexuality, however, are qualified to assume occupational responsibilities without endangering national security. Nor have security administrators produced any convincing proof that self-controlled homosexuality, as a personality trait, endangers security any more than does self-controlled heterosexuality. It is the uncontrolled sex drive in either case that may make a man a security risk. Moreover, there is the added inconsistency that, in assuming that homosexuals make a poor risk, the emphasis has been placed upon the male homosexual. It would be necessary to cast a suspicious eye on women employees as well, since it can be assumed that there is an equal incidence of female homosexuality.

We are in agreement with Edmund Bergler, who quite significantly states: "Army and Navy officials and administrators in schools, prisons, and other institutions should be more concerned with the degree of heterosexuality and homosexuality in an individual than they are with the question of whether he has ever had an experience of either sort."

Nevertheless, it is the consensus of opinion among numerous psychiatrists and attorneys that among existing regulations in various branches of the government and military service, those dealing with sexual behavior problems require revision. Many who have received "undesirable discharges" because of "homosexual tendencies" engage the services of attorneys to represent them at hearings before military review boards, their contention being that they have been victimized by unfortunate circumstances and subjected to a miscarriage of justice. They state that they have been advised to resign "for the good of the service" rather than risk a court-martial.

Dr. Caprio has examined many such persons accused of homosexuality. Defense attorneys have asked him if their client is or is not a homosexual. In many instances, he has been able to testify that they were not.

Defects of the present system have been pointed out by Thomas King, a well-known Washington attorney, whose extensive practice in military cases qualifies him to offer the following constructive criticism and recommendations. (Having worked with Colonel King on a number of such cases, Dr. Caprio feels that his comments and proposals are invaluable.)

"Many problems are presented as a result of resignations under the foregoing regulations. It is getting to the point where many people are eliminated from military service and then apply for the change of their discharge through the Discharge Review Board and/or the Board for the Correction of Military Records.

"The resignation in lieu of board proceeding, the resignation in lieu of trial by court-martial, constitutes serious problems to the individual concerned. He has been restricted in his movements; it is generally known around the station or base that he is under investigation of some kind, and psychologically he is deeply depressed. Frequently, there are family problems that the threat of a court-martial—or the threat of board proceedings—may bring disgrace or unpleasantness upon his family, whether it be his wife and children, his parents, or his sisters and brothers—all are conducive to his taking a step which he would not otherwise take except for the pressure placed upon him.

"Bar Associations throughout the country have what is known as a 'Committee on Legal Assistance to Military Personnel.' In many instances, the members of this committee are former officers of the Military Establishment, familiar with the board proceedings, court-martial and the like, and are more than willing to be of assistance to the military service in the matter of advising personnel as to their rights, for a nominal feel. The use of the Bar Association Committee eliminates the situation where service is terminated under unpleasant circumstances, since the usual requirement is that the resignation be submitted within a limited period, from 24 to 48 or 72 hours. The inability to procure independent legal advice from the local Judge Advocate Office raises the question as to the effectiveness of the legal advice of the local JAG Officer—which also is in the process of preparing papers either in the form of court-martial charges or board proceedings against the individual.

"Another rather serious situation is the adequacy, as well as the lack of bias in the investigation developing such charges. Without casting any aspersions on any individual or any branch of the service, when a person is assigned the task of making an investigation, particularly those who are doing investigative work in the criminal field, the tendency is toward a prosecution of the individual. The financial capacity of the individual is such that he is unable to conduct a cross-investigation which will match that of the government investigators. Hence, he is against substantial odds in defending himself.

"Many board proceedings are instituted where there is inadequate as well as insufficient psychiatric evaluation of the person appearing before the board. Of necessity, in many instances, doctors who are not qualified and trained in psychiatry are used. Polygraph examinations are sometimes used, although they should not be given except under the direction of a trained psychiatrist rather than the investigative authorities. If an individual who is being subjected to elimination proceedings, either by court-martial or by boards, were to be sent to a major hospital for psychiatric evaluation, much more would undoubtedly be learned. Without this, however, much material information is lost in the investigation. The use of young and inexperienced doctors who are graduates of medical schools with but slight psychiatric training is always unsatisfactory, not because of the bias or prejudice of the young medical officer but because of the lack of training.

"Another consideration is the loss of manpower to the government and the cost of the development of such manpower. Frequently the problem arises as the result of a drinking episode and things are said or done while under the influence of liquor that would never otherwise be thought of. Also, on occasion, the heavy drinking of liquor is the result of some psychiatric problem which is not recognized because it is so much deeper than the drinking and does not necessarily show itself on the surface without prolonged hospitalization and study. Brilliant men and women, definitely salvageable, have been requested to resign for the good of the service, although their records, prior to the particular incident, were superb. In addition the government had spent thousands of dollars in special training, college education, and the like. Such individuals, even when they commit an intolerable offense, should be fined and reprimanded but not dismissed from the service.

"One of the problems confronting the service is the number of applications for the review of discharges. In the Air Force, the Personnel Council acts upon the resignation. It is also the Discharge Review Board. In the Army, the Personnel Board passes upon the discharge and, under its jurisdiction is the Discharge Review Board. Different individuals sit upon the consideration of these cases in each of the two proceedings. However, where the case is presented to a board which has been passed upon by the members of the over-all council or board, the likelihood of retaining the same status is always present because of the general tendency to adhere to the original decision. This results in applications to the Board for the Correction of Military Records, or, in the case of the Navy, the Board for the Correction of Naval Records. Much time and expense are wasted in having so many boards pass upon the same case.

"In summarization:

a) No individual should be permitted to resign 'for the good of the service' until a preliminary board has actually heard the case and considered the evidence, after which the opportunity for resignation could be afforded;

b) No person should be permitted to go before a board who has not had independent legal advice either from a

Judge Advocate of a Command different from that in which the board proceeding is being held, or from private counsel obtained independently, or through the Bar Association Committee on Legal Assistance to Military Personnel.

c) In such board proceedings any statement of a derogatory nature made against an individual which is to be used in evidence should be made available to the accused in order that he might be cognizant of statements against him, as well as have the opportunity to answer them.

d) In the investigation process the accused should have full opportunity to read any statement about which he is being interrogated. Frequent instances arise where the investigator reads a part of a statement and asks the accused if that is substantially or substantively correct. Then it is reported that the statement was read and the accused stated that it was substantially, or substantively, correct. Such practices tend to bring into bad repute the investigative services.

e) No evidence in a file should be permitted to be used, unless the individual has had the opportunity of reviewing it, as well as answering it.

f) The Commander of an installation initiating elimination proceedings should be required to discuss the disciplinary problem with the individual under consideration for elimination. The elimination proceeding is a serious one to the service as well as to the individual.

g) Full and competent psychiatric evaluation by qualified psychiatrists."

The above specific recommendations by Colonel Thomas King offer constructive proposals for improvement.

CASE ILLUSTRATIONS

The following case illustrates what often happens when a person in the service is "suspected" or "charged" with having "homosexual tendencies" or having made gestures construed as "homosexual advances," and how circumstantial evidence can lead to a misevaluation and mismanagement not only of this particular case but many other cases of a similar nature.

Briefly the facts are as follows: this young man, age forty, comes from a normal well-adjusted family. He served sixteen years in various branches of the military service and had planned to complete four more years of service in order to be eligible for retirement. His military record has been a good one, having served in the South Pacific, Europe, and the Aleutians. He was charged with having "caressed" a sailor friend who was under the influence of alcohol and who had made the complaint. When the authorities searched his room, they found pictures and magazines of so-called "musclemen." His case was referred to me for a psychiatric evaluation by an attorney who specializes in military cases. The defendant insisted that he was not a homosexual, that he had sexual relations with approximately 200 women, and that he was a victim of unfortunate circumstances. I suggested that he furnish me with a detailed account of the true facts and whatever comments he wished to make regarding his situational problem.

To abstract and condense his version of what took place would detract from its value and deprive the reader of an opportunity to draw his own conclusions regarding the validity of his own statements.

"At about noon on Saturday, two Air Policemen came to the —— (where I have a part-time job) and asked me to accompany them to Air Police Operations. At Operations, we were joined by the OSI agents X. and Z. After signing a statement that I understood Article 31 of the Uniform Code of Military Justice, Z (who did most of the interrogating) informed me that I had been accused of making a homosexual overture to a Navy man. I was then asked to give a resumé of my actions from noon the previous day on. These actions, described to them verbally, were substantially as follows:

"I had worked on my regular duty assignment until 1700 on Friday after which I stopped at the NCO Club and had three or four beers with a sergeant. After that, I changed into civilian clothes at my room in the NCO barracks, walked a few blocks off base to ——, had several beers at —— Tavern, and, not seeing anyone I knew, proceeded on downtown to the area of ——. The portion of this street near the Marine Barracks has a number of bars with hillbilly or rock 'n' roll bands which are popular with military personnel. I drifted into a number of these places and finally went into what was formerly called the ——. There, I joined a friend of about one year's standing who works in the neighborhood and who was in the bar with his young son. We sat there talking and drinking beer until about 2200, when he stated he had to take the child home; he asked me to wait around awhile, as perhaps he could return. Although he was unable to come back, I waited at the bar in a position where I could watch the door.

"On entering the place earlier, I had noticed a Navy man sitting at the bar with his head on his arms as if asleep or passed out, and on at least two different occasions, I saw the police shake him and tell him to straighten up or leave. Once, when the door slammed, I looked up, and the man was sitting up and had a cup of coffee along with his beer glass and bottle. He said something to me about the music, as I remember, and we eventually struck up a conversation. As his ship (the ——) had been in the Mediterranean locale of my last overseas' assignment, we found quite a lot in common to talk about. He bought several beers, and I bought at least as many as he did. In the course of the conversation, he pointed out one of the girls who works that portion of —— and said he'd been up with her earlier in the evening. He danced with her several times while we were sitting there. He also made several references to the fact that he had had no sleep to speak of since —— and that he had been on a real bender. He was quite interested in the Air Force, said he had never been on a base, and asked if he might visit —— sometime during his leave. I told him any time, and he said how about coming out that night and staying at transient billets; in which case we could look around the base next day. I told him I thought it was possible he could stay at the Visiting Airman's Quarters, as many men on leave came to Base Operations for prospective flights, and sometimes ended up staying a night or two at the transient billets. In any event, we could check with Base Operations.

"So we left there sometime after midnight, and caught a cab to the base. He asked that I show him where I lived so he could find me next day. As my quarters are near Base Operations, we got off there and split the dollar taxi fare. In the room, he sat down and lit up a cigarette, and I checked the refrigerator in the barracks next door to see if I had any beer on hand. (I didn't have.) When I returned, he was nodding and, at one point, nearly fell from the chair. I didn't think he could make it to Base Operations, much less on over to the VAQ, so I told him to take my bed and that I'd get some cushions off the divan in the lounge and make myself a bed on the floor. When I returned with the cushions, he was undressed, except for T shirt and shorts, and was apparently asleep by the time I got into my bed. I had only been in this single room a few months, and when living next door in a two-man room, I quite often had friends (going to or returning from overseas) stop by and stay a few days. If there was not an empty bed available, I'd give them mine and sleep in the lounge or on an improvised bed on the floor. Conversely, I'd spent many a night in my friends' barracks under similar circumstances in various parts of the world.

"Anyway, an hour or so later, I was awakened by some noise or other—probably by the sailor shuffling his feet around in putting on his shoes. I asked him what he was doing, and he said he had told the girl at —— that he'd meet her when the bars closed at 0200. I switched on the light, and after he'd dressed, I took him to the door and pointed out where he could catch a cab, indicating that we never paid more than one dollar for that particular distance.

"Agent Z. told me that my account agreed almost exactly with the sailor's with the following exceptions (he seemed to place great importance on these points and went over them continually): 1. I had started the conversation in the bar; 2. I had bought all the beer; 3. I had paid the entire amount of the taxi fare; 4. I knew better than to think that anyone had to check through Base Operations to get a VAQ billet; 5. after the sailor had gone to bed, I sat down (or lay) on the bed beside him and tried to caress his cheek; and 6. that the sailor had not taken off his pants and socks prior to getting into bed. The sailor had evidently stopped (or been stopped) at the main gate, and had made his allegations to the Air Police who in turn took him to the Officer of the Day.

"Z. indicated that he had four years of college, that he specialized in these types of cases, that he batted 100%, and that he was positive I was lying about everything. I got the impression that he had had a course in high school psychology (at least), was trying to play Sigmund Freud, and mold me into the image of his investigative specialty. He asked all manner of obscene and lascivious questions and with such evident relish and enjoyment that I got the distinct impression that he was a shade warped. These questions centered around my relationships with my parents; why at my age I was not married; why I included a younger airman in my circle of acquaintances (see more on this below); had I frequented such and such bars and theaters in the district (I hadn't); had I ever had a 'blow-job' (I had from women in Paris and Naples); when was the last time I masturbated; etc. He intimated that I must be quite a souse. He asked me to enumerate my associates in the area and I gave the names of the people with whom I spent almost 100% of my off-duty time. With one exception, these friends were all of my age or older, all married, and were friends with whom I had been rather closely associated for ten or more years. The one exception was the unmarried friend, A., living on base and the agents latched onto this association with relish.

"Prior to finding me at the Credit Union that day, the agents had apparently talked to my First Sergeant who likes neither me nor A. (I had a run-in with him once over some of his duty-roster manipulations, and he had once prevented A. from getting promoted, after which A. had gotten a transfer to another squadron.) In any event, I strongly suspect that —— used this occasion to make inferences and innuendoes detrimental to A. and me. He was destitute enough for material—so much so that he had to tell them things like this: that A. had attended my graduation from the NCO Academy; he was very careful to omit, however, that A. was accompanied by his girl friend and that I had dozens of other friends there also (single, married, male, female, all ages and ranks).

"A. was about the first person I'd met on ——. We came from similar family backgrounds (hillbilly), had many mutual likes (beer, beans, bowling, hillbilly music, western movies, cards, tall tales, etc.). He was then in love with the young daughter of a very close friend of mine (I had introduced him to the girl). We nearly always went out there together except when he had some planned date or activity. I was invited to his home in a little —— coal-mining town over the 4th of July holiday weekend and became good friends with his mother and various other members of his family in that area. One unemployed brother of A.'s came up to —— later that month, and we got him a job in one of the mess halls on base as assistant manager. The brother didn't stay long due to difficulties with his wife back in ——, but while he was here, A. and I bought his food, and he used my bed over in the two-man room for over a week while I made out the best I could in empty rooms, the TV lounge, or on the floor. Soon after this, A. began to have a long series of family illnesses and difficulties, and he relied on me rather heavily for advice and moral support, and often had to borrow money from me for his emergency leaves. On the occasions when we did manage to get out together, however, we sat around discussing his (or my) problems, and usually chose to remain alone, as neither of us liked to run in packs. We almost invariably hung out in places frequented by squadron or other base personnel and were constantly plagued by free loaders and "joiners" whom we usually shook by drifting on to other places. I believe now that our independence and capacity to enjoy ourselves was pretty generally resented, as I've long observed that people in general can tolerate almost anything except a person who minds his own affairs or one who can seemingly enjoy life. So for lack of anything else, this association was seized upon by the agents to exemplify my "exclusive" interest in young men though, as indicated, this was the only young associate on the base with whom I had anything resembling a lasting friendship. It was conveniently overlooked, too, that my many other friends were of my age or older (and married); that, being single, I might have a single man's outlook and interests; and that nearly all single men living on base are young.

"At this point in the interrogation, the agents asked me if I would be willing to sign a statement on all that had passed between us up to this point. I indicated I would. At the end of the interview (many hours later), I asked them if they still wanted a signed statement, and they said no.

"The agents asked if I'd object to them searching my room, and I told them no (objections would have been useless, anyway), but did indicate that I had some items to which they

would probably attach undue significance. These items consisted of some physique model photographs which I had come
by as follows (part of the verbal statement to the agents):

> I had for years participated in weight-lifting activities and
> eventually purchased my own set of weights. Included with
> the purchase was a year's subscription to a magazine ———.
> About 1953-54, I subscribed to two other weight-lifting pub-
> lications. To promote subscriptions and renewals, these latter
> publications sent out 8 x 10 photos of various great weight
> lifters and models, or albums of such models. While the early
> editions of ——— and ——— seemed legitimate and above
> board, I noticed after a while that their advertising (usually
> of physique model photographs) became questionable. These
> publications evidently released their mailing lists to various
> studios throughout the country, as I was deluged with catalogs
> literature, and sample photographs. These pictures were
> standard physique poses at first, but soon I was receiving
> photos of completely nude models, with the information that,
> if I wanted to purchase any of these (usually at exorbitant
> rates), I was to fill out an enclosed form to indicate that I
> was an artist, sculptor, anatomist, etc. I never ordered any of
> these, and after a while, a notice would be sent out that if I
> didn't order something soon, I would be dropped from their
> mailing lists.
>
> When I went to Europe, these mailings suddenly stopped
> altogether, and I found out later that the shipments violated
> some postal regulation and that the matter was being litigated.
>
> As indicated earlier, my job is writing, and I'd spent so
> much time out of the U.S. that all facets of American life
> fascinated me, and I got the idea of doing a series of articles
> on American morals. I outlined one article on the matter just
> discussed (and several others, centering mostly on American
> activities overseas). While in Europe, however, the postal
> ban on such matter was evidently lifted, and I suddenly began
> to receive the literature again (I had had my address changed
> on the magazine subscriptions). Most of this came from a
> new concern in New York, and though clothed or covered,
> their models were in poses which were highly suggestive, and
> some poses even verged on pornography. I had collected other

material for my article by this time (including data on the laws governing physique photography), and when I began to receive notices from this latter concern that I would be removed from their mailing lists unless I ordered from them, I sent off for two or three minimum orders of about six photos each (though I didn't tell the OSI agents this). The model agency in question once included an autographed photo and addresses of two of their models, and I wrote these men, thinking I could eventually get their confidence and some clues as to their backgrounds and personalities, as well as why they would have to resort to such employment. Neither ever answered, and one of the letters was eventually returned unclaimed. The model agency in question evidently got into trouble with the postal authorities or went out of business, as in early —— I stopped getting literature and sample photos from them. But no sooner had their material ceased than I started getting matter from agencies right here in ——.

All this material certainly exceeded the volume I needed for my purposes, but I kept it with my notes and outline, and neglected to screen it or work on the series of articles, as I was currently more interested in a couple of peacetime service novels, some short stories, etc., that I was working on. Ironically, I had just recently found a pocketbook edition (in the Base Exchange) of a book called *Muscle Boy* which covered essentially the angle I had in mind and just about obviated the necessity for me to do my article at all. I had filed this book in my "Articles and Essays" folder.

"In seizing all this material, the agent said it was a good thing for me that I told them I had it, and I got the distinct impression that the other agent told him to be quiet. The other agent doubted that I had collected this material for an article, and he told me what a wonderful collection of pornography the Library of Congress had. 'You have heard of the Library of Congress, haven't you?' he asked.

"They also seized the outline, notes, and early chapters of the one novel I had with me; some of the notes were in the form of journals but covered mostly impressions of people and places, tall stories, records of GI ups and downs, etc. They took some letters I'd kept (I often make carbon copies of my own letters if I feel I'm going to relate something which might be of use in my later writings); and they took my addresses of friends and family (which I keep on index cards). Although I requested an early return of these addresses so that I could mail out my Christmas cards and gifts, they have failed to do so to date and have left me holding about 200 cards which I would ordinarily have mailed out early in the month. Further seizures included the physique magazines, a Charles Atlas course, catalogs of a sports shirt and swimming trunk concern from which I occasionally order, and a book, *The Flowers of Evil,* by Baudelaire (I'm sure they confiscated this book through an ignorance of world literature—probably because of the title; when I offered them an English translation, they embarrassedly turned it down). The agent insisted that I must have some dirty stories around, kept asking me where they were.

"In inventorying this seized material, they (over my objections) withdrew the outlines and notes on the 'American Morals' series, and the book *Muscle Boy* from my folder for 'Articles and Essays,' and listed them separately. I feel they were a little too general on the classification of other items.

"Back at interrogating (they held me from — to —) they attempted again to get a 'true statement,' said I might as well come clean, as they would check back on me from here to eternity. I intimated this might not be necessary as OSI had given me a complete background investigation for my final TOP SECRET clearance as recently as ———. They told me, like spoiled children, that my reaction was completely different from what they usually got in a case like this. I gathered they expected me to cry, implicate a lot of other people, ask for an early out, etc. I did make one request—but the wrong one, as it turned out. I told them as ——— was especially gossip prone, I felt I owed it to my officer-in-charge, —— and certain good friends to hear the matter from me rather than the rumor mill. This evidently surprised them, but they said I only wanted to tip off other members of the 'ring.' When I offered to make the calls in their presence, they told me that their cases were classified CONFIDENTIAL and that I well knew the penalties for divulging classified information. I was to keep my mouth shut, and they assured me that no one would hear about the matter except certain key administrative personnel. I laughed and told them they didn't know much about down-to-earth military operations and human nature; the matter would be all over the base by morning. (It was—greatly distorted.)

"They finally tired, and released me. I asked them if there was to be any restriction on my comings and goings. They said no, and I do not know whether or not my actions have been watched or not. I returned to the barracks, rode off base with a Master Sergeant from my barracks. I had a few beers at —— and called Lt. —— my boss. He came over from —— immediately, and I told him the whole story. He was glad to have it from my mouth, said he would help me if he could. He has kept me posted on developments. Early the next week, the Provost Marshal called him and told him that my TOP SECRET clearance had been pulled, and that the OSI told him it looked like an 'open and shut' case. Someone in the —— Division let it out that the Information Office would be losing me. When the Legal Officer got the preliminary OSI reports, he in turn called Lt. —— and told him that, when the case came up, he would not process it routinely but would give it particular attention. The Legal Officer also indicated that the investigation would take as long as thirty to sixty days. I was surprised at this time element, as someone had indicated to me earlier that, if they really had a case, I'd be booted out in two or three days. We generally interpreted the delay as indicating that they were screening the addresses, journals, notes, etc., trying to tie me in with the ring. (To my almost certain knowledge, there is not a single homosexual among my acquaintances or correspondents nor have I ever moved in their circles, frequented their hangouts, etc.)

"After I left Lt. —— on that night, I stopped off at the NCO Club where A. had a part-time job and told him briefly of what had happened. When he got off work Sunday night, we went up to —— Tavern and had a few beers, and I filled him in on the detail. He insisted that we continue our friendship as before. Earlier that same day I'd called —— and Mrs. —— whom I'd known in Saudi Arabia; they came for me and heard me out. Next day, I told Miss —— who works in our office, is a very good friend, and who has gone out with me a few times. Monday night I told ——, a friend from airlift days; he took me out to dinner, and counselled me till rather late (or rather tried to bolster up my morale). He said '—— I'm going to make you the best goddam defense witness you ever had.' On two weekends since then, he has taken me to his home in —— where his wife lives, and I also spent Christmas with them.

"I told various other friends about matters, as the occasions arose—usually after they came and told me.

"On ——, A. was called to come to the OSI's headquarters at ——. I only saw him briefly after that, but he gave me a run-down on his interrogation. He was not asked to sign Article 31; they asked him a few questions about our association without ever telling him the nature of the charge against me. They came out and searched his effects, found a letter from a girl back home, and two letters I'd written him while he was on emergency leave this last time. (These included data on some money I'd collected and sent down to him, some 'keep your chin up' advice, etc.) They—the agents—turned up, too (either through my papers or the rumor mill) that A. sometimes utilized my Sears, Roebuck account when he needed clothing or car parts or something, paying me back as he could afford it. He trusts me to keep the record and currently owes me $50.02, and I'm sure he is good for it. In this connection, I've had friends everywhere I've been stationed who utilized my account in a like manner, and do not recall that I ever lost a dime. A. indicated that the agents told him to keep away from me, and he thought it might be just as well until things were resolved. This surprised and hurt me, even though I'd told all my friends that if they wished to keep away from me, I'd understand.

"In summary, I was sometimes amazed at the agents' marked inclination to attach significance to anything they handled. For example, they apparently took as gospel the inferences from their brief by the First Sergeant (or whoever it was) and no doubt have had an avalanche of other such inferences. A man who attended the NCO Academy with me (and whom I edged out for honor student) is telling around, for instance, that he noticed a constant stream of younger airmen visiting me at the Academy barracks; the only one who ever came over there was A. and then only when I'd be too rushed to take care of such matters as mail, laundry, dry cleaning, BX supplies, etc., and would call on him to help me. Even on the rare occasions I called on him, he couldn't often help me as he had a full schedule, what with his part-time job, sports, dates, etc. In my room as indicated, they grabbed such a standard world classic of literature as the Baudelaire volume; they attached significance to my having pictures of all my thirty-six nieces and nephews; they toyed a long time with such neutral items as bookmarkers (some from the Base Library), wanting to know in detail what they were. I keep the Sunday TV Show supplements posted on a bulletin board in my room, and they pounced on one of these because a movie actor was depicted on the cover. They made me shake out my soiled laundry, piece by piece.

"I was as amazed, too, at the shallowness of some aspects of their investigation and at some of their omissions; they made no reference whatever to the condition of the sailor-making charge; they completely overlooked a massive correspondence file which I have accumulated since assignment to ——; it evidently never occurred to them that if I had had any such inclinations, my room in the barracks was not a very propitious place to carry them out.

"They consistently displayed a profound ignorance of even the simplest aspects of military life, as in the case of checking through Operations for information on transient billets, the GI grapevine on gossip items, the willingness of GI friends to give one another the shirts off their backs, etc., and they didn't believe that a GI out on the town alone, will almost invariably team up with other GI's.

"So, taking into account the agents' suspected propensity for building up a case at any cost, I feel that they might play up the salient points in this one, quote my notes and writing (fiction mostly) out of context, distort things generally, withhold other data, etc., and make a pretty plausible case to a board. I do not doubt that they are capable of playing off personnel (and witnesses) against one another, though, once, during the interrogation, they assured me volubly that they did not resort to such things. I don't, however, deeply resent their alienation of my good friends and do not feel that this comes within the purview of their investigative authority."

In our final evaluation, we believe the evidence doesn't justify any serious disciplinary action. This man should have been interrogated and examined by a psychiatrist in the military service. Nonmedical agents or investigators are not qualified to render an opinion regarding homosexual matters. Homosexual problems in the military service should be properly evaluated only by the medical officers specializing in psychiatry. No one in the medical profession will deny that *sex problems are psychiatric problems.*

To give someone an "undesirable discharge" after sixteen years of service because of the kind of evidence described above is "unscientific" and supports our premise that there is a need for the better handling of sex cases in the military service.

There is no question but that many unscrupulous persons derive a profitable income from selling by mail photos of nude or semi-nude men which appeal to persons with a pronounced latent homosexual component. We consider such practice a form of sex exploitation and detrimental to the good of society, particularly when many of the photos come within the realm or fringe of obscenity and pornography (as the defendant himself testified in writing). But if a person in the military, for example, is so victimized by mail, it would seem unjust to subject him to the severest penalty by forcing him to "resign for the good of the service." Overt homosexuals or persons who flagrantly indulge in homosexual practices should be separated from the service. But care should be taken that other individuals who are either wrongfully accused or who become innocent victims of unfortunate circumstances are given a proper interview examination by psychiatrists in the military service and not by agents, using what some servicemen refer to as "Gestapo methods of investigation." We have every confidence that in due time the miltiary will accept constructive criticism and remedy the present misevaluation and mishandling of sex problems. Existing antiquated regulations and methods of investigation should be scrapped (as we scrap outmoded destroyers that no longer serve any purpose) for a more modern and realistic approach to sex problems in the light of the newest information advanced by specialists in the field.

THE NEED FOR IMPROVED SEX LEGISLATION

It is significant that psychiatrists and lawyers who have studied the gross inadequacies of our sex laws are generally coming to the conclusion that there is urgent need for a real revision. Nor is the problem uniquely an American one, though we have been far too slow in moving toward the necessary revisions. Sweden, for example, after a decade of thorough investigation by government commissions, in which jurists, sociologists, and psychiatrists participated, revised its criminal code in 1943 to remove all ambiguous references to "unnatural acts." Prohibitory clauses now apply only to "socially dangerous manifestations of homosexuality" and other deviations and are similar to those now proposed in the Model Penal Code of the American Law Institute in this country. Like that body, the Swedish Royal Commission on Revision of the Penal Code found no justification for unnecessary public harassment of sexual deviates nor for the perpetuation of theological prejudices about sexual acts in the code.

In England, too, there is increasing concern about the apparent marked increase in prosecution of "unnatural offenses," some of the cases involving men of high position. Kingsley Martin, editor of the *New Statesman and Nation,* wrote recently of homosexuality: "It is a social evil, but its bad effects are greatly exaggerated by our stupid, savage, and out-of-date criminal law." And E. M. Forster, writing in the same journal, urged that the law be changed to ignore homosexuality per se between adults, and to treat offenses arising out of homosexuality on the same basis as heterosexual offenses.

In the United States, the present legal and economic status of sexual deviates raises weighty questions of social justice. The failure on the part of legislators and law-enforcement officers in general—though there are notable exceptions—to appreciate the distinction between *normal variations* in sexual behavior, on the one hand, and *pathological deviations,* on the other, has led to serious demoralization among large sections of the population. In our overzealous pursuit of the necessary goal of national security, it is questionable whether we have not created an entirely new category of "second-class citizens."

Many psychiatrists are of the opinion that so-called deviant sexual acts between two adults, indulged in private by mutual consent, should not be regarded as criminal offenses.

Bowman and Engle have pointed out that "not one statute regarding sodomy, crimes against nature, and other so-called unnatural acts makes an exception for married couples," and that cases on record declare that "a husband and wife can be guilty of the crime of sodomy, no matter what phase of it they happen to be practicing." Various authorities have advised clearly that such statutes are not enforced, except in a few unfortunate cases. If these statutes were revised, it might then be possible to enforce needed and important provisions of law. The deletion of unenforceable statutes does not necessarily condone the acts so excluded from criminal prosecution nor would it adversely affect sexual morality. Indeed, it would promote public morality in the wider sense of marshalling public opinion behind criminal codes that focus upon truly antisocial acts. One of the dangers of leaving unenforceable criminal statutes on the books is the widespread disregard for law so engendered. As with prohibition laws, sex laws that penalize what millions of people do not regard as *mala in se* must eventually lead to a grave deterioration in the respect for law.

These similar considerations have led the American Law Institute, in its Model Penal Code, recently completed in part, to urge that state legislatures make drastic revisions in sex laws. The Model Penal Code is the work of 1,300 eminent lawyers and judges, and though it may be years before the states generally adopt the Code, the respectability of its authorship will give it a wide hearing.

The Code proposes that homosexuality should not be

punishable by law unless it involves force or coercion, or involves minors or offenses in public.

The members voted thirty-five to twenty-four to eliminate sodomy as a punishable offense. Justice Learned Hand expressed the view that sodomy is a matter of morals—"a matter very largely of taste, and it is not a matter that people should be put in prison about."

Many other distinguished lawyers supported the following opinion: "The law today should pertain only to acts that injure society. Anything a man does to himself, or to a willing adult partner, is strictly his own business. Removing homosexuality from the criminal list will reduce blackmail while at the same time it may encourage homosexuals to seek psychiatric help."

Many state legislatures have attempted to solve the problem of the sex offender by enacting special legislation, commonly referred to as "sex psychopath" laws. Though their purpose is to correlate criminal sex conduct with abnormal mental behavior, these laws have not yet proven effective or just. They differ from state to state in basic conception; they are loosely constructed, badly defined, too broad, and inconclusive. Further, they are impractical to administer.

A comparison of two main provisions in some of these laws indicates the following:

There is a wide variation of behavior which can bring an offender under the jurisdiction of a so-called "sex psychopath" law. Examination of five different statutes, for example, shows five different definitions: psychopathic offender; psychopathic personality; person with abnormal mental illness; criminal sexual psychopath; and mentally defective delinquent.

Not only do the definitions vary, but the behavior which bring the offender's actions within such definitions varies still further. For example, jurisdictional variations may be: conviction of a felony; no crime or charge necessary; conviction of rape, sodomy, incest, lewdness, indecent exposure, obscene literature or pictures, indecent communications to females, carnal abuse or attempt to commit such an offense; charge of criminal offense and detention in penitentiary; and conviction of a felony or conviction of a misdemeanor for the third time.

The above by no means exhaustive list indicates the lack of consistency in legislation dealing with this problem. The result of this confusion is an inability to apply, with just effect, the existing laws. In all fairness to the lawmakers, it should be noted that the fault is not theirs alone. The legislator does not usually possess the training to devise a proper set of statutes in this field. There is no precise or uniform definition of the term "sex psychopath" and the widespread variance in the medical profession as to the basic cause, nature of, and proper treatment for the sex offender are further obstacles. Moreover, local facilities for examination, evaluation, and treatment of the sex offender are often inadequate and law enforcement officials seldom have the understanding necessary to deal with such cases.

But there is a growing realization that the problem of the so-called "abnormal" sex offender is one that can best be dealt with by a *psycho-legal* approach, rather than a strictly legal one. The answer is not bigger jails or more policemen, but treatment directed to a determination of psychological causes.

The sex laws of different states today include such unscientific terms as "unnatural acts," "abhorrent practices," "infamous conduct," "gross indecency," "crimes against nature," lewd or disorderly conduct," "lewd vagrancy," "lascivious acts." These terms should be changed and the obsolete term "sexual pervert" replaced by the more modern term of "sexual deviate."

COMPULSORY SEX EDUCATION

Proper sex education in our schools from the first grades to the university can do much to prevent sex offenses and reduce the incidence of sex incompatibility, responsible for so many divorces. In his book *Successful Marriage,* Dr. Spurgeon English states: "Anyone who assumes the sexual emotions can be ignored for a lifetime and that they will start functioning satisfactorily on the day of the marriage ceremony is truly living in the dark ages of thought regarding the welfare of the human animal."

There are those who advocate the suppression of books dealing with sexual enlightenment. Such people generally are using an unconscious defense mechanism against their own unresolved sexual conflicts. As Dr. Ernest Jones expressed it: "It is people with secret attractions to various temptations who busy themselves most with removing these temptations from other people; really they are defending themselves under the pretext of defending others, because at heart they feel their own weaknesses."

This perhaps explains why Dr. Sigmund Freud met with such severe criticism when he attempted to expose the secrets of the unconscious—or our instinctive cravings that we tend to repress.

In a letter to a young writer (Bruno Goetz) Freud wrote:

"My purpose is to help as well as I can the many people who today live internally in hell. Not in some hereafter but here on earth, most people live in hell . . . My scientific findings my theories and methods aim at making them conscious of this hell so that they will be able to free themselves from it."

The discussion of sex is no longer considered "dirty talk." We have gotten away from Victorian Puritanism. We now realize how important it is that sex education be given to school children. The problem, as stated by Gerald Walker, author of "A New Look at Sex Education" * is: "What, when and by whom should our young people be told about sex?"

"Youngsters need accurate information about sex," says Charles Messner, associate director of the Division of Education for the American Social Hygiene Association, "because this is one of the areas of life in which they are going to have to make decisions. But the modern view of sex education goes beyond merely imparting the 'facts of life.' It also emphasizes the importance of moral values in interpersonal relationships and aids the student in forming a wholesome code of ethics."

Sex education of children should not be the sole responsibility of parents who are too often ignorant themselves or may be in such a relation to their children as to make sex discussion difficult or even traumatic. Qualified teachers and lecturers in the school system should assume the major share of this important responsibility.

Sex-instruction programs in school curriculums are already in operation in certain states. In Oregon, since 1945, and in Michigan, since 1949, according to Gerald Walker: "Instruction in the anatomy and physiology of the sexual system has been made legally mandatory, except for students whose parents object on constitutional or religious grounds. On the other hand, there are places where sex education in public schools is banned by law."

At the Cleveland Health Museum, one of the four such institutions in the United States, visiting fifth-to-seventh grade children are told elementary facts of reproduction, birth, and growth. Lecturers use clay models to explain stages of labor up to delivery of a baby. The museum also has a life-size plastic human model for demonstration purposes.

Sweden's National League for Sexual Education (Riksforbundet Fur Saxell Upplysning) includes doctors, nurses, midwives, psychologists, and social workers. It has government

* *Cosmopolitan*, March, 1959.

backing. It educates, advises, and gives medical aid to many citizens and handles confidential problems on sex and marriage difficulties.

Its founder and current president, a Norwegian-born schoolteacher, Mrs. Elise Ottesen-Jensen (whom I had the good fortune to interview while visiting Sweden), organized countrywide programs of sex education, research, birth control, and treatment of infertility and venereal disease. She was the recipient of the 1954 Lasker Award in Planned Parenthood.

She believes that eliminating the false mystery, taboos, and prejudices concerning sex, and teaching children the truth at an early age will help create a generation of more wholesome, happier, and healthier people.

At one time in Sweden, sexual relations were regarded as something "sinful" or "shameful" and intercourse was supposed to be indulged in for procreation only. For a wife to manifest enjoyment of the sex act was considered "indecent." The use of contraceptives was condemned, and this resulted in a high rate of illegal abortions. Sweden finally assumed a new attitude toward sex, namely that "sex union by itself can enrich and deepen the sexual relationship regardless if this union has reproduction as its aim or not."

The League, in 1934, adopted the following program:

1. Sex education in all schools, teachers' colleges, and universities throughout the nation.

2. Consultation centers—stationary in cities, ambulatory in the country—which give guidance and information in all questions relating to sex.

3. Repeal of the "bill concerning contraceptives" (which prohibited all birth-control propaganda).

4. Legalization of abortion and sterilization on eugenic, biological, medical, and social grounds.

5. Revision of all legislation in this field in accordance with a scientific judgment of sexual disharmonies.

6. A thorough change of social and economic conditions in order to utilize research in the field of sex science.

Today it can be said that the Swedish people, as far as sex is concerned, have the world's most advanced laws.

Miriam Benedict, a writer, author of "Sweden Prevents Sex Delinquency" (*Sexology,* August, 1954), informs us that Sweden's present organization "believes in the happy, wanted family as the basis of society, and sex information is given with this goal in view. Courses in marriage and sexual science are held for students in Stockholm and other Scandinavian towns. Nearly one thousand students, in 1952, took advantage of these courses in the hope of building their marriage on a firm foundation."

Since no similar organization exists in either Denmark or Norway, Stockholm has become the "sex information center of the North," answering nearly 3,000 letters annually from all over Scandinavia. The League's archives are the most complete in the world.

Many critics and skeptics in this country fear that adopting Sweden's policy of sex education may increase promiscuity and infidelity.

Mrs. Elise Ottesen-Jensen made the following reply: "Sexual knowledge does not increase the promiscuity of husband and wife or the incidence of premarital sexual intercourse between young people. Taking away sexual fears and increasing sexual knowledge make it possible for love to permeate the sex activities and create greater fulfillment, permanency, and security in youthful as well as marital sex relations between men and women. Let us remember that promiscuity and extramarital relations on the part of husbands and wives are caused by unhappiness at home due to lack of knowledge, neurotic sex fears, or unwholesome sex education. Eliminate the unhappiness, spread wholesome sex enlightenment, and unfaithfulness is lessened to a considerable degree."

Sex education is now compulsory in Sweden. Professional teachers use a handbook on sex instruction, published by the Royal Board of Education. They frequently consult school physicians for expert advice. Special lectures are sometimes given by doctors. The information given varies according to different age groups. It covers the biological, medical, moral, and ethical aspects of sex.

The purpose of sex education, according to the Royal Board of Education," is to help children so that sexual development may occur as naturally as possible. Forming a healthy outlook on this side of life will be a great help to them in mastering the various problems connected with sex. The instruction must recognize that love relationships of the right kind can ennoble a youth's character and raise his ideals and, far from undermining personality, help to build it up and to endow it with dignity and stability. The school is also the means by which society acquaints its younger members with the measures, laws, and institutions which in various ways affect their lives, sometimes protecting, sometimes restricting."

Schools attempt not only to impart factual information about sex, but to train character, to inspire pupils to achieve healthy ideals and personal happiness, and fulfill their responsibility to society.

In some classes, boys and girls receive common instruction but, in cases where the information is specific to one sex, the instruction is given separately. In describing venereal diseases, care is taken not to frighten children. The subject of sexual deviations is handled in a delicate manner. The courses include information on the use of contraceptives. Teachers often consult parents, when necessary, for the purpose of enlightening them and enlisting their cooperation toward creating a happy home environment for their children.

Pupils with special disturbances or problems in sexual behavior (homosexuality, pregnancy, venereal disease) are referred to the school medical officer.

Preliminary sex instruction given in the first class, covers the following:

1. How the sexes differ.
2. Where the children come from and how they develop before they are born.
3. How children are born.
4. How children depend upon their mother and father for their homes.

Sex instruction for ages 11 to 13 includes such topics as:

1. Differences between the sexes.
2. Structure and function of the sexual organs.
3. Puberty.
4. Menstruation.
5. Night pollutions (wet dreams).
6. Masturbation.
7. Conception.
8. Development of the foetus and pregnancy.
9. Labor.
10. Determination of sex.
11. Twins.
12. Traumatic experiencs during pregnancy.

Sex instruction for ages 14 to 16 includes the additional items:

1. Sex and youth. Moral considerations. Abstention from sexual relations during adolescence.
2. Illegitimate children.
3. Spontaneous and induced abortions.
4. Venereal diseases.
5. Contraceptives.
6. Sterilization.
7. The climacteric or menopause.
8. Sexual abnormalities.
9. Moral and social aspects of sex.

10. Welfare measures to help in setting up a family.

11. Welfare measures during pregnancy, confinement, and nursing.

12. Welfare measures for the care and upbringing of children and adolescents.

Sex instruction for ages 17 to 20 covers such subjects as:

1. Menstruation and hormones.
2. Impotence and frigidity.

There is special advice and directions for dealing with pupils engaging in undesirable sexual practices, as well as measures by the school in proven cases of intercourse between pupils and when a schoolgirl becomes pregnant.

It is our hope that our country will adopt a similar educational policy.

WORLD SEX HEALTH

The peoples of the world will eventually come to realize that sexual ignorance condemns thousands to lives of unnecessary unhappiness, and damages the basic fabric of social life. Deliberate repression entails a large train of vexing consequences. Nonrational efforts to deny reality only produce harmful confusion. "Knowledge dispels fear," as science replaces superstition. As society struggles to emancipate men from other wants, it must seek to emancipate man from the want of knowledge and dispel the prejudice, bigotry, and fear that take the place of knowledge.

When needed education in the principles of sex becomes universal, mankind will pass a milestone in medical progress. A healthier world inhabited by healthier generations will be the reward.

Donald Geddes, author of *New Light On Sexual Knowledge* (New American Library, 1948) writes: "The world can hardly be called a peaceful place today, nor is there likelihood that it ever will be until we know more about sex, one of the basic motivating factors in the human being. Like atomic energy, sex is a force which can be used to destroy society or to improve it."

The following are some recommended objectives for world sex health:

1. Adequate sex knowledge should be made more accessible to people throughout the world via lectures, books, and magazines.

2. Sex education should be included in every public education program. Courses in sex education should be taught in the elementary grades, high schools, and universities. Today all children are required to participate in some form of physical education; similarly, every boy and girl should be required to attend classes devoted to the study of sex in relation to physical and mental health.

3. Sex facts should be made available to parents in need of guidance.

4. Society should be re-educated in sexual matters with the hope of eliminating neurotic sex taboos, ignorance, prejudice, and other unhealthy attitudes.

5. Legislatures should meet the urgent need for improved legislation in the handling of sex offenders.

6. There should be more enlightened management of sex cases in the military services.

7. Police officials should discourage entrapment of sex offenders.

8. More marriage clinics should be established to provide couples with the sex guidance they need.

9. As in the case of cancer, polio, and other diseases, funds should be raised to establish clinics for the treatment of sex deviates.

10. Scientific reseach in the study of sexual aberrations and

crimes should be encouraged. A National Institute of Sexual Science should be established similar to the National Institute of Mental Health, now in existence in the nation's capital. There should be other centers of research and therapy in the larger cities throughout the country and other parts of the world.

Abortion   The expulsion of the fetus at a period of uterogestation so early that it has not acquired the power of sustaining an independent life; (legal definition) the unlawful destruction or premature bringing forth of the human fetus before the natural time of birth

Adultery   Voluntary sexual intercourse of a married person with someone other than their spouse

Ambisexual   Another term for bisexual

Ambivalence   Love-hate feelings for the same person

Annulment   To cancel, make void, or nullify a marriage

Bestiality   A sexual deviation that involves sexual contact between a human being and an animal

Bisexual   A person who has a sexual interest in both sexes and the capacity for pleasurable physical relations with either sex

Buggery   Carnal copulation against nature, i.e., a man or woman with a beast, or a man "unnaturally" with a woman

Call girl   A professional prostitute who makes her business appoinments via the telephone

Capital punishment   The death penalty

Carnal knowledge   An overall term used in law to refer to sexual contact or intimacy between a male and female; literally, knowing a woman in the flesh

Castration complex   Sexual frustration associated with fears of loss of virility or related fears, sometimes causing a man to become sexually inadequate

Coitus   Sexual intercourse

Common law   That body of law or juridic theory which originated, developed, and was administered in England

Congenital   Inborn, occurring at birth

Contraception   The prevention of conception and impregnation

Coprolalia   The use of obscene language as a form of sexual stimulation

Coprophilia   A sexual deviation where sexual gratification is associated with the act of defecation; an abnormal interest in feces

Court martial   A military court under authority of government and Articles of War, established for trying and punishing a person who commits an offense while in military service

Cunnilingus   The act of licking, tonguing, sucking, or mouthing the external female genitalia (vulva)

Deviation   A departure from that which is considered "normal"

Ecclesiastical law   Pertaining to or set apart for the church

Electra complex   A strong neurotic attachment or fixation of a daughter for her father; counterpart of the Oedipus complex in men. (In Greek mythology, Electra was the daughter of Agamemnon and incited her brother Orestes to murder their mother, Clytemnestra, to avenge their father's death.)

Entrapment   The act of police officers or agents inducing a person to commit an offense not otherwise contemplated by him, for the purpose of instituting a criminal prosecution against him

Erogenous zones   Sexually sensitive areas of the body, such as the mouth, lips, breasts, buttocks, genitals, and anus

Erotic   Sexually stimulating

Exhibitionism   Indecent exposure; the unlawful exposure of one's sexual organs before a member of the opposite sex

Fellatio   The act of taking the penis into one's mouth and sucking it

Felony   Conviction of an offense in which the offender may be sentenced to death or to imprisonment in a penitentiary or state prison

Fetishism Sexual stimulation induced by handling objects of various kinds such as articles of clothing (gloves, shoes, undergarments, etc.) which enter into masturbation fantasies

Fixation A strong attachment

Flagellation A sexual deviation involving the act of whipping for sexual excitement. In sadism, pleasure is derived from administering the whipping; in masochism, from being whipped

Forensic Application of medical knowledge to the purposes of the law

Fornication Unlawful sexual intercourse between married persons

Free association A term used by psychoanalysts to describe that which a patient talks about spontaneously via the free flow of associated ideas

Frigidity Inability of a woman to achieve an orgasm during intercourse

Frottage A sexual deviation in which orgasm is induced by rubbing against an individual of the opposite sex

Heterosexual Relating to sexuality (in its broadest sense) for the opposite sex

Homosexual Relating to or directed toward one of the same sex

Homosexual panic A term used by psychiatrists to describe an acute state of anxiety experienced by a person who suffers from feelings of guilt associated with homosexual practices or thoughts

Homosexuality A sexual relationship between persons of the same sex

Hypnoanalysis A technique used by a psychiatrist or hypnotherapist for studying and analyzing a person while in a hypnotic trance

Hypnotherapy Refers to posthypnotic suggestions given by a psychiatrist to his patient for the purpose of helping him solve his problem

Id A Freudian term used by psychoanalysts to refer to unconscious instinctive drives

Incest Sexual relations between members of one's own family, as between a father and daughter, a mother and son, or brother and sister

Indecent exposure The willful and unlawful showing of one's sexual organs before a member of the opposite sex

Insanity Unsoundness of mind; (legal definition) such want of reason, memory, or understanding so as to excuse a person who has committed an act otherwise prohibited by law

Inversion (*sexual*) A term used synonymously with homosexuality

Invert A homosexual; one sexually attracted to the same sex

Impotence Sexual inadequacy in the male; incapacity to achieve or maintain an erection sufficient to provide sexual satisfaction to the woman partner

Kleptomania The impulse to steal, often motivated by an unconscious sexual conflict

Lascivious conduct Tending to deprave the morals in respect to sexual relations

Latent That which is unconscious

Lesbian A female homosexual

Lesbianism Lesbian love; female homosexuality; the erotic love of a woman for another. The relationship may consist of kissing, breast fondling, mutual masturbation, cunnilingus, or tribadism

Lewdness That form of immorality which has relation to sexual impurity

Libido The sexual impulse, hunger, or appetite; also referred to as the sexual energy of a person

Masochism Sexual pleasure in being humiliated or experiencing physical or mental pain

Masturbation Sexual self-gratification

Misdemeanor General name for criminal offenses which do not in law amount to the grade of felony

Mixoscopia Pleasure derived from witnessing two people engaged in sexual relations

Mother-surrogate Mother substitute

Narcissism Excessive self-love

Necrosadism Lust murder; mutilation of a corpse

Nymphomania Sexual desire in the female so excessive that it cannot be satisfied; the counterpart of satyriasis in the male

Oedipus complex A strong emotional attachment of a son to his mother (From the Greek myth of Oedipus who married his mother and suffered divine punishment)

Obscenity Conduct tending to corrupt public morals by indecency or lewdness

Oral Eroticism "Mouth pleasures" Patients who derive sexual pleasure by mouth contacts, or who substitute eating or other activities of the mouth for sexual gratifications, are said to be fixated at the oral-erotic stage.

Orgasm The pleasurable climax of the sexual act; in the male, it results in an ejaculation of semen; in women, it is characterized by intense sexual excitement, followed by a satisfying state of relaxation, with an increase in the secretion of the Bartholin glands of the vagina.

Paraphilia Another name for sexual deviations, used by Stekel.

Partialism A fixation of the libido to a specific portion of the female anatomy

Pedophilia A desire for sex relations with children

Pederasty Rectal intercourse

Penis envy The envy of a woman toward a man. Women with that emotion show evidence of a desire to possess a penis.

Peeping Tom A person who derives sexual pleasure from looking into bedroom windows or "peeping" for the purpose of observing a woman undressing or a couple engaged in sexual relations

Pervert A person who is considered "sexually abnormal"; invert

Phallus Another term for the penis

Phobia A persistent morbid dread or fear

Polymorphous perversity Many forms of sexual deviations

Pornography Obscene pictures or literature

Precocious sexuality Premature awakening of sexual desire

Probation Reducing the length of a prison term as a reward for good behavior

Procreate To reproduce

Prostitution Refers to sexual relations for profit or gain

Prurient Pertaining to lascivious thoughts or desires

Psychic Relating to the mind; mental or psychological

Psychic masturbation Self-gratification obtained via sexual fantasies

Psychic trauma A mental injury caused by some drastic emotional or sexual experience

Psychodynamic Referring to unconscious motivating forces

Psychogenesis   The psychological origin or development of a condition

Psycho-legal   A combined cooperative psychiatric and legal approach

Psychosexual infantilism   Sexual abnormality associated with the arrested development of the libido or sexual instinct

Psychosomatic   Pertains to illness that is caused or complicated by emotional conflict in so-called "body-mind" reactions

Psychopathic   Mentally abnormal

Psychotic   Insane

Queer   A slang expression for a homosexual

Rape   The unlawful carnal knowledge of a woman with force or without her consent

Repressions   Forces acting to discard certain emotions and experiences from consciousness and relegate them to the unconscious

Resistance   The efforts by a patient undergoing psychotherapy to prevent his neurotic patterns of life from being changed

Sadism   Sexual pleasure derived from causing someone physical or mental pain

Sadomasochism   A neurotic pattern combining sadism and masochism. One who at times is cruel (sadistic) and causes another person pain, and at other times develops feelings of self-pity or experiences a "need to suffer" as means of atonement, is referred to as "sadomasochistic."

Saliromania   Sexual deviation associated with a compulsive impulse to besmirch a painting or statue of a nude woman, or express contempt for a woman by defiling her in some form

Sapphism   Female homosexuality; Lesbianism

Satyriasis   Excessive sexual desire in men which makes complete sexual fulfilment impossible to them; the counterpart of "nymphomania" in women

Sexual aberration   Sexual deviation

Sexual apathy   Sexual indifference; without sexual feeling or desire

Sexual deviate   A person who is considered sexually "abnormal"

Sexual inversion   Homosexuality

Sexual offender   One who commits or is charged with an unlawful sexual act

Sexual perversion   That which is considered sexually "abnormal"

Sex psychopath   A person suffering from a serious sexual abnormality generally requiring institutionalization

Sodomy   "Unnatural" and unlawful sexual relations

Somatic   Pertaining to the organs of the body

Statutory law   The written will of a legislative body

Statutory rape   Sexual intercourse with a female under the statutory age of consent, with or without her actual consent

Sterility   Incapacity to procreate

Sterilization   The process of rendering a person barren or nonproducing

Taboo   Something forbidden

Third sex   A term used by Hirschfeld to refer to homosexuals; the intermediate sex

Transference   An emotional relationship that develops between a patient and the psychoanalyst, in which feelings formerly directed toward the patient's father or mother or other figure of authority or love are transferred to the analyst. If the reactions are affectionate, the transference is called "positive"; if hostile, the transference is called "negative."

Transvestism   Cross-dressing. A sexual deviation in which a person obtains erotic satisfaction or stimulation by dressing in the clothes of the opposite sex

Tribadism   The act of one woman lying on top of another and simulating coital movements so that the friction against the clitoris brings about an orgasm

Troilism   Sexual relations involving three persons

Unnatural act   A term used in law to refer to a sexual act which is considered "abnormal"

Unconscious   Latent; that which is motivated by some forbidden drive or force

Voyeurism   Sexual excitement produced by watching others undressing or enjoying sexual intimacies. The common English term for the *voyeur* is "Peeping Tom."

bibliography

Abrahamsen, David. "Study of 102 Sex Offenders at Sing Sing," *Federal Probation*. Vol. 14, No. 3 (Sep., 1950), 26-32.

Allen, C. *The Sexual Perversions and Abnormalities*. London: Oxford University Press, 1940.

———. "The Treatment of the Sexual Abnormalities," *Medical Press and Cir*. Vol. 210 (London, 1943), 23-35.

———. "On the Cure of Homosexuality," *International Journal of Sexology* (1952), 148-150.

———, and Berg, Charles. *The Problem of Homosexuality*. New York: The Citadel Press, 1958.

Allen, Frances A. "Confinement of the Sexually Irresponsible," *Journal of Criminal Law and Criminology*. Vol. 32 (1941), 196-199.

American Law Institute (A.L.I.). *Model Penal Code* (May, 1957).

Apfelberg, B., Sugar, C., and Pfeffer, A. Z. "A Psychiatric Study of 250 Sex Offenders," *Journal of Psychiatry*. Vol. 100 (1944), 762-770.

Arieff, A. J., and Rotman, D. B. "One Hundred Cases of Indecent Exposure," *Journal of Nervous and Mental Diseases*. Vol. 96 (1942), 523-529.

Bailey, D. S. *Homosexuality and the Western Christian Tradition*. New York: Longmans, Green & Co., 1955.

Baldwin's Ohio Code 13032-1.

Barratt, Norris S. "A Suggested Technique of Handling the Abnormal Sex Offender under Existing Pennsylvania Law," *Legal Intelligencer* (July 30, 1948).

Barrett, David A., and Shaeffer, C. (eds.). *Play Safe, A Simplified Guide to Our Sex Laws*. Kansas City, Mo.: Pioneer Associates, 1939.

Beauvoir, Simone de. *The Second Sex*. New York: Alfred A. Knopf, 1953.

Bender, Lauretta, and Blau, Abram. "The Reaction of Children to Sexual Relations with Adults," *American Journal of Orthopsychiatry*. Vol. 7, No. 4 (1937), 500-518.

Bennett, E. A. "The Psychopathology of Sexual Perversions," *Proceedings of Royal Society of Medicine*. Vol. 26 (1933), 1030-1034.

Bensing, R. C. "A Comparative Study of American Sex Statutes," *Journal of Criminal Law and Criminology*. Vol. 42 (May, 1951), 57-72.

Bergler, E. "Differential Diagnosis between Spurious Homosexuality and Perversion Homosexuality," *Psychiatric Quarterly*. Vol. 21 (July, 1947), 399-409.

———. "The Myth of a New National Disease," *Psychiatric Quarterly* (Jan., 1948), 66-68.

———. "Eight Prerequisites for the Treatment of Homosexuality," *Psychiatric Quarterly* (1947), 399.

367

————. *Homosexuality: Disease or Way of Life?* New York: Hill & Wang, 1957.

————. "Obscene Words," *Psychoanalytical Quarterly.* Vol. 5 (1936), 226.

Berliner, B. "Libido and Reality in Masochism," *Psychoanalytical Quarterly.* Vol. 9 (1940), 322.

————. "The Role of Object Relations in Moral Masochism," *Psychoanalytical Quarterly.* Vol. 27 (1958), 38.

Biggs, Earl R. *How to Protect Your Child from the Sex Criminal.* Portland, Oreg.: New Science Book Co., 1950.

Bloch, Iwan. *Anthropological Studies in the Strange Sexual Practices of all Races in All Ages.* New York: Anthropological Press, 1933.

————. *The Sexual Life of Our Times.* New York: Rebman Co., 1914.

Bonaparte, M. *Female Sexuality.* New York: International University Press, 1953.

Bonica vs. *Olesen* (D.C. Calif. 1954) 126 Fed. Supp 398.

Bonner, Clarence A. "Who and What Are Sexual Psychopaths?" *Focus.* Vol. 27, No. 2 (July, 1948), 103-105.

Boss, Medard. *The Meaning and Content and Sexual Perversions.* 2nd ed. New York: Grune & Stratton, 1949.

Bowling, R. W. "The Sex Offender and the Law," *Federal Probation.* Vol. 14, No. 33 (Sep., 1950), 11-16.

Bowman, Claude C. "Social Factors Opposed to the Extension of Heterosexuality," *American Journal of Psychiatry.* Vol. 106 (Dec., 1949), 441-447.

Bowman, K. M. "The Problem of the Sex Offender," *American Journal of Psychiatry.* Vol. 108, No. 4 (Oct., 1951).

————. "The Challenge of Sex Offenders: Psychiatric Aspects of the Problem," *Mental Hygiene* (1938).

————. "A Psychiatric Evaluation of Laws on Homosexuality." Read at American Psychiatric Association Meeting, Atlantic City, New Jersey, May 9, 1955.

Brande, Jacob M. "The Sex Offender and the Court," *Federal Probation.* Vol. 14, No. 3 (Sep., 1950), 17-22.

Branham, Vernon Carnegie, and Kutash, Samuel B. (eds.). *Encyclopedia of Criminology.* Toronto: George J. McLeod, Ltd., 1949.

Brill, A. A. *Sexuality and Its Role in the Neuroses.* In Psychoanalysis Today. New York: International Press, 1944.

————. "The Psychiatric Approach to the Problem of Homosexuality. *P.A. Student Health Association.* Vol. 15 (1934), 31-34.

Britain vs. *State* (1842) r Humph. Tenn. 203 (93 AIR 998).

Bromberg, Walter. *Crime and the Mind.* Philadelphia: J. B. Lippincott Co., 1948.

————. "Emotional Immaturity and Anti-Social Behavior," *Journal of Clinical Psychopathology.* Vol. 8 (1946), 423-453.

Brown, L. G. "Sex Pathologies," *Social Pathology* (1942, New York), 139-155.

Brown, Sanger, *Sex Worship and Symbolism*. Boston: D.C. Badge, 1922.

Burlingame, C. C. "The Violent Sex Offender—Criminal or Sick," The Institute of Living, *Digest of Neurology and Psychiatry*, Series No. 18 (May, 1950), 267-268.

Busser, Ralph C., Jr. "What Should be Done with Sex Offenders?" *Legal Intelligencer* (Sep. 7, 1948).

Bychowski, G. "Homosexuality—Psychology," *International Journal of Psychoanalysis*. Vol. 26 (1945, London), 114-127.

California Legislative Assembly, Preliminary Report of the Sub-committee on Sex Crimes (1950).

Caprio, Frank S. "A Case of Exhibitionism with Special Reference to the Family Setting," *American Journal of Psychotherapy*. Vol. 2, No. 4 (Oct., 1948), 587-602.

———. "Scoptophilia and Exhibitionism," *Journal of Clinical Psychopathology* (Jan., 1949).

———. "Sexual Cannibalism," *Sexology Magazine* (April, 1958).

———. "Sadistic Sex Tease," *Sexology Magazine* (1958).

———. "Hand Fetishism." *Sexology Magazine* (April, 1958).

———. *Sexual Deviations*. Washington, D.C.: Linacre Press, 1950.

———. *Variations in Sexual Behavior*. New York: The Citadel Press, 1955.

———. *The Sexually Adequate Male*. New York: The Citadel Press, 1952.

———. *The Sexually Adequate Female*. New York: The Citadel Press, 1953.

———. *The Power of Sex*. New York: The Citadel Press, 1952.

———. *Female Homosexuality*. New York: The Citadel Press, 1954.

———. *Marital Infidelity*. New York: The Citadel Press, 1953.

———. *Modern Woman's Guide to Sexual Maturity*. New York: The Citadel Press, 1959.

Caprio, Frank S. *Sex and Love*. Englewood Cliffs, N. J.: Parker Publishing Co., 1959.

California Department of Mental Hygiene. "Sexual Deviation Research, Final Report." Vol. 20, No. 1 (Mar., 1954).

Calverton, V. F., and Schmalhausen. *Woman's Coming of Age*. New York: Horace Liveright, 1931.

Carpenter, E. *Love's Coming of Age*. New York: Boni and Liveright, Inc., 1911.

Cason, Hulsey. "A Case of Sexual Psychopathy," *Journal of Clinical Psychopathy*. Vol. 8 (July-Oct., 1947), 785-800.

Cassity, John Holland. "Psychological Considerations of Paedophilia," *Psychoanalytical Review*. Vol. 14, No. 2 (April, 1927), 189-199.

Cauldwell, O. D. "Lesbian Love Murder," *Sexology Magazine* (July, 1950).

Chesser, Eustace. *Sexual Behavior, Normal and Abnormal*. London and New York: Medical Publications, 1949.

Chideckel, Maurice. *Female Sex Perversion: The Sexually Aberrated Woman As She Is*. New York: Eugenics Publishing Co., 1938.

Christoffel, H. "Exhibitionism and Exhibitionists," *International Journal of Psychoanalysis*. Vol. 17 (July, 1936), 321-345.

Clark, S. D. "Homosexuality: Medico-Legal Problems," *M. Press*. Vol. 218 (Sep. 3, 1947), 220-222.

Cohen, Louis H. *Murder, Madness and the Law*. Cleveland, Ohio: The World Publishing Co., 1952.

Commonwealth of Massachusetts, Final Report of the Special Commission Investigating the Prevalence of Sex Crimes (April, 1948).

Commonwealth vs. *Fiede* 271 Mass. 318 (1930).

Conn, J. H. *Brief Psychotherapy of the Sex Offender*. A Report of a Liaison Service between a Court and a Private Psychiatrist, *Journal of Clinical Psychopathology*. Vol. 10 (Oct., 1949).

Cook, George A. "Problem of the Criminal Sexual Psychopath," *Dis. Nervous System*. Vol. 10 (May, 1949).

Cory, Donald Webster. *The Homosexual in America*. New York: Greenberg, 1951.

Creadick, R. N. "Management of the Intersexuals," *Southern Medical Journal* (1953), 455-460.

Crew, F. A. E. "Sex: Its Nature and Abnormalities Considered from Biological and Legal Points of View," *Proceedings of Royal Society of Medicine*. London and New York: Medical Publications, 1949.

Crucial Issues in the Treatment and Control of Sexual Deviation in the Community. A Report of the State Psychiatric Research Clinic in Detroit, with Recommendations as Formulated by H. Warren Dunham, State Department of Mental Health, Lansing, Mich. (June, 1951).

Cruvant, Bernard A., Meltzer, Milton and Tartaglino, Francis J. "An Institutional Program for Committed Sex Deviants," *American Journal of Psychiatry*. Vol. 107, No. 3 (Sep., 1950), 190-194.

Curran, D., and Parr, D. "Homosexuality: An Analysis of 100 Male Cases Seen in Private Practice," *British Medical Journal* (April, 1957), 797-801.

Cushing, J. G. N. "Psychotherapy of Sexual Delinquency," *Journal of Clinical Psychopathology* (April, 1950), 49-56.

Davenport vs. *U.S.* (D.C. 1948-56 A. 2nd 851).

Davidson, Henry A. "Legislation Dealing with Sex Offenders," *American Journal of Psychiatry*. Vol. 106 (Nov., 1949), 390.

Davis, K. *Factors in the Sex Life of Twenty Two Hundred Women*. New York: Harper & Brothers, 1929.

De River, Paul. *The Sexual Criminal*. Springfield, Ill.: Charles C Thomas, 1949.

Deb, A. K. "Suicide and Homicide in Relation to Sexual Difficulties," *Ind. Medical Rec.* (1946), 66-134.

D.C. Code 22-504 (1951): D.C. Code 22-1112 (Supp. 10, 1955).

Department of Justice, Bureau of Prisons. *National Prisoner Statistics* (Feb., 1958, No. 18).

Deutsch, Albert. "Sober Facts about Sex Crimes," *Colliers* (Nov. 25, 1950).

Deutsch, H. *The Psychology of Women*. Vols. 1 and 2. New York: Grune & Stratton, 1944-1945.

Dishay, L. J. *The Boy Sex Offender and His Later Career*. New York: Grune & Stratton, 1943.

Drummond, Isabel. *The Sex Paradox*. New York: G. P. Putnam's, 1953.

Dunham, Warren H. *Crucial Issues in the Treatment and Control of Sexual Deviation in the Community*. State Department of Mental Health, Lansing, Mich.

Dutton, Charles J. "Can We End Sex Crimes?" *Christian Century* (1937), 1594-1595.

East, W. Norwood. "Observations on Exhibitionism," *Lancet*. Vol. 11 (Aug. 23, 1924), 370-375.

Eliasberg, W. "The Irresistible Impulse and Crime," *Psychiatric Quarterly Supplement*. Vol. 21 (1947), 108-122.

Ellis, Albert. *The Folklore of Sex*. New York: Charles Boni, 1951.

———. "On the Cure of Homosexuality," *Int. Journal of Sexology* (1952).

———. "The Effectiveness of Psychotherapy with Individuals Who Have Severe Homosexual Problems," *Journal of Consulting Psychology* (1956).

Ellis, Havelock. *Studies in the Psychology of Sex*. Vol. 1. Philadelphia: F. A. Davis Co., 1910.

———. *Studies in the Psychology of Sex*. Vol. 2. New York: Random House, 1936.

Farnham, Marynia F. "The Unmentionable Minority," *Cosmopolitan Magazine* (May, 1948).

Fenichel, O. *The Psychoanalytic Theory of Neurosis*. New York: Norton, 1945.

Fere, C. S. *Sexual Degeneration in Mankind and in Animals*. Trans. by Ulrich van de Horst, Ph. D. New York: Anthropological Press, 1932.

Fishman, Joseph. *Sex in Prison*. New York: National Library Press, 1934.

Flexner, Abraham. *Prostitution in Europe*. New York: Century Co., 1914.

Ford, Clellan, and Beach, Frank A. *Patterns of Sexual Behavior*. New York: Harper & Brothers, 1951.

Foxe, Arthur N. *Crime and Sexual Development*. The Monogram Editions. New York: Glen Falls, 1936.

Frederica, Diana. *Diane: A Strange Autobiography*. New York: The Citadel Press, 1939.

Freeman, T. "Clinical and Theoretical Observations on Male Homosexuality," *International Journal of Psychotherapy*. Vol. 36 (1955), 335.

Freud, S. *Three Contributions to the Theory of Sex*. Nervous and Mental Disease. Monograph Series No. 7, New York, Nervous and Mental Disease Publishing Co., Washington, D.C., 1930.

———. "The Psychogenesis of a Case of Homosexuality in a Woman." In Collected Papers. The Hogarth Press, Ltd., London, 1924.

Freyhan, F. A. "Homosexual Prostitution," *Delaware State Medical Journal*. Vol. 19 (May, 1947), 92-94.

Frosch, J. and Bromberg, W. "The Sex Offender: A Psychiatric Study," *American Journal of Orthopsychiatry* (1939).

Gebhard et al. *Pregnancy, Birth and Abortion*. New York: Hoeber-Harper, 1958.

Gillespie, W. M. "Contribution to the Study of Fetishism," *International Journal of Psychoanalysis*. Vol. 22 (Oct., 1940), 401-415.

Gilmore vs. *State* 118 Sa. 299. 45 S.E. 226.

Glover, Benjamin H. "Observations on Homosexuality among University Students," *Journal of Nervous and Mental Diseases*. 11B (May, 1951), 377-387.

Glover, Edward J. "Notes on an Unusual Form of Perversion," *International Journal of Psychoanalysis*, London (1937).

Glueck, Bernard C., Jr. *Psychodynamic Patterns in the Homosexual Sex Offender*. Read at the American Psychiatric Association Meeting, Atlantic City, N. J., May 9, 1955.

Greensoan, Herbert, and Campbell, John D. "The Homosexual as a Personality Type," *American Journal of Psychiatry*. Vol. 101 (Mar., 1945), 682-689.

Griffith, E. F. "The Treatment of Sexual Disorders in Women," Medical Press and Cir., London (1943).

Groves, Ernest R. *The American Woman*. New York: Greenberg, 1937.

Gurvity, M. *Sexual Offenders in Private Practice, Treatment and Outcome*. Paper delivered at American Psychological Association (Sep. 3, 1957).

Gutheil, Emil A. "Neuroses and Crime: Stekel's Contribution to the Problem of Criminality in Neurosis," *Journal of Criminal Psychopathology*. Vol. 2 (1941), 444-454.

Guttmacher, Manfred S. *Sex Offenses: The Problem, Causes and Prevention*. New York: W. W. Norton Co., Inc., 1951.

Guyon, R. *The Ethics of Sexual Acts*. New York: Alfred A. Knopf, 1949.

———. *Sexual Freedom*. New York: Alfred A. Knopf, 1950.

———. "The Sexual Problem during the Historical Period," *Sexology* (Nov. and Dec., 1949).

Hadfield, J. A. "Some Aspects of the Psychopathology of Sex Perversions," *Proceedings of Royal Society of Medicine*, (London, 1933).

Hadley, Ernest E. "Comments on Pedophilia," *Medical Journal Records.* Vol. 124 (Aug., 1926), 157-162.

Haines, William H., Hoffman, Harry R., and Esser, Robert A. "Commitments under the Criminal Sexual Psychopath Law in the Criminal Court of Cook County, Ill.," *Journal of Psychiatry.* Vol. 105 (Dec., 1948), 420-425.

Haire, N., Costler, A. Willy, et al. *Encyclopedia of Sexual Knowledge.* New York: Eugenics Publishing Co., 1937.

Hall, Gladys Mary. *Prostitution: A Survey and a Challenge.* London: Williams & Norgate, 1933.

Hall, R. *The Well of Loneliness.* New York: Blue Ribbon Books, 1928.

Handbook on Sex Instruction in Swedish Schools. The Royal Board of Education in Sweden, 1956.

Harper, Dana. "The Truth about Homosexual Women," *Sexology* (Aug., 1948).

———. "What Do Homosexuals Want?" *Sexology* (Feb., 1950).

Harris, Charles. "A New Report on Sex Crimes," *Coronet* (Oct., 1947).

Harris, H. Wilson. *Human Merchandise: A Study of the International Traffic in Women.* London: Ernest Benn, 1928.

Hartwell, Samuel W. *A Citizen's Handbook of Sexual Abnormalities and the Mental Hygiene Approach to their Prevention.* A Report to the Committee on Education of the Governor's Study Commission on the Deviated Criminal Sex Offender, State of Michigan (1950).

Harvey, Holman. "Help Stamp Out This Vile Traffic," *Reader's Digest* (Mar., 1959).

Hearings before Sub. Comm. Judiciary—Jan. 27-30 (85th Cong.) (1958).

Henninger, James M. "Exhibitionism," *Journal of Criminal Psychopathology.* Vol. 23, No. 3 (Jan., 1941), 436-444.

Henry, George W. *Sex Variants.* 2nd ed. P. B. Hoeber, 1948.

———. "Psychogenic Factors in Overt Homosexuality," *American Journal of Psychiatry.* Vol. 93, Part 2, No. 4 (Jan., 1937).

———. and Gross, Alfred A. "Social Factors in the Case Histories of 100 Under-Privileged Homosexuals," *American Mental Hygiene.* Vol. 22 (Oct., 1938), 591-611.

———. The Homosexual Delinquent," *American Mental Hygiene.* Vol. 25, No. 1 (July, 1941), 420-442.

———. "The Sex Offender: A Consideration of Therapeutic Principles." National Probation Association Yearbook, pp. 114-137 (1940).

Hirschfield, M. *Sexual Anomalies.* London: Francis Aldor, 1944.

Hitschmann, E., and Bergler, E. *Frigidity in Women: Its Characteristics and Treatment.* Nervous and Mental Diseases Monograph Series. New York: Nervous and Mental Disease Publishing Co., 1936.

Hoch, P. H. and Zubin, F. *Psychosexual Development in Health and Disease.* New York: Grune & Stratton, 1949.

Honnigmann, John J. "A Cultural Theory of Obscenity," *Journal of Criminal Psychopathology*. Vol. 5 (1944), 715-733.

Hoover, J. Edgar. "How Safe Is Your Daughter?" *American Magazine*. Vol. 144 (July, 1947).

Horack, Frank E. "Sex Offenses and Scientific Investigation," Illinois Law Review. Vol. 44, No. 2 (May-June) p. 152.

House, S. D. "A Psychosexual Inventory," *Psychoanalytic Review* (Washington, D. C., 1927).

Horney, Karen. *The Neurotic Personality of Our Times*. New York: W. W. Norton & Co., 1937.

———. "The Problem of Female Masochism," *Psychoanalytical Review*. Vol. 22 (1935), 241.

Hughes, James E. "The Minnesota 'Sexual Irresponsibles' Law," *Mental Hygiene*. Vol. 25, No. 1 (Jan., 1941), 76-86.

Hulbert, Harold S. "Post-Sex Crime Amnesia." Editorial. *Journal of Criminal Law Criminol*. Vol. 37 (Sep.-Oct., 1948), 191-192.

Indiana Statutes (Burns) 104221.

Kahn, S. *Mentality and Homosexuality*. Boston: Meadow Publishing Co., 1937.

Karpman, Benjamin. "A Case of Paedophilia," *Psychoanalytic Review*. Vol. 37, No. 3 (July, 1950).

———. "Criminality as an Expression of Psychosexual Infantilism," *Journal of Criminal Psychopathology*. Vol. IV (1942).

———. "Dream Life in a Case of Transvestism," *Journal of Nervous and Mental Disorders*. Vol. 106, No. 3 (Sep., 1947), 292-339.

———. "Felonious Assault Revealed as a Symptom of Abnormal Sexuality," *Journal of Criminal Law Criminology*. Vol. 37, No. 3 Sep.-Oct., 1946).

———. "Mediate Psychotherapy and the Acute Homosexual Panic," *Journal of Nervous and Mental Disorders*. Vol. 98, No. 5 (Nov., 1943).

———. "Perversions as Neuroses (The Paraphiliac Neuroses)," *Journal of Criminal Psychopathology*. Vol. 3, No. 2 (1942).

———. "Sex Life in Prison," *Journal of Criminal Law Criminology*. Vol. 38, No. 5 (Jan.-Feb., 1948).

———. "The Sexual Offender: A Case of Obscene Letter Writing," *Psychoanalytic Review*. Vol. 10 (July, 1923), 1-46.

———. *The Sexual Offender and His Offenses*. New York: Julian Press, 1954.

Kentucky Revised Statutes (1948) R 32-990.

Kercher, John. "Sex Crimes," *Illinois Medical Journal*. Vol. 73, No. 1 (Feb., 1928), 171-172.

Kinsey, Alfred C., Pomeroy, Wardell B., and Martin, Clyde W. *Sexual Behavior in the Human Male*. Philadelphia: W. B. Saunders, 1948.

Kolb, L. C., and Johnson, A. M. "Etiology and Therapy of Overt Homosexuality," *Psychoanalytic Quarterly*. Vol. 24 (1955), 506.

Krafft-Ebing, Richard von. *Psychopathia Sexualis.* Brooklyn, N. Y.: Physicians and Surgeons Book Co., 1922.

Krinsky, Charles M., and Michaels, Joseph J." A Survey of 100 Sex Offenders Admitted to the Boston Psychopathic Hospital," *Journal of Criminal Psychopathology.* Vol. 2 (Oct., 1940), 198-201. Kronengold, Edward, and Sterba, Richard. "Two Cases of Fetishism," *Psychoanalytic Quarterly.* Vol. 5 (1936).

Kronhausen, Eberhard and Phylis. *Pornography and the Law.* New York: Ballantine Books, 1959.

Lauval, Marc. "Some Legal Aspects of Homosexuality," *International Journal of Sexology* (Bombay, India, 1950).

Leroy vs. *Sidley* 1 Sid. 168-82 Eng. Reprint (1036) 1663. Lewinsky, H. "Features from a Case of Homosexuality," *Psychoanalytical Quarterly.* Vol. 21 (1952), 344-354.

Lewinsohn, Richard. *A History of Sexual Customs.* New York: Harper & Brothers, 1958.

Lewis, N. D., and Yarnell, H. "Pathological Fire-Setting (Pyromania)," *Nervous and Mental Disease Monographs.* New York: Nervous and Mental Diseases Publishing Co., 1951.

Licht, R. *Sexual Life in Ancient Greece.* London: Routledge & Kegan Paul, 1949.

London, Louis and Caprio, Frank S. *Sexual Deviations.* Washington, D. C.: Linacre Press, 1949.

Lorand, S. "Perverse Tendencies and Fantasies: Their Influence on Personality," *Psychoanalytical Review.* Vol. 26 (1939), 178-90.

Lundberg, F., and Farnham, M. *Modern Women: The Lost Sex.* New York: Harper & Brothers, 1947.

Mackwood, J. C. "A Note on the Psychotherapuetic Treatment of Homosexuality in Prison," *Medical Press* (London, Sep. 3, 1947).

Mac Iver, R. *Sex and Social Attitudes about the Kinsey Report.* New York: New American Library of World Literature, Inc., 1948.

Malinowski, B. *The Sexual Life of Savages in Northwestern Melanesia. An Ethnographic Account of Courtship, Marriage and Family Life among the Natives of the Trobriand Islands.* British New Guinea. New York: Halcyon House.

Mannheim, H. "Some Criminological Aspects of Homosexuality," *Medical Press.* Vol. 218 (Sep. 3, 1947), 210-212.

Mangus, A. R. "Sexual Deviation and the Family," *Marriage and Family Living.* Vol. 15 (Nov., 1953), 325-331.

Mantegazza, P. *The Sexual Relations of Mankind.* S. Putnam, trans. New York: Eugenics Publishing Co., 1935.

————. *Physiology of Love.* H. Alexander, trans. New York: Eugenics Publishing Co., 1936.

Martin, W. F. "An Unusual Case of Sex Perversion," *Journal of Michigan Medical Society,* Grand Rapids, 1926.

Martin vs. *State* (1928) 38 Ga App. 392-93 ALR 1005.

Massina vs. *Maryland* (1957) 130 A 2nd 578.

Mayer, E. E. "The Sex Deviate," *The Pennsylvania Medical Journal.* Vol. 53 (Jan., 1950), 32-37.

McCormick, Austin H. "New York's Present Problem. Symposium Challenge of Sex Offenders," *Mental Hygiene.* Vol. 22 (Jan., 1938), 4-10.

McNickles, R. N. "Control of Sex Offenses," *Editorial Reserch Reports.* Vol. 11 (1949), 853-870.

McPartland, J. *Sex in Our Changing World.* New York: Rinehart & Co., 1947.

Menninger, K. *Love Against Hate.* New York: Harcourt, Brace & Co., 1942.

Mercer, J. D. *They Walk in Shadow.* New York: Comet Press Books, 1959.

Miliken, R. J. "The Sex Offender's Victim," *Federal Probation.* Vol. 14, No. 3 (Sep., 1950), 22-26.

Minnesota Statutes—part 5—Chapter 6.4.17.

Minow, Newton. "The Illinois Proposal to Confine Sexually Dangerous Persons," *Journal of Criminal Law.* Vol. 40 (July-Aug., 1949), 186-187.

Moll, Albert. *Libido Sexualis: Studies in the Psychosexual Laws of Love Verified by Clinical Case Histories.* New York: American Ethnological Press, 1933.

————. *Perversions of the Sexual Instinct—A Study of Sexual Inversion.* trans., Maurice Popkin, Ph.D. Newark, N. J.: Julian Press, 1931.

Monroe, Russell R., and Enelow, Morton L. "Therapeutic Motivations in Male Homosexuals," read at the American Psychiatric Association Meeting, Atlantic City, N. J. (May 9, 1955).

Moore, T. V. "Homosexuality, Pathogenesis," Pearson, Durham. Vol. 14 (1945), 47-83.

Mozes, Eugene R. "The Lesbian," *Sexology Magazine* (Dec., 1951).

National Prisoner Statistics (F.B.I.) 1955, 6, 7, and 8.

N. C. Law Review 36: 189 (Feb., 1958).

Nedoma, K. "Homosexuality in Sexological Practice," *International Journal of Sexology* (1951), 219-224.

New Jersey Commission on the Habitual Sex Offender, "The Habitual Sex Offender." New Jersey Report and Recommendations as formulated by Paul W. Tappan, Trenton, New Jersey (1950).

New York City, Mayor's Committee for the Study of Sex Offenses, "Report of the Mayor's Committee for the Study of Sex Offenses." New York (1941).

Niederland, William G. "Masculine Women Are Cheating Love," *Coronet Magazine* (May, 1953).

Noblett vs. *Corum* S. C. Appls. Va 72 S.E. 2nd 241 (1952). Nunberg, H. "Circumcision and Problems of Bisexuality," *International Journal of Psychoanalysis.* Vol. 28 (1947), 1.

N. Y. vs. *Doubleday* 297 N. Y. 687 (1947).

N. Y. Penal Law 690-722—1140 b.

Oberndorf, C. P. "Voyeurism As a Crime," *Journal of Criminal Psychopathology.* Vol. 12, No. 2 (Oct., 1939), 103-111.

Overholser, Winfred. "Legal and Administrative Problems. Symposium, Challenge of Sex Offenders." *Mental Hygiene.* Vol. 22 (Jan., 1938), 20-24.

————. *The Psychiatrist and the Law.* New York: Harcourt, Brace & Co., 1953.

Peck, Martin. "Exhibitionism: Report of a Case," *Psychoanalytical Review.* Vol 11, No. 2 (April, 1924), 156-165.

People of the State of Michigan vs. *Fred C. Ring* 255 W. 373 93 ALR 943 (1939).

Peyton vs. *D. C.* 100 A. 2nd 36 (1953).

Picton, Harold. "The Morbid, the Abnormal and the Personal," *British Society for the Study of Sex Psychology* (London, 1923).

Piker, Philip. "Sex Offenses as Seen by a Psychiatrist," *Journal of Health and Physical Education.* "Vol. 18 (Nov., 1947), 645-646-689-690.

Pillay, A. P., and Ellis, Albert (eds.). "Sex, Society and the Individual," *The International Journal of Sexology,* Bombay, India, 1953.

Platt, J. A. "Sappho." *Encyclopedia Britannica,* 11th ed.

Ploscowe, Morris. *Sex and the Law.* New York: Prentice-Hall, 1951.

Pollens, B. *The Sex Criminal.* New York: Macaulay, 1938.

Poe, J. S. "The Successful Treatment of a Forty-Year Old Passive Homosexual," *Psychoanalytical Review.* Vol. 29 (1952), 23-30.

Porterfield, A. L. "Sexual Psychopaths: Psychiatrists and Courts," *Journal of Criminal Law Criminology.* Vol. 38 (May-June, 1947), 55-56.

Potter, LaForest. *Strange Loves. A Study in Sexual Abnormalities.* New York: Robert Dodsley Co., 1933.

Psychiatrically Deviated Sex Offenders. Formulated by the Committee on Forensic Psychiatry of the Group for the Advancement of Psychiatry. Report No. 9 (May, 1949) (Rev. Feb., 1950), Topeka, Kansas.

Psychiatric Characteristics of Sex Offenders. A statistical Analysis of 250 Sex Offenders Examined at the New Jersey State Diagnostic Center at Menlo Park. Department of Institutions and Agencies, State of New Jersey, mimeographed (1950).

Radlo, Sandor. *An Adaptational View of Sexual Behavior in Psycho-sexual Development in Health and Disease.* New York: Grune & Stratton, 1949.

————. "A Critical Examination of the Concept of Bisexuality," *Psychosomatic Medicine* (1940).

Regina vs. *Hicklin* (1865) L.R. 3 B.Q. 360, 371.

Reik, T. *Masochism in Modern Man.* New York: Farrar and Rinehart, 1941.

Reinhardt, James M., and Fisher, Edward C. "The Sexual Psychopath and the Law," *Journal of Criminal Law Criminology.* Vol. 39 (1949), 734-742.

Remington's Revised Statutes of Washington—Cg. 6—Vol. 4.

Report of the Departmental Committee on Sexual Offenses Against Young Persons. London: H.M. Stationery Office, 1925.

Report of the Governor's Study Commission on the Deviated Criminal Sex Offender. State of Michigan. Hon. G. Mennen William, 1951.

Report of the Interim Commission of the State of New Hampshire to Study the Cause and Prevention of Serious Sex Crimes (Mar., 1949).

Report of the Mayor's Committee for the Study of Sex Offenses, City of New York (1940).

Report on the Study of 102 Sex offenders at Sing Sing Prison as Submitted to Governor Thomas E. Dewey, Albany, New York (Mar., 1950).

Report Judiciary Committee 85th Cong. (April 17, 1958).

Rex vs. *Gallard* (1733) 25 Eng. Reprint 547 93 A.L.R. 998.

Rickles, N. K. "Exhibitionism," *Journal of Nervous and Mental Diseases.* Vol. 95 (Ja., 1942).

Roche, Philip Q. "Sexual Deviations," *Federal Probation.* Vol. 14, No. 3 (Sep., 1950), 3-11.

Romm, May E. "Compulsion Factors in Exhibitionism," *Journal of Criminal Psychopathy.* Vol. 3 (April, 1942), 585-596.

Ross vs. *U. S.* 354 U. S. 476 (1957).

Ruskin, Samuel H. "Analysis of Sex Offenders among Male Psychiatric Patients," *American Journal of Psychiatry.* Vol. 97 (Jan., 1941), 955-968.

Sadger, S. A. "A Contribution to the Understanding of Sadomasochism," *International Journal of Psychoanalysis.* Vol. 7 (1926), 484.

Schmalhausen, S. D. *Why We Misbehave.* New York: Garden City Publishing Co., 1928.

Secor, H. W. "Sex Life in the Far East," *Sexology Magazine,* (July, 1950), 762-772.

Selling, Lowell S. "Endocrine Glands and Sex Offenders," *Medical Records.* Vol. 147 (May, 1938), 441-444.

Seward, G. H. *Sex and the Social Order.* New York: McGraw-Hill Book Co., 1946.

Sex Offenders: A Report of the Joint State Government Commission to the General Assembly of the Commonwealth of Pennsylvania (1951).

Shaskin, Donald. "One Hundred Sex Offenders," *American Journal of Orthopsychiatry.* Vol. 9, No. 3 (July, 1939), 565-569.

Sheldon, W. H. *Varieties of Delinquent Youth.* New York: Harper & Brothers, 1949.

Sherwin, Robert V. *Sex and the Statutory Law.* New York: Oceana Publications, 1949.

Silverman, Daniel. "The Treatment of Exhibitionism: An Experiment in Operation between Police and Psychiatric Clinic," *Bulletin of Menninger Clinic,* Topeka, Kansas. Vol. 4-5 (1941), 85-93.

Slater, E. P. "Assessment of Homosexual Traits," *British Journal of Medical Psychology.* Vol. 21 (1947), 61-74.

Sorensen, S. *Abnormal Sexuality in Love and Marriage.* New York: S. Forbat, 1938.

Sperling, Melitta. "The Analysis of an Exhibitionist," *International Journal of Psychoanalysis.* Vol. 27 (1947), 32-45.

Sperling, O. "Psychodynamics of Group Perversions," *Psychoanalysis Quarterly.* Vol. 25 (1956), 56.

Srnec, Dr., and Freund, Dr. "Treatment of Male Homosexuality through Conditioning," *International Journal of Sexology.* (1953), 92-93.

Stanley-Jones, D. "Sexual Inversion and the English Law," *Medical Press and Circ* (1946).

————. "Homosexuality," British Medical Journal (1946).

————. "Sexual Inversion: An Ethical Study," *The Lancet.* Vol. 1 (1947), 366.

————. "Sexual Inversion: The Problem of Treatment," *Medical Press* (1947), 212.

State vs. *Goldstein* (1906) 72 336 (98 A.L.R. 999).

State vs. *Wolf* (1922) 211 Mo. App. 429 (98 A.L.P. 999).

Stearns, A. W. "Personality Study of Sex Offenders," *Journal of Nervous and Mental Diseases* (Albany, New York, 1929).

Stekel, W. *Bisexual Love. The Homosexual Neurosis.* Boston: R. G. Badger, 1922).

————. *Frigidity in Woman.* New York: Liveright Publishing Co., 1926. Vols. I and II.

————. *Sadism and Masochism.* New York: Liveright Publishing Co., 1929.

————. *Sexual Aberrations.* New York: Liveright Publishing Co., 1930.

Stewart, William Scott. "Comments Concerning Proposed Legislation for the Commitment of Sex Offenders," *John Marshall Law Quarterly.* Vol. 3 (Mar., 1938), 407-421.

Strakosch, F. M. *Factors in the Sex Life of Seven Hundred Psychopathic Women.* New York: State Hospital Press, Utica, 1934.

Sutherland, Edwin H. "The Diffusion of Sexual Psychopath Laws," *American Journal of Sociology.* Vols. 56 (Sep., 1950), 142-148.

Tappan, Paul. "Sex Offender Laws and Their Administration," *Federal Probation.* Vol. 14, No. 3 (Sep., 1950), 32-37.

Taylor, F. H. "Observations on Some Cases of Exhibitionism," *Journal of Mental Diseases.* Vol. 93 (July, 1947), 631-638.

The Criminal Law and Sexual Offenders. Report of the Joint Committee on Psychiatry and the Law Appointed by the British Medical Association and the Magistrates Association, *British Medical Journal Supplement* (Mar. 12, 1949), 135-140.

The Habitual Sex Offender: Report and Recommendations of the Commission on the Habitual Sex Offender, State of New Jersey (1950).

Thompson, C. *Changing Concepts of Homosexuality: A Study of Impersonal Relations.* Ed. by Patrick Mullahy. New York: Hermitage Press, Inc., 1949.

Thornton, Nathaniel. "Homosexuals Your Mind," *Psychology Digest* (New York, June, 1948).

Thorner, H. A. "Notes on a Case of Male Homosexuality," *International Journal of Psychoanalysis.* Vol. 30 (1949), 31.

Uniform Crime Reports for the United States, Department of Justice, Nos. 1 and 2 Special Issue (1958).

University of Pennsylvania Law Review, Vol. 106, No. 1 (Nov., 1957).

U.S. vs. *Kennerley* 209 Fed. 119 (1913).

U.S. vs. *One Book Called Ulysses* 5 Fed. Supp. 182 (1933).

U.S. vs. *31 Photos and Institute for Sex Research* U.S.D.C. So. Dist N. Y. (1947).

U.S. vs. *Ross* 205 F d. 2nd 619 (1958).

U.S.C.A. Title 18 sec. 1461, 2, 3, 4, 5.

Van de Velde, T. H. *Ideal Marriage. Its Physiology and Technique.* New York: Covici Friede, 1930.

Volanski vs. *U.S.* (C.A. Ohio-1957) 246 Fed. 2nd 842.

Waggoner, Raymond W. and Boyd, David R., Jr. "Juvenile Sexual Behavior," *American Journal of Orthopsychiatry.* Vol. 2 (Apr., 1941), 275-292.

Wall, Thomas R., Jr., and Wyler, Charles P. "Institutional and Post-Institutional Treatment of the Sex Offender," *Vanderbilt Law Review.* Vol. 2 (Dec., 1948), 47-61.

Weihofen, Henry. *The Urge to Punish.* New York: Farrar, Straus and Cuddahy, Inc., 1956.

Weirauch, Anna Elizabeth. *The Outcast.* New York: Greenberg, 1933.

————. *The Scorpion.* New York: Greenberg, 1932.

Wertham, Frederic. "Psychiatry and the Prevention of Sex Crimes," *Journal of Criminal Law Criminology.* Vol. 28 (1938), 847-853.

Westmarck, Edward. *The Origin and Development of the Moral Ideas.* 2nd ed. London: Macmillan Co., 1917.

White, H. D. Jennings. "Psychological Causes of Homoeroticism and Inversion," *British Society for the Study of Sex Psychology.* London, 1925.

Wile, Ira S. "Sex Offenses against Young Children: What Shall Be Done about Them?" *Journal of Social Hygiene.* Vol. 23, No. 1 (1939), 33-34.

Wilhelm, Gale. *Torchlight to Valhalla.* New York: Random House, 1938.

Winner, A. L. "Homosexuality in Women," *Medical Press* (Sep. 3, 1947), 218.

Wittels, David G. "What Can Be Done about Sex Crimes?" *Saturday Evening Post* (Dec. 11, 1948).

Wittels, Fr. "The Mystery of Masochism," *Psychoanalysis Review*. Vol. 24 (1937), 139.

Wolbarst, A. L. "Sexual Perversions: Their Medical and Social Implications," *Medical Journal and Records* (New York, 1935).

Wolfenden Report on Homosexuality. Report of the Committee on Homosexual Offenses and Prostitution in Allen, C. and Berg, C. The Problem of Homosexuality. New York: The Citadel Press, 1958.

Wortis, Joseph. "Sex Taboos, Sex Offenders and the Law," *American Journal of Orthopsychiatry*. Vol. 9, No. 3 (July, 1939), 554-564.

Weingraf, Fritz. "Fragment of an Analysis of a Prostitute," *Journal of Criminal Psychology*. Vol. 5 (Oct., 1938), 247-253.

Wulff, M. "A Case of Male Homosexuality," *International Journal of Psychoanalysis*. Vol. 23 (1942), Parts 3-4, 112-120.

Wulffen, Erich. *Woman as a Sexual Criminal.* New York: Falstaff Press, Inc., 1935.

Wybret, Esther B. "The Homosexual Woman Speaks," *Sexology Magazine* (April, 1949).

———. "What Makes a Lesbian?" *Sexology* (Oct., 1949), 149-154.

Wylie, Philip. *The Disappearance.* New York: Rinehart & Co., 1951.

Wynne vs. *State* Ct. Apps Ga 1941 15 S.E. 2nd 623.

Yawger, N. S. "Transvestism and Other Cross-Sex Manifestations," *Journal of Nervous and Mental Diseases*. Vol. 92, No. 1 (July, 1940), 41-48.

index